FREE Study Skills DVD Offer

Dear Customer,

Thank you for your purchase from Mometrix! We consider it an honor and a privilege that you have purchased our product and we want to ensure your satisfaction.

As a way of showing our appreciation and to help us better serve you, we have developed a Study Skills DVD that we would like to give you for FREE. This DVD covers our *best practices* for getting ready for your exam, from how to use our study materials to how to best prepare for the day of the test.

All that we ask is that you email us with feedback that would describe your experience so far with our product. Good, bad, or indifferent, we want to know what you think!

To get your FREE Study Skills DVD, email freedvd@mometrix.com with *FREE STUDY SKILLS DVD* in the subject line and the following information in the body of the email:

- The name of the product you purchased.
- Your product rating on a scale of 1-5, with 5 being the highest rating.
- Your feedback. It can be long, short, or anything in between. We just want to know your impressions and experience so far with our product. (Good feedback might include how our study material met your needs and ways we might be able to make it even better. You could highlight features that you found helpful or features that you think we should add.)
- Your full name and shipping address where you would like us to send your free DVD.

If you have any questions or concerns, please don't hesitate to contact me directly.

Thanks again!

Sincerely,

Jay Willis
Vice President
jay.willis@mometrix.com
1-800-673-8175

Psychiatric-Mental Health Nurse Practitioner

Exam Secrets Study Guide

Exam Review and NP
Practice Test for the
Nurse Practitioner Test

Written and edited by Mometrix Test Prep

Printed in the United States of America

This paper meets the requirements of ANSI/NISO Z39.48-1992 (Permanence of Paper).

Mometrix offers volume discount pricing to institutions. For more information or a price quote, please contact our sales department at sales@mometrix.com or 888-248-1219.

Mometrix Media LLC is not affiliated with or endorsed by any official testing organization. All organizational and test names are trademarks of their respective owners.

Paperback
ISBN 13: 978-1-5167-3292-0
ISBN 10: 1-5167-3292-8

DEAR FUTURE EXAM SUCCESS STORY

First of all, **THANK YOU** for purchasing Mometrix study materials!

Second, congratulations! You are one of the few determined test-takers who are committed to doing whatever it takes to excel on your exam. **You have come to the right place.** We developed these study materials with one goal in mind: to deliver you the information you need in a format that's concise and easy to use.

In addition to optimizing your guide for the content of the test, we've outlined our recommended steps for breaking down the preparation process into small, attainable goals so you can make sure you stay on track.

We've also analyzed the entire test-taking process, identifying the most common pitfalls and showing how you can overcome them and be ready for any curveball the test throws you.

Standardized testing is one of the biggest obstacles on your road to success, which only increases the importance of doing well in the high-pressure, high-stakes environment of test day. Your results on this test could have a significant impact on your future, and this guide provides the information and practical advice to help you achieve your full potential on test day.

Your success is our success

We would love to hear from you! If you would like to share the story of your exam success or if you have any questions or comments in regard to our products, please contact us at **800-673-8175** or **support@mometrix.com**.

Thanks again for your business and we wish you continued success!

Sincerely,
The Mometrix Test Preparation Team

Need more help? Check out our flashcards at:
http://mometrixflashcards.com/NP

i

TABLE OF CONTENTS

Introduction

Thank you for purchasing this resource! You have made the choice to prepare yourself for a test that could have a huge impact on your future, and this guide is designed to help you be fully ready for test day. Obviously, it's important to have a solid understanding of the test material, but you also need to be prepared for the unique environment and stressors of the test, so that you can perform to the best of your abilities.

For this purpose, the first section that appears in this guide is the **Secret Keys**. We've devoted countless hours to meticulously researching what works and what doesn't, and we've boiled down our findings to the five most impactful steps you can take to improve your performance on the test. We start at the beginning with study planning and move through the preparation process, all the way to the testing strategies that will help you get the most out of what you know when you're finally sitting in front of the test.

We recommend that you start preparing for your test as far in advance as possible. However, if you've bought this guide as a last-minute study resource and only have a few days before your test, we recommend that you skip over the first two Secret Keys since they address a long-term study plan.

If you struggle with **test anxiety**, we strongly encourage you to check out our recommendations for how you can overcome it. Test anxiety is a formidable foe, but it can be beaten, and we want to make sure you have the tools you need to defeat it.

Secret Key #1 – Plan Big, Study Small

There's a lot riding on your performance. If you want to ace this test, you're going to need to keep your skills sharp and the material fresh in your mind. You need a plan that lets you review everything you need to know while still fitting in your schedule. We'll break this strategy down into three categories.

Information Organization

Start with the information you already have: the official test outline. From this, you can make a complete list of all the concepts you need to cover before the test. Organize these concepts into groups that can be studied together, and create a list of any related vocabulary you need to learn so you can brush up on any difficult terms. You'll want to keep this vocabulary list handy once you actually start studying since you may need to add to it along the way.

Time Management

Once you have your set of study concepts, decide how to spread them out over the time you have left before the test. Break your study plan into small, clear goals so you have a manageable task for each day and know exactly what you're doing. Then just focus on one small step at a time. When you manage your time this way, you don't need to spend hours at a time studying. Studying a small block of content for a short period each day helps you retain information better and avoid stressing over how much you have left to do. You can relax knowing that you have a plan to cover everything in time. In order for this strategy to be effective though, you have to start studying early and stick to your schedule. Avoid the exhaustion and futility that comes from last-minute cramming!

Study Environment

The environment you study in has a big impact on your learning. Studying in a coffee shop, while probably more enjoyable, is not likely to be as fruitful as studying in a quiet room. It's important to keep distractions to a minimum. You're only planning to study for a short block of time, so make the most of it. Don't pause to check your phone or get up to find a snack. It's also important to **avoid multitasking**. Research has consistently shown that multitasking will make your studying dramatically less effective. Your study area should also be comfortable and well-lit so you don't have the distraction of straining your eyes or sitting on an uncomfortable chair.

The time of day you study is also important. You want to be rested and alert. Don't wait until just before bedtime. Study when you'll be most likely to comprehend and remember. Even better, if you know what time of day your test will be, set that time aside for study. That way your brain will be used to working on that subject at that specific time and you'll have a better chance of recalling information.

Finally, it can be helpful to team up with others who are studying for the same test. Your actual studying should be done in as isolated an environment as possible, but the work of organizing the information and setting up the study plan can be divided up. In between study sessions, you can discuss with your teammates the concepts that you're all studying and quiz each other on the details. Just be sure that your teammates are as serious about the test as you are. If you find that your study time is being replaced with social time, you might need to find a new team.

Secret Key #2 – Make Your Studying Count

You're devoting a lot of time and effort to preparing for this test, so you want to be absolutely certain it will pay off. This means doing more than just reading the content and hoping you can remember it on test day. It's important to make every minute of study count. There are two main areas you can focus on to make your studying count:

Retention

It doesn't matter how much time you study if you can't remember the material. You need to make sure you are retaining the concepts. To check your retention of the information you're learning, try recalling it at later times with minimal prompting. Try carrying around flashcards and glance at one or two from time to time or ask a friend who's also studying for the test to quiz you.

To enhance your retention, look for ways to put the information into practice so that you can apply it rather than simply recalling it. If you're using the information in practical ways, it will be much easier to remember. Similarly, it helps to solidify a concept in your mind if you're not only reading it to yourself but also explaining it to someone else. Ask a friend to let you teach them about a concept you're a little shaky on (or speak aloud to an imaginary audience if necessary). As you try to summarize, define, give examples, and answer your friend's questions, you'll understand the concepts better and they will stay with you longer. Finally, step back for a big picture view and ask yourself how each piece of information fits with the whole subject. When you link the different concepts together and see them working together as a whole, it's easier to remember the individual components.

Finally, practice showing your work on any multi-step problems, even if you're just studying. Writing out each step you take to solve a problem will help solidify the process in your mind, and you'll be more likely to remember it during the test.

Modality

Modality simply refers to the means or method by which you study. Choosing a study modality that fits your own individual learning style is crucial. No two people learn best in exactly the same way, so it's important to know your strengths and use them to your advantage.

For example, if you learn best by visualization, focus on visualizing a concept in your mind and draw an image or a diagram. Try color-coding your notes, illustrating them, or creating symbols that will trigger your mind to recall a learned concept. If you learn best by hearing or discussing information, find a study partner who learns the same way or read aloud to yourself. Think about how to put the information in your own words. Imagine that you are giving a lecture on the topic and record yourself so you can listen to it later.

For any learning style, flashcards can be helpful. Organize the information so you can take advantage of spare moments to review. Underline key words or phrases. Use different colors for different categories. Mnemonic devices (such as creating a short list in which every item starts with the same letter) can also help with retention. Find what works best for you and use it to store the information in your mind most effectively and easily.

Secret Key #3 – Practice the Right Way

Your success on test day depends not only on how many hours you put into preparing, but also on whether you prepared the right way. It's good to check along the way to see if your studying is paying off. One of the most effective ways to do this is by taking practice tests to evaluate your progress. Practice tests are useful because they show exactly where you need to improve. Every time you take a practice test, pay special attention to these three groups of questions:

- The questions you got wrong
- The questions you had to guess on, even if you guessed right
- The questions you found difficult or slow to work through

This will show you exactly what your weak areas are, and where you need to devote more study time. Ask yourself why each of these questions gave you trouble. Was it because you didn't understand the material? Was it because you didn't remember the vocabulary? Do you need more repetitions on this type of question to build speed and confidence? Dig into those questions and figure out how you can strengthen your weak areas as you go back to review the material.

Additionally, many practice tests have a section explaining the answer choices. It can be tempting to read the explanation and think that you now have a good understanding of the concept. However, an explanation likely only covers part of the question's broader context. Even if the explanation makes sense, **go back and investigate** every concept related to the question until you're positive you have a thorough understanding.

As you go along, keep in mind that the practice test is just that: practice. Memorizing these questions and answers will not be very helpful on the actual test because it is unlikely to have any of the same exact questions. If you only know the right answers to the sample questions, you won't be prepared for the real thing. **Study the concepts** until you understand them fully, and then you'll be able to answer any question that shows up on the test.

It's important to wait on the practice tests until you're ready. If you take a test on your first day of study, you may be overwhelmed by the amount of material covered and how much you need to learn. Work up to it gradually.

On test day, you'll need to be prepared for answering questions, managing your time, and using the test-taking strategies you've learned. It's a lot to balance, like a mental marathon that will have a big impact on your future. Like training for a marathon, you'll need to start slowly and work your way up. When test day arrives, you'll be ready.

Start with the strategies you've read in the first two Secret Keys—plan your course and study in the way that works best for you. If you have time, consider using multiple study resources to get different approaches to the same concepts. It can be helpful to see difficult concepts from more than one angle. Then find a good source for practice tests. Many times, the test website will suggest potential study resources or provide sample tests.

Practice Test Strategy

If you're able to find at least three practice tests, we recommend this strategy:

UNTIMED AND OPEN-BOOK PRACTICE

Take the first test with no time constraints and with your notes and study guide handy. Take your time and focus on applying the strategies you've learned.

TIMED AND OPEN-BOOK PRACTICE

Take the second practice test open-book as well, but set a timer and practice pacing yourself to finish in time.

TIMED AND CLOSED-BOOK PRACTICE

Take any other practice tests as if it were test day. Set a timer and put away your study materials. Sit at a table or desk in a quiet room, imagine yourself at the testing center, and answer questions as quickly and accurately as possible.

Keep repeating timed and closed-book tests on a regular basis until you run out of practice tests or it's time for the actual test. Your mind will be ready for the schedule and stress of test day, and you'll be able to focus on recalling the material you've learned.

Secret Key #4 – Pace Yourself

Once you're fully prepared for the material on the test, your biggest challenge on test day will be managing your time. Just knowing that the clock is ticking can make you panic even if you have plenty of time left. Work on pacing yourself so you can build confidence against the time constraints of the exam. Pacing is a difficult skill to master, especially in a high-pressure environment, so **practice is vital**.

Set time expectations for your pace based on how much time is available. For example, if a section has 60 questions and the time limit is 30 minutes, you know you have to average 30 seconds or less per question in order to answer them all. Although 30 seconds is the hard limit, set 25 seconds per question as your goal, so you reserve extra time to spend on harder questions. When you budget extra time for the harder questions, you no longer have any reason to stress when those questions take longer to answer.

Don't let this time expectation distract you from working through the test at a calm, steady pace, but keep it in mind so you don't spend too much time on any one question. Recognize that taking extra time on one question you don't understand may keep you from answering two that you do understand later in the test. If your time limit for a question is up and you're still not sure of the answer, mark it and move on, and come back to it later if the time and the test format allow. If the testing format doesn't allow you to return to earlier questions, just make an educated guess; then put it out of your mind and move on.

On the easier questions, be careful not to rush. It may seem wise to hurry through them so you have more time for the challenging ones, but it's not worth missing one if you know the concept and just didn't take the time to read the question fully. Work efficiently but make sure you understand the question and have looked at all of the answer choices, since more than one may seem right at first.

Even if you're paying attention to the time, you may find yourself a little behind at some point. You should speed up to get back on track, but do so wisely. Don't panic; just take a few seconds less on each question until you're caught up. Don't guess without thinking, but do look through the answer choices and eliminate any you know are wrong. If you can get down to two choices, it is often worthwhile to guess from those. Once you've chosen an answer, move on and don't dwell on any that you skipped or had to hurry through. If a question was taking too long, chances are it was one of the harder ones, so you weren't as likely to get it right anyway.

On the other hand, if you find yourself getting ahead of schedule, it may be beneficial to slow down a little. The more quickly you work, the more likely you are to make a careless mistake that will affect your score. You've budgeted time for each question, so don't be afraid to spend that time. Practice an efficient but careful pace to get the most out of the time you have.

Secret Key #5 – Have a Plan for Guessing

When you're taking the test, you may find yourself stuck on a question. Some of the answer choices seem better than others, but you don't see the one answer choice that is obviously correct. What do you do?

The scenario described above is very common, yet most test takers have not effectively prepared for it. Developing and practicing a plan for guessing may be one of the single most effective uses of your time as you get ready for the exam.

In developing your plan for guessing, there are three questions to address:

- When should you start the guessing process?
- How should you narrow down the choices?
- Which answer should you choose?

When to Start the Guessing Process

Unless your plan for guessing is to select C every time (which, despite its merits, is not what we recommend), you need to leave yourself enough time to apply your answer elimination strategies. Since you have a limited amount of time for each question, that means that if you're going to give yourself the best shot at guessing correctly, you have to decide quickly whether or not you will guess.

Of course, the best-case scenario is that you don't have to guess at all, so first, see if you can answer the question based on your knowledge of the subject and basic reasoning skills. Focus on the key words in the question and try to jog your memory of related topics. Give yourself a chance to bring the knowledge to mind, but once you realize that you don't have (or you can't access) the knowledge you need to answer the question, it's time to start the guessing process.

It's almost always better to start the guessing process too early than too late. It only takes a few seconds to remember something and answer the question from knowledge. Carefully eliminating wrong answer choices takes longer. Plus, going through the process of eliminating answer choices can actually help jog your memory.

Summary: Start the guessing process as soon as you decide that you can't answer the question based on your knowledge.

How to Narrow Down the Choices

The next chapter in this book (**Test-Taking Strategies**) includes a wide range of strategies for how to approach questions and how to look for answer choices to eliminate. You will definitely want to read those carefully, practice them, and figure out which ones work best for you. Here though, we're going to address a mindset rather than a particular strategy.

Your chances of guessing an answer correctly depend on how many options you are choosing from.

How many choices you have	How likely you are to guess correctly
5	20%
4	25%
3	33%
2	50%
1	100%

You can see from this chart just how valuable it is to be able to eliminate incorrect answers and make an educated guess, but there are two things that many test takers do that cause them to miss out on the benefits of guessing:

- Accidentally eliminating the correct answer
- Selecting an answer based on an impression

We'll look at the first one here, and the second one in the next section.

To avoid accidentally eliminating the correct answer, we recommend a thought exercise called **the $5 challenge**. In this challenge, you only eliminate an answer choice from contention if you are willing to bet $5 on it being wrong. Why $5? Five dollars is a small but not insignificant amount of money. It's an amount you could afford to lose but wouldn't want to throw away. And while losing $5 once might not hurt too much, doing it twenty times will set you back $100. In the same way, each small decision you make—eliminating a choice here, guessing on a question there—won't by itself impact your score very much, but when you put them all together, they can make a big difference. By holding each answer choice elimination decision to a higher standard, you can reduce the risk of accidentally eliminating the correct answer.

The $5 challenge can also be applied in a positive sense: If you are willing to bet $5 that an answer choice *is* correct, go ahead and mark it as correct.

Summary: Only eliminate an answer choice if you are willing to bet $5 that it is wrong.

Which Answer to Choose

You're taking the test. You've run into a hard question and decided you'll have to guess. You've eliminated all the answer choices you're willing to bet $5 on. Now you have to pick an answer. Why do we even need to talk about this? Why can't you just pick whichever one you feel like when the time comes?

The answer to these questions is that if you don't come into the test with a plan, you'll rely on your impression to select an answer choice, and if you do that, you risk falling into a trap. The test writers know that everyone who takes their test will be guessing on some of the questions, so they intentionally write wrong answer choices to seem plausible. You still have to pick an answer though, and if the wrong answer choices are designed to look right, how can you ever be sure that you're not falling for their trap? The best solution we've found to this dilemma is to take the decision out of your hands entirely. Here is the process we recommend:

Once you've eliminated any choices that you are confident (willing to bet $5) are wrong, select the first remaining choice as your answer.

Whether you choose to select the first remaining choice, the second, or the last, the important thing is that you use some preselected standard. Using this approach guarantees that you will not be enticed into selecting an answer choice that looks right, because you are not basing your decision on how the answer choices look.

This is not meant to make you question your knowledge. Instead, it is to help you recognize the difference between your knowledge and your impressions. There's a huge difference between thinking an answer is right because of what you know, and thinking an answer is right because it looks or sounds like it should be right.

Summary: To ensure that your selection is appropriately random, make a predetermined selection from among all answer choices you have not eliminated.

Test-Taking Strategies

This section contains a list of test-taking strategies that you may find helpful as you work through the test. By taking what you know and applying logical thought, you can maximize your chances of answering any question correctly!

It is very important to realize that every question is different and every person is different: no single strategy will work on every question, and no single strategy will work for every person. That's why we've included all of them here, so you can try them out and determine which ones work best for different types of questions and which ones work best for you.

Question Strategies

READ CAREFULLY

Read the question and answer choices carefully. Don't miss the question because you misread the terms. You have plenty of time to read each question thoroughly and make sure you understand what is being asked. Yet a happy medium must be attained, so don't waste too much time. You must read carefully, but efficiently.

CONTEXTUAL CLUES

Look for contextual clues. If the question includes a word you are not familiar with, look at the immediate context for some indication of what the word might mean. Contextual clues can often give you all the information you need to decipher the meaning of an unfamiliar word. Even if you can't determine the meaning, you may be able to narrow down the possibilities enough to make a solid guess at the answer to the question.

PREFIXES

If you're having trouble with a word in the question or answer choices, try dissecting it. Take advantage of every clue that the word might include. Prefixes and suffixes can be a huge help. Usually they allow you to determine a basic meaning. Pre- means before, post- means after, pro - is positive, de- is negative. From prefixes and suffixes, you can get an idea of the general meaning of the word and try to put it into context.

HEDGE WORDS

Watch out for critical hedge words, such as *likely, may, can, sometimes, often, almost, mostly, usually, generally, rarely,* and *sometimes.* Question writers insert these hedge phrases to cover every possibility. Often an answer choice will be wrong simply because it leaves no room for exception. Be on guard for answer choices that have definitive words such as *exactly* and *always.*

SWITCHBACK WORDS

Stay alert for *switchbacks.* These are the words and phrases frequently used to alert you to shifts in thought. The most common switchback words are *but, although,* and *however.* Others include *nevertheless, on the other hand, even though, while, in spite of, despite, regardless of.* Switchback words are important to catch because they can change the direction of the question or an answer choice.

FACE VALUE

When in doubt, use common sense. Accept the situation in the problem at face value. Don't read too much into it. These problems will not require you to make wild assumptions. If you have to go beyond creativity and warp time or space in order to have an answer choice fit the question, then you should move on and consider the other answer choices. These are normal problems rooted in reality. The applicable relationship or explanation may not be readily apparent, but it is there for you to figure out. Use your common sense to interpret anything that isn't clear.

Answer Choice Strategies

ANSWER SELECTION

The most thorough way to pick an answer choice is to identify and eliminate wrong answers until only one is left, then confirm it is the correct answer. Sometimes an answer choice may immediately seem right, but be careful. The test writers will usually put more than one reasonable answer choice on each question, so take a second to read all of them and make sure that the other choices are not equally obvious. As long as you have time left, it is better to read every answer choice than to pick the first one that looks right without checking the others.

ANSWER CHOICE FAMILIES

An answer choice family consists of two (in rare cases, three) answer choices that are very similar in construction and cannot all be true at the same time. If you see two answer choices that are direct opposites or parallels, one of them is usually the correct answer. For instance, if one answer choice says that quantity x increases and another either says that quantity x decreases (opposite) or says that quantity y increases (parallel), then those answer choices would fall into the same family. An answer choice that doesn't match the construction of the answer choice family is more likely to be incorrect. Most questions will not have answer choice families, but when they do appear, you should be prepared to recognize them.

ELIMINATE ANSWERS

Eliminate answer choices as soon as you realize they are wrong, but make sure you consider all possibilities. If you are eliminating answer choices and realize that the last one you are left with is also wrong, don't panic. Start over and consider each choice again. There may be something you missed the first time that you will realize on the second pass.

AVOID FACT TRAPS

Don't be distracted by an answer choice that is factually true but doesn't answer the question. You are looking for the choice that answers the question. Stay focused on what the question is asking for so you don't accidentally pick an answer that is true but incorrect. Always go back to the question and make sure the answer choice you've selected actually answers the question and is not merely a true statement.

EXTREME STATEMENTS

In general, you should avoid answers that put forth extreme actions as standard practice or proclaim controversial ideas as established fact. An answer choice that states the "process should be used in certain situations, if…" is much more likely to be correct than one that states the "process should be discontinued completely." The first is a calm rational statement and doesn't even make a definitive, uncompromising stance, using a hedge word *if* to provide wiggle room, whereas the second choice is a radical idea and far more extreme.

11

BENCHMARK

As you read through the answer choices and you come across one that seems to answer the question well, mentally select that answer choice. This is not your final answer, but it's the one that will help you evaluate the other answer choices. The one that you selected is your benchmark or standard for judging each of the other answer choices. Every other answer choice must be compared to your benchmark. That choice is correct until proven otherwise by another answer choice beating it. If you find a better answer, then that one becomes your new benchmark. Once you've decided that no other choice answers the question as well as your benchmark, you have your final answer.

PREDICT THE ANSWER

Before you even start looking at the answer choices, it is often best to try to predict the answer. When you come up with the answer on your own, it is easier to avoid distractions and traps because you will know exactly what to look for. The right answer choice is unlikely to be word-for-word what you came up with, but it should be a close match. Even if you are confident that you have the right answer, you should still take the time to read each option before moving on.

General Strategies

TOUGH QUESTIONS

If you are stumped on a problem or it appears too hard or too difficult, don't waste time. Move on! Remember though, if you can quickly check for obviously incorrect answer choices, your chances of guessing correctly are greatly improved. Before you completely give up, at least try to knock out a couple of possible answers. Eliminate what you can and then guess at the remaining answer choices before moving on.

CHECK YOUR WORK

Since you will probably not know every term listed and the answer to every question, it is important that you get credit for the ones that you do know. Don't miss any questions through careless mistakes. If at all possible, try to take a second to look back over your answer selection and make sure you've selected the correct answer choice and haven't made a costly careless mistake (such as marking an answer choice that you didn't mean to mark). This quick double check should more than pay for itself in caught mistakes for the time it costs.

PACE YOURSELF

It's easy to be overwhelmed when you're looking at a page full of questions; your mind is confused and full of random thoughts, and the clock is ticking down faster than you would like. Calm down and maintain the pace that you have set for yourself. Especially as you get down to the last few minutes of the test, don't let the small numbers on the clock make you panic. As long as you are on track by monitoring your pace, you are guaranteed to have time for each question.

DON'T RUSH

It is very easy to make errors when you are in a hurry. Maintaining a fast pace in answering questions is pointless if it makes you miss questions that you would have gotten right otherwise. Test writers like to include distracting information and wrong answers that seem right. Taking a little extra time to avoid careless mistakes can make all the difference in your test score. Find a pace that allows you to be confident in the answers that you select.

12

KEEP MOVING

Panicking will not help you pass the test, so do your best to stay calm and keep moving. Taking deep breaths and going through the answer elimination steps you practiced can help to break through a stress barrier and keep your pace.

Final Notes

The combination of a solid foundation of content knowledge and the confidence that comes from practicing your plan for applying that knowledge is the key to maximizing your performance on test day. As your foundation of content knowledge is built up and strengthened, you'll find that the strategies included in this chapter become more and more effective in helping you quickly sift through the distractions and traps of the test to isolate the correct answer.

Now it's time to move on to the test content chapters of this book, but be sure to keep your goal in mind. As you read, think about how you will be able to apply this information on the test. If you've already seen sample questions for the test and you have an idea of the question format and style, try to come up with questions of your own that you can answer based on what you're reading. This will give you valuable practice applying your knowledge in the same ways you can expect to on test day.

Good luck and good studying!

Scientific Foundation

Advanced Pathophysiology

CEREBRAL ANEURYSMS

Cerebral aneurysms, weakening and dilation of a cerebral artery, are usually **congenital** (90%) while the remaining (10%) result from **direct trauma or infection**. Aneurysms usually range from 2-7 mm and occur in the **Circle of Willis** at the base of the brain. A rupturing aneurysm may decrease perfusion as well as increasing pressure on surrounding brain tissue, resulting in mental changes. Cerebral aneurysms are classified as follows:

- **Berry/saccular**: The most common congenital type occurs at a bifurcation and grows from the base on a stem, usually at the Circle of Willis.
- **Fusiform**: Large and irregular (>2.5 cm) and rarely ruptures, but causes increased intracranial pressure. Usually involves the internal carotid or vertebrobasilar artery.
- **Mycotic**: Rare type that occurs secondary to bacterial infection and septic emboli.
- **Dissecting**: Wall is torn apart and blood enters layers. This may occur during angiography or secondary to trauma or disease.
- **Traumatic Charcot-Bouchard (pseudoaneurysm):** Small lesion resulting from chronic hypertension.

CLASSIFICATIONS OF BRAIN TUMORS

Any type of **brain tumor** can occur in children and adults. Brain tumors may cause psychiatric symptoms, such as hallucinations and changes in mental status, depending on the type and site. Brain tumors are classified as follows:

- **Astrocytoma:** Arises from astrocytes, which are glial cells. It is the most common type of tumor, occurring throughout the brain but most common in the cerebellum of children. There are many types of astrocytomas, and most are slow growing. Some are operable while others are not. Radiation may be given after removal. Astrocytomas include glioblastomas, aggressively malignant tumors occurring most often in adults 45-70.
- **Brain stem glioma**: May be fast or slow growing but generally not operable because of location, although it may be treated with radiation or chemotherapy.
- **Craniopharyngioma**: A congenital, slow-growing, and benign cystic tumor; however, it is difficult to resect and is treated with surgery and radiation. May be recurrent, especially if >5 cm.
- **Meningioma**: Slow-growing meningeal tumor, usually benign and more common in women; surgically removed if causing symptoms.

ARTERIOVENOUS MALFORMATION

Arteriovenous malformation (AVM) is a congenital abnormality characterized by a tangle of dilated arteries and veins without a **capillary bed**. AVMs can occur anywhere in the brain and may cause no significant problems. Usually the AVM is "fed" by 1 or more cerebral arteries, which enlarge over time, shunting more blood through the AVM. The veins also enlarge in response to increased arterial blood flow because of the lack of a capillary bridge between the 2. Because vein walls are thinner and lack the muscle layer of an artery, the veins tend to rupture as the AVM becomes larger, causing a **subarachnoid hemorrhage**. Chronic ischemia that may be related to the AVM can result in **cerebral atrophy**. Sometimes small leaks, usually accompanied by headache,

15

nausea, and vomiting, may occur before rupture. AVMs may cause a wide range of neurological symptoms, including changes in mentation, dizziness, sensory abnormalities, confusion, and dementia. Treatment includes:

- Supportive management of symptoms.
- Surgical repair or focused irradiation (definitive treatments).

STROKES

ISCHEMIC STROKES

Strokes (brain attacks, cerebrovascular accidents) result when there is interruption of the blood flow to an area of the brain. The 2 basic types are ischemic and hemorrhagic. About 80% are ischemic, resulting from blockage of an artery supplying the brain. **Ischemic strokes** are classified as follows:

- **Thrombosis** in large artery, usually resulting from atherosclerosis, may block circulation to a large area of the brain. It is most common in the elderly and may occur suddenly or after episodes of transient ischemic attacks.
- **Lacunar infarct** (penetrating thrombosis in small artery) is most common in those with diabetes mellitus and/or hypertension.
- **Embolism** travels through the arterial system and lodges in the brain, most commonly in the left middle cerebral artery. An embolism may be cardiogenic, resulting from cardiac arrhythmia or surgery. An embolism usually occurs rapidly with no warning signs.
- **Cryptogenic** has no identifiable cause.

HEMORRHAGIC STROKES

Hemorrhagic strokes account for about 20% of all strokes and result from a ruptured cerebral artery, causing not only lack of oxygen and nutrients but also edema that causes widespread pressure and damage. Hemorrhagic strokes are classified as follows:

- **Intracerebral** is bleeding into the substance of the brain from an artery in the central lobes, basal ganglia, pons, or cerebellum. Intracerebral hemorrhage usually results from atherosclerotic degenerative changes, hypertension, brain tumors, anticoagulation therapy, or some illicit drugs, such as crack and cocaine. Onset is often sudden and may cause death.
- **Intracranial aneurysm** occurs with ballooning cerebral artery ruptures, most commonly at the Circle of Willis.
- **Arteriovenous malformation (AVM)** is a tangle of dilated arteries and veins without a capillary bed. This is a congenital abnormality. Rupture of AVMs is a cause of stroke in young adults.
- **Subarachnoid hemorrhage** is bleeding in the space between the meninges and brain, resulting from aneurysm, AVM, or trauma. This type of hemorrhage compresses brain tissue.

RIGHT HEMISPHERE STROKES

Strokes most commonly occur in the right or left hemisphere, but the exact location and the extent of brain damage affects the type of presenting symptoms. If the frontal area of either side is involved, there tends to be **memory and learning deficits**. Some symptoms are common to specific areas and help to identify the area involved:

- **Right hemisphere:** This results in left paralysis or paresis and a left visual field deficit that may cause spatial and perceptual disturbances so that people may have difficulty judging distance. Fine motor skills may be impacted, resulting in trouble dressing or handling tools. People may become impulsive and exhibit poor judgment, often denying impairment. Left-sided neglect (lack of perception of things on the left side) may occur. Depression is common as well as short-term memory loss and difficulty following directions. Language skills usually remain intact.

STROKE OF THE LEFT HEMISPHERE, BRAIN STEM, AND CEREBELLUM

Symptoms of **strokes** vary according to the area of the brain affected:

- **Left hemisphere:** This results in right paralysis or paresis and a right visual field defect. Depression is common and people often exhibit slow, cautious behavior, requiring repeated instruction and reinforcement for simple tasks. Short-term memory loss and difficulty learning new material or understanding generalizations is common. Difficulty with mathematics, reading, writing, and reasoning may occur. Aphasia (expressive, receptive, or global) is common.
- **Brain stem**: Because the brain stem controls respiration and cardiac function, a brain attack frequently causes death, but those who survive may have a number of problems, including respiratory and cardiac abnormalities. Strokes may involve motor or sensory impairment or both.
- **Cerebellum:** This area controls balance and coordination. Strokes in the cerebellum are rare but may result in ataxia, nausea, and vomiting, as well as headaches and dizziness or vertigo.

HYDROCEPHALUS

Hydrocephalus occurs when there is an imbalance between production and absorption of **cerebrospinal fluid (CSF)** in the ventricles, resulting from impaired absorption or obstruction, which may be congenital or acquired. The ventricular system produces and circulates CSF. There are right and left lateral ventricles, which open into the third ventricle at the interventricular foramen (foramen of Monro). The aqueduct of Sylvius connects the third and fourth ventricles. The fourth ventricle, anterior to the cerebellum, supplies CSF to the subarachnoid space and the spinal cord (dorsal surface). The CSF circulates and then returns to the brain and is absorbed in the arachnoid villi. There are 2 common types of hydrocephalus:

- **Communicating**: CSF flows (communicates) between the ventricles but is not absorbed in the subarachnoid space (arachnoid villi).
- **Non-communicating**: CSF is obstructed (non-communicating) between the ventricles with obstruction, often resulting in stenosis of the aqueduct of Sylvius, but it can occur anywhere in the system.

NEEDS OF TRAUMATIC BRAIN INJURY PATIENTS

The needs of the patient with a **traumatic brain injury** depend on the extent of the damage but problems and interventions can include:

- **Impaired verbal communication**: Speech therapy and communication enhancement approaches.
- **Impaired physical mobility**: Physical therapy, assistive devices, and occupational therapy.
- **Impaired bowel/urinary elimination**: Bowel/bladder training, and assistance with toileting.
- **Disturbed thought processes**: Memory training, medications, safety precautions, cognitive stimulation, and behavioral therapy.
- **Disturbed sensory perceptions**: Nutritional and environmental management and hearing and vision support.
- **Insomnia**: Environmental management and sleep enhancement techniques.
- **Impaired swallowing**: Swallowing therapy.
- **Risk for injury**: Safety precautions, seizure precautions, and seizure prophylaxis.
- **Impaired parenting skills**: Parenting classes and child protection strategies.
- **Delayed growth and development**: Monitoring and enhancement strategies.
- Substance abuse: Intervention, 12-step programs and support programs.
- **Risk for violence**: Intervention, behavioral therapy, and family therapy.
- **Risk for suicide**: Monitoring, support groups, therapy, and medications.

MULTIPLE SCLEROSIS

Multiple sclerosis (MS) is a central nervous system (CNS) immune-mediated inflammatory demyelinating disease, believed triggered by an unidentified environmental source, such as a virus. MS is associated with mood swings, depression, and changes in mental status. Within the CNS, small glial cells, **oligodendrocytes**, send out processes that wrap around the axons of neurons, creating the **myelin sheath**. One oligodendrocyte may "grasp" 10-15 neurons, and adjoining segments of the sheath are created by other oligodendrocytes, with spaces in between (Nodes of Ranvier). The sheath, primarily composed of lipids, is white in appearance, creating the "white matter" of the brain. Impulses travel along the sheath, jumping from 1 node to another. With MS, for reasons that are not clear, an immune reaction causes **killer T cells** to attack the oligodendrocytes, which begin to demyelinate, leaving scarred areas along the axons, slowing neuronal transmission. Damage to 1 oligodendrocyte can affect many neurons. Initially, unaffected mature oligodendrocytes repair the damage, so symptoms tend to wax and wane. Over time, however, cells cannot remyelinate and new cells don't develop adequately, so symptoms worsen.

PARKINSON'S DISEASE

Parkinson's disease (PD) is an **extrapyramidal movement motor system disorder** caused by loss of brain cells that produce dopamine. The basal ganglia, which lies at the base of the cerebral cortex and controls movement and coordination, has a number of structures that are involved in PD, particularly the **substantia nigra**, where neuronal cells project fibers to the putamen and caudate of the corpus striatum, releasing dopamine (a neurotransmitter that is produced from levodopa), which is then transmitted to the thalamus and cerebral cortex, modulating movement. With PD, impairment in neuronal connections and death of cells develop between the substantia nigra and the putamen of the basal ganglia, resulting in decreased levels of dopamine. Symptoms appear when 60-80% of neuronal cells are impaired and dopamine levels drop by 20-50%. As dopamine levels fall, other areas of the basal ganglia function abnormally as well, further impairing motor function. Depression is common with PD.

ALZHEIMER'S DISEASE

The network of neurons, branches, and synapses within the central nervous system is called the **neuron forest**. Electrical charges are transmitted at about 1 trillion points (synapses) with the release of neurotransmitters. In **Alzheimer's disease**, there is disruption in both the electrical activity and the neurotransmitters. The cerebral cortex begins to atrophy, especially in the area of the **hippocampus**, which controls storage of new memories, resulting in characteristic short-term memory loss. **Amyloid plaques** (clusters of protein fragments) form between the neurons, and as the neurons die and deteriorate, tangled strands of another protein occur. Researchers believe that these structures cause the brain damage associated with Alzheimer's disease:

- **Plaques** form from **beta-amyloid**, which is a sticky protein found in the fatty membrane surrounding neurons, and are believed to block neurotransmission or trigger an immune response.
- **Tangles** form when the **tau protein**, which supports the transport system within a neuron, begins to collapse, causing the transport system to disintegrate and the cell to die.

STAGES

There are a number of methods for **staging Alzheimer's disease.** Staging is done by a combination of physical exam, history (often provided by family or caregivers), and mental assessment, as there is no definitive test for Alzheimer's. The 7-stage classification system (developed by Gary Reisberg, MD) is used by the Alzheimer's Association:

- **Stage 1:**
  o Pre-clinical with no evident impairment although slight changes may be occurring within the brain.
- **Stage 2:**
  o Very mild cognitive decline with some misplacing of items and forgetting things or words, but impairment is not usually noticeable to others or found on medical examination.
- **Stage 3:**
  o Mild, early-stage cognitive decline with short-term memory loss, problems with reading retention, remembering names, handling money, planning, and organizing. May misplace items of value.
- **Stage 4:**
  o Moderate cognitive decline with decreased knowledge of current affairs or family history, difficulty doing complex tasks, and social withdrawal. This stage is more easily recognized on exam and may persist for 2-10 years, during which the patients may be able to manage most activities of daily living and hygiene.
- **Stage 5:**
  o Moderately-severe cognitive decline as the cerebral cortex and hippocampus shrink and the ventricles enlarge. Patients are obviously confused and disoriented to date, time, and place. Patients may have difficulty using/understanding speech and managing activities of daily living. They may forget their address and telephone number. They may dress inappropriately, forget to eat resulting in weight loss, or eat a poor diet. They may be unable to do simple math, such as counting backward by 2s.

- **Stage 6:**
  - Moderately severe cognitive decline as the brain continues to shrink and neurons die. Patients are profoundly confused and unable to care for themselves and may undergo profound personality changes. They may confuse fiction and reality. They may fail to recognize family members, experience difficulty toileting, and begin to pace obsessively or wander away. Sundowner's syndrome, in which the person has disruption of waking/sleeping cycles and tends to get restless and wander about at night, is common. Patients may develop obsessive behaviors, such as tearing items, pulling at the hair, or wringing hands. This stage (with stage 7) may be prolonged, lasting 1-5 years.
- **Stage 7:**
  - Very severe cognitive decline during which most patients are wheelchair bound or bedbound and lose most ability to speak beyond a few words. They are incontinent of urine and feces and may be unable to sit unsupported or hold head up. They choke easily and have increased weakness and rigidity of muscles.

NON-ALZHEIMER'S DEMENTIAS

The following are characteristics of non-Alzheimer dementias:

- **Creutzfeldt-Jakob disease:** This causes rapidly progressive dementia with impaired memory, behavioral changes, and incoordination.
- **Dementia with Lewy Bodies:** Cognitive and physical decline is similar to Alzheimer's, but symptoms may fluctuate frequently. This form of dementia may include visual hallucinations, muscle rigidity, and tremors.
- **Frontotemporal dementia:** This may cause marked changes in personality and behavior and is characterized by difficulty using and understanding language.
- **Mixed dementia:** Dementia mirrors Alzheimer's and another type because of 2 different causes of dementia.
- **Normal pressure hydrocephalus:** This is characterized by ataxia, memory loss, and urinary incontinence.
- **Parkinson's dementia:** This form of dementia may involve impaired decision making, and difficulty concentrating, learning new material, understanding complex language, and sequencing. Inflexibility. Short or long-term memory loss may occur.
- **Vascular dementia:** Memory loss may be less pronounced than that common to Alzheimer's, but symptoms are similar.

NEEDS OF ALZHEIMER'S DISEASE OR DEMENTIA PATIENTS

The **needs of the patient with Alzheimer's disease or dementia** will vary depending on the stage of the disorder, but by the time the patient has moderate disease, some needs are evident:

- **Safety**: Because patients may wander and may have impaired judgment, safety issues are a primary concern. Patients may need movement or door alarms and locks on outside doors. Knives, scissors and other dangerous tools may need to be removed.
- **Nutritional support**: Patients often forget they've eaten and eat again or forget to eat, so supervision of nutrition is necessary. Patients are often unable to shop or prepare food.
- **Assistance with ADLs and IADLs**: Patients may need assistance with all ADLs, especially those related to personal hygiene. They may also need assistance with all IADLs and may need a conservator if no family is available to assist.
- **Exercise**: Patients need to remain active. Walking is an ideal exercise as patients often pace.
- **Emotional support**: Patients need and often respond to love and kindness.

HUNTINGTON'S DISEASE

Huntington's disease is an **autosomal-dominant genetic disease** caused by a mutation (repeats) of the **huntingtin (IT15) gene** of chromosome 4. The severity of the disease relates to the number or repeats. This defect causes destruction of neurons in the basal ganglia and the cerebral cortex, especially the cerebellum. The cerebellum excites movement, and the basal ganglia inhibit it, maintaining a balance that allows smooth coordination of muscle activity. Any disruption in the system can result in unwanted movements or the inability to control movements. The putamen and caudate comprise the neostriatum (part of the basal ganglia) and these are the first neural cells to die, interfering with both direct and indirect motor pathways. Damage to the **direct motor pathway** causes under-stimulation of the motor cortex, resulting in slow movement. Damage to the **indirect motor pathways** leads to over-stimulation of the motor cortex, resulting in chorea (rapid body movements). As cells of the basal ganglia die, the cerebellum atrophies, the ventricles enlarge, and gray and white matter are reduced. Huntington's disease may cause depression, suicidal ideation, mood swings, and memory loss.

HYPERNATREMIA

Hypernatremia is excess **salt**, indicated by a serum sodium level greater than 145 mEq/L. In bedridden seniors, hypernatremia can be from lack of access to water. Other causes of hypernatremia are: Too much sodium in IV fluid; too much salt in the diet; too much Mannitol; glycosuria; inadequate water intake due to a defective thirst mechanism from a hypothalamic problem; excessive water loss from sweating, vomiting and diarrhea; burns; and diabetes insipidus. Patients present with thirst, signs of dehydration, lethargy and weakness, and seizures or coma in severe cases. Diagnosis should be based on the history, physical exam and serum sodium level. Normal sodium ranges between136 to 145 mEq/L. Replace the **free water deficit**. The free water deficit = total body water (TBW) × [(plasma Na/140) – 1]. The total body water is the patient's weight in kilograms multiplied by 0.6. Free water replacement can be accomplished orally in conscious patients who can swallow or intravenously in more seriously ill patients.

HYPONATREMIA ETIOLOGY

Hyponatremia is **lack of salt**, indicated by a plasma sodium less than 135 mEq/L. Hyponatremia can be from severe dehydration, but is usually secondary to some other disorder. Hyponatremia can be hypervolemic, euvolemic or hypovolemic. This is determined by calculating the plasma osmolality and volume status of the patient. The Biochemistry lab calculates the **plasma osmolality** as follows: Plasma osmolality = $(2 \times Na^+) + (BUN/2.8) + (glucose/18)$. Causes of hyponatremia include kidney disease, excess free water intake, diuretics, SIADH, severe vomiting or diarrhea, low-sodium diet, liver disease and congestive heart failure. Symptoms depend on the acuity and severity of hyponatremia. Patients may be asymptomatic. Symptoms can include nausea, vomiting, headache and confusion. Severe cases can present with seizures and coma. Order serum electrolytes, BUN, glucose, and urine sodium (UNa). Be concerned if plasma sodium is <135 mEq/L; death often occurs below 105 mEq/L. Treatment depends on volume status and underlying cause of the hyponatremia.

PATIENTS BEING EVALUATED FOR ACUTE PSYCHOSIS
CLINICAL SIGNIFICANCE OF HYPONATREMIA

While severe hyponatremia may occur without psychiatric illness, it is not uncommon in psychiatric patients and may relate to worsening symptoms of disease, water intoxication related to compulsive polydipsia, compulsive smoking/drinking, and drug abuse. Additionally, some antipsychotic agents and antidepressants are associated with hyponatremia. Signs and symptoms include not only acute psychosis but also alterations in consciousness, hallucinations, tremor, seizures, impaired cognition, coma, and life-threatening electrolyte imbalance.

CLINICAL SIGNIFICANCE OF HYPOGLYCEMIA

While the classic signs of hypoglycemia include tremor, tachycardia, weakness, anxiety, and hunger, hypoglycemia may manifest with a wide variety of symptoms affecting multiple body systems, sometimes making diagnosis difficult. Because the central nervous system depends on carbohydrates for fuel, when the blood glucose level drops, one of the first indications is neurologic dysfunction, usually resulting in alterations of consciousness. Patients may be confused, lethargic, combative and/or extremely agitated. Sensorium may be depressed, and some patients develop seizures and focal neurologic deficits. Symptoms generally reverse promptly with administration of glucose.

SIGNIFICANCE OF HYPOXEMIA PER ABG

The normal value of PaO_2 is 80 to 100 mm Hg and SaO_2 is 96 to 98%. **Hypoxemia** occurs when the level of oxygen in the arterial system falls below 80 mm Hg. This in turn may result in **hypoxia**, a lack of adequate oxygenation at the tissue level. The brain is particularly susceptible to hypoxia with impaired functioning of the cerebral tissue within one minute of onset of hypoxia. The severity of neuropsychiatric symptoms relates to the rate and degree of hypoxic onset. Patients may tolerate a slow onset with minimal symptoms even at 60 mm Hg; but, if hypoxia occurs abruptly, the patient may have a concomitant abrupt onset of acute psychosis and delirium. Even mild hypoxia may produce changes in cognition with the patient having difficulty using language and understanding abstractions as well as coordinating motor activity. Patients may be extremely drowsy or emotionally labile. If hypoxia is severe, the patient may lose consciousness and/or experience seizures.

HYPERCALCEMIA

Hypercalcemia is an elevated **serum calcium level**. There are numerous causes; the most common are hypoparathyroidism and cancer. Clinical manifestations of hypercalcemia include fatigue, weakness, confusion, passage of renal stones, nausea, vomiting and abdominal pain. The diagnosis is made by laboratory examination of serum calcium, parathyroid hormone (PTH) and phosphate levels. Order CT scan or chest x-ray to rule out malignancy. The goal of treatment is to **lower the calcium level**. Possible treatments include IV fluids, calcitonin, corticosteroids, IV bisphosphonates, oral phosphate, and dialysis as a last resort. Primary hyperparathyroidism can be treated surgically. Underlying malignancy should be treated appropriately.

RULING OUT DRUG TOXICITIES AND OVERDOSES WHILE EVALUATING PATIENTS

When evaluating the patient, the NP must often rule out **drug toxicities** and **overdoses** when determining the diagnosis. Toxic reactions to drugs and overdoses can mimic other mental health disorders. Methods include:

- **Screening**: Various screening tests are available to screen for a wide variety of drugs (amphetamines, barbiturates, marijuana, cocaine, PCP, methadone, benzodiazepines, and barbiturates) and alcohol. Blood, urine, and sputum tests may be ordered.
- **Physical examination**: The NP should be aware of physical and other signs of substance use disorder, such as needle tracks, fingertip burns, dilated or constricted pupils, repeated sniffing, tremors, odor of marijuana/alcohol, and lack of personal hygiene. Patients may exhibit labile mood swings and impulsive or inappropriate behavior. Overdose is often associated with excess sedation and somnolence leading to coma.

- **History**: A careful history and review of previous medical records may provide information about drug use. If asked, patients may admit to using drugs, so the direct approach may be useful.

ALCOHOL WITHDRAWAL

Chronic abuse of ethanol (alcoholism) is associated with **alcohol withdrawal syndrome** *(delirium tremens)* with abrupt cessation of alcohol intake, resulting in hallucinations, tachycardia, diaphoresis, and sometimes-psychotic behavior. It may be precipitated by trauma or infection and has a high mortality rate, 5-15% with treatment and 35% without treatment. Management includes:

- Monitor vital signs and blood gases.
- Use the Clinical Instrument for Withdrawal for Alcohol (CIWA) to measure symptoms of withdrawal.
- Assess and monitor level of consciousness, orientation, alterations in sensory impressions, agitation, and anxiety.
- Provide an environment with minimal sensory stimulus (lower lights, close blinds).
- Implement fall and seizure precautions.
- Provide nutritional support and monitor intake and output.
- Implement measures to assure proper sleep and stress management.
- Express acceptance and reassurance.
- Maintain body temperature.

People easily aroused can usually safely sleep off the effects of ingesting too much alcohol but if semi-conscious or unconscious, emergency medical treatment (such as intravenous fluids and medications, intubation, and/or dialysis) may be necessary.

HALLUCINATIONS

Different types of **hallucinations** include:

- **Auditory**: This is the most common type of hallucination and often involves patients' hearing voices or commands to action, but some patients may hear music, clicks, or other sounds, which may be very persistent.
- **Visual**: Patients may believe that they see people or other things, such as bugs or snakes, which are not present. In some cases, visual hallucinations may be of unformed images, such as bright or flashing lights, or distortions.
- **Gustatory**: Patients may experience bad tastes.
- **Olfactory**: Patients may complain of smells that are not present, especially noxious or unpleasant smells.
- **Tactile**: Patients may feel as though something is touching them or crawling on their skin.
- **Hallucinogen-induced**: Various hallucinations may occur within a short time (minutes to an hour) of ingesting a hallucinogen, such as LSD.
- **Schizophrenia-induced**: During psychotic episodes, patient may experience a variety of hallucinations.

DEPRESSION AND AGING/CO-MORBID CONDITIONS

Depression affects about 19% of adults >55 and 37% of **older adults with co-morbid conditions**, putting older adults (who have the highest rates of suicide) at risk. **Depression onset** varies but is most common in young adulthood (mid-20s) and the recurrence rate is about 60%. Depression is associated with conditions that **decrease quality of life**, such as heart disease, neuromuscular diseases, arthritis, cancer, diabetes, Huntington's disease, stroke, and diabetes. Some drugs may also precipitate depression: diuretics, Parkinson's drugs, estrogen, corticosteroids, cimetidine, hydralazine, propanolol, digitalis, and indomethacin. Patients experience changes in mood, sadness, loss of interest in usual activities, increased fatigue, changes in appetite and fluctuations in weight, anxiety, and sleep disturbance. Depression often goes undiagnosed, so screening for at-risk individuals should be done routinely. Treatment includes tricyclic antidepressants (TCAs) and selective serotonin reuptake inhibitors (SSRIs), but SSRIs have fewer side effects and are less likely to cause death with an overdose. Older adults may take longer to respond to medication than younger adults. Counselling, treating underlying cause, and instituting an exercise program may help reduce depression.

PREVALENCE OF MOOD DISORDERS

The prevalence of mood disorders is discussed below:

- **Bipolar I disorder** occurs in up to 1.6% adults, with onset usually in early adulthood, although older psychiatric patients have higher rates of about 20%.
- **Bipolar II disorder** is less common, occurring in about 0.5% of the population, and occurs more frequently in females than males.
- **Cyclothymic disorder** occurs in 0.4 to 1% with onset in adolescence or early adulthood.

PREVALENCE OF PSYCHOTIC DISORDERS

The prevalence of psychotic disorders is discussed below:

- **Schizophrenia** occurs in up to 1.5% of adults with onset usually in early adulthood (20s). Those with first-degree family members with the disease have a risk of developing schizophrenia 10 times higher than the general public.
- **Schizoaffective disorder** usually begins in early adulthood, more commonly in females than males, and affects <1% of the population, although these patients are at high risk for substance use disorder and suicide.
- **Delusional disorders** affect only about 0.3% of the population, with onset usually in adolescence or later, with incidence increasing to 2 to 4% in older adults.
- **Shared psychotic disorder** (Folie a deux) is rare (prevalence unclear) but appears to affect females more than males. Age of onset varies widely.

PREVALENCE OF DISSOCIATIVE DISORDERS

The prevalence of dissociative disorders is discussed below:

- **Dissociative amnesia** is an area of controversy. Prevalence is unknown but reported cases are rising, although some researchers believe it is over-diagnosed in people who are suggestible.
- **Dissociative identity disorder** is an area of controversy as some people experiencing dissociative identity disorders are responding to suggestions. Prevalence is not clear but dissociative identity disorder is more common in females than males.
- **Dissociative fugue** (a specifier of dissociative amnesia) occurs rarely, affecting only about 0.2% of the general population although increased rates may occur in times of severe stress, such as during war or natural disasters.
- **Depersonalization/derealization disorder** may occur in about half the population in response to stress, but statistics are not available. However, depersonalization is observed in about 40% of hospitalized psychiatric patients.

PREVALENCE OF ANXIETY DISORDERS, PTSD, OCD, AND PHOBIAS

The prevalence of anxiety disorders, PTSD, OCD, and phobias is discussed below:

- **Phobias** of all types are fairly common in the general population, affecting between 7.2 and 11.3% of the population over a lifetime, with rates decreasing with age.
- **Obsessive-compulsive disorder** occurs in up to 2.3% of adults, with rates higher in those whose first-degree family members have the same disorder.
- **Post-traumatic stress syndrome** ranges from 1 to 14% in the general population over the course of a lifetime, but at-risk populations, such as those that have experienced abuse, have much higher rates, ranging from 3 to 64%. Incidence is about twice as high in females as in males, often associated with physical, emotional, or sexual abuse.
- **Generalized anxiety disorder (GAD)** occurs in up to 5% of the adult population with about two-thirds of people with GAD being female. Panic disorder affects up to 2% of the population but about 10% of those referred for psychiatric evaluation. Panic disorder is often associated with agoraphobia.

> **Review Video: Obsessive Compulsive Disorder (OCD)**
> Visit mometrix.com/academy and enter code: 499790

PREVALENCE OF SLEEP DISORDERS

The prevalence of sleep disorders is discussed below:

- **Insomnia** is a common problem occurring in up to 35% of adults at some time in their life, with chronic insomnia occurring in 10 to 15% of adults. Insomnia may be precipitated by physical conditions, such as heart disease, gastroesophageal reflux disease (GERD), urinary incontinence, or psychiatric disorders. Insomnia is common with depression and bipolar disorder.
- **Narcolepsy** is a rare disorder occurring in only 0.02 to 0.16% of adults, with onset usually occurring in adolescence (although symptoms may be evident earlier).
- **Breathing-related sleep disorders** affect up to 10% of the population, with increased incidence in older adults. Onset of symptoms is usually between ages 40 and 60.
- **Circadian Rhythm Sleep Disorder**, common among shift workers, occurs in up to 4% of adults and 7% of adolescents, with onset typically during adolescence and often proceeded by an episode of stress.

PREVALENCE OF EATING DISORDERS AND SUBSTANCE USE DISORDERS

The prevalence of eating disorders is discussed below:

- **Anorexia nervosa** is 10 times more common in females than males and affects about 0.5 to 1% of the population. Onset is usually during adolescence between ages 14 and 16.
- **Bulimia nervosa** affects between 3 and 8% of the population, with onset in the late teens or early adulthood between ages 18 and 24. Like anorexia, bulimia is 10 times more common in females than males.

The prevalence of substance use/abuse disorders is discussed below:

- **Alcoholism** affects about 16% of the population with about 20% of those over age 12 engaging in periodic binge drinking.
- **Illicit drugs** are used by about 6.3% of the population over age 12, with marijuana being the most commonly used illicit drug.

PREVALENCE OF PERSONALITY DISORDERS

The prevalence of personality disorders is discussed below:

- **Borderline personality disorder** affects 2 to 20% of the general population but up to 20% of hospitalized psychiatric patients. The disorder becomes evident during adolescence, but symptoms often lessen with age.
- **Schizotypal personality disorder** affects about 3% of the general population with a higher rate (about 17%) in diagnosed psychiatric patients.
- **Antisocial personality disorder** occurs in about 3.6% of the adult population with males at higher risk for the disorder than females and onset during childhood.
- **Paranoid personality disorder** affects up to 2.5% of the general population but up to 30% of those hospitalized for psychiatric disorders.

Pharmacology

PHARMACOTHERAPEUTICS

Pharmacokinetics relates to the **effects that the body has on a drug**, and pharmacodynamics relates to the effects that a drug has on the body. Both must be considered to ensure adequate dosing to achieve the optimal response from medications. With all drugs there is an intake (dose) and a response. Pharmacokinetics relates to the route of administration, the absorption, the dosage, the frequency of administration, the distribution, and the serum levels achieved over time. The drug's rate of clearance (elimination) and doses needed to ensure therapeutic benefit must be considered. Most drugs are cleared through the kidneys, with water-soluble compounds excreted more readily than protein-soluble compounds. Volume of distribution (intravenous [IV] drug dose divided by plasma concentration) determines the rate at which the drug passes into tissue. Drug distribution depends on the degree of protein binding and ion trapping that takes place.

PHARMACOKINETICS

Pharmacokinetics include:

- **Elimination half-time** is the time needed to reduce plasma concentrations to 50% during elimination. Usually the equivalent of 5 half-times is needed to completely eliminate a drug. Five half-times are also needed to achieve steady-state plasma concentrations if giving doses intermittently.
- **Context-sensitive half-time**, in contrast, is the time needed to reach a specific amount of decrease (50%, 60%) after stopping administration of a drug.
- **Recovery time** is the length of time it takes for plasma levels to decrease to the point that the person awakens. This is affected by plasm concentration.
- **Effect-site equilibrium** is the time between administration of a drug and clinical effect (the point at which the drug reaches the appropriate receptors) and must be considered when determining dose, time, and frequency of anesthetic agents. The bioavailability of drugs may vary, depending upon the degree of metabolism that takes place before the drug reaches its site of action.

TOLERANCE, DEPENDENCY, AND WITHDRAWAL

A patient can develop a **tolerance** to a particular medication when that medication is used over a period of time. The effects of the medication diminish and can lead to a need to increase the dosage to achieve the same response. Some diagnoses, such as schizophrenia, require medications throughout the patient's life, so changing medications may become necessary. Sometimes dependency and withdrawal symptoms can be seen along with the development of tolerance. **Dependency** can be psychological or physical in nature. The **withdrawal** of this medication can produce stress or anxiety along with real physical symptoms. The medication will often have to be weaned by slowly decreasing the dosage. In severe cases, abrupt discontinuation of the medication can lead to death.

PHARMACODYNAMICS

Pharmacodynamics relates to biological effects (therapeutic or adverse) of drug administration over time. Drug transport, absorption, means of elimination, and half-life must all be considered when determining effects. Responses may include continuous responses, such as blood pressure variations, or dichotomous response, in which an event either occurs or does not (such as death). Information from pharmacodynamics provides feedback to modify medication dosage (pharmacokinetics). Drugs provide biological effects primarily by interacting with receptor sites (specific protein molecules) in the cell membrane. Receptors include voltage-sensitive ion channels (sodium, chloride, potassium, and calcium channels), ligand-gated ion channels, and transmembrane receptors. Agonist drugs exert effects after binding with a receptor while antagonist drugs bind with a receptor but have no effects, so they can block agonists from binding. The total number of receptors may vary, up-regulating or down-regulating in response to stimuli (such as drug administration). Dose-response curves show the relationship between the amount of drug given and the resultant plasma concentration and biological effects.

TRIAL PERIOD OF NEW MEDICATION

When initiating any sort of pharmaceutical treatment, it is important to have an adequate **trial period** for each therapy before switching to alternative therapies due to **unresponsiveness**. Generally speaking, a medication is tested for 8 weeks before switching. However, 4 to 6 weeks is sufficient for stimulants before opting for a second-line treatment. Before switching medications, one should check with a pharmacist to ensure the dose of the current therapy has been **optimized**. It is not uncommon for agents to be prescribed in doses that fail to optimize the drug. Drug optimization may occur at either a lower or higher dose for an individual patient than the dose that is commonly prescribed. Dose optimization is 1 of the many reasons why upward and downward titrations are important.

PHASES OF PHARMACOLOGICAL TREATMENT

The **phases of pharmacological treatment** are as follows:

- **Initiation**: Involves a complete assessment and patient history. Lab work includes blood chemistry, complete blood count, liver, kidney, and thyroid function tests. The choice of medication and dosage may be adjusted based on these results. The inpatient should be closely monitored with the first dose of any medication for adverse reactions.
- **Stabilization**: Determination of the proper dosage of medication, with increases or decreases to achieve the desired response with minimal side effects. There should be an ongoing assessment process, including physical and psychological assessments along with re-evaluation of certain lab values or drug levels. The patient should be closely monitored for any unwanted side effects, drug interactions, or adverse reactions such as abnormal muscle movements or elevated blood pressure or temperature. The initial medication chosen may not produce the desired response, and a second drug may be added or a drug may be discontinued altogether.
- **Maintenance:** Utilizing medication to prevent reoccurrence of unwanted symptoms. Symptoms may reappear because of a change in metabolism caused by the medication, development of tolerance, physical illness, stress, or use of additional prescription or over the counter medications. Some side effects may not be evident until the patient has been on the medication for a period of time. Patients must be educated about potential side effects and possible decrease in the drug's efficacy and able to recognize red-flag signs and symptoms. Patients should understand the importance of follow-up visits and testing to evaluate their particular medication regimen.
- **Discontinuation**: Stopping medication. Most psychiatric medications are not stopped abruptly, but the dosage is slowly decreased over time. During the weaning period, the patient should be closely monitored for reappearance of the unwanted symptoms. Weaning helps to avoid withdrawal symptoms. Support, reassurance, and education are vital to the successful discontinuation of many psychiatric medications.

GERONTOLOGICAL PHARMACOLOGY

There are a number of issues that can affect **gerontological pharmacology**:

- **Antidepressants** are associated with excess sedation, so typical doses are only 16-33% of a younger adult's dose. Selective serotonin reuptake inhibitors (SSRIs) are safest, but Prozac® may cause anorexia, anxiety, and insomnia so should be avoided.
- **Older antipsychotics**, such as haloperidol, have high incidence of side effects. Atypical antipsychotics appear to be safer with risperidone (<2 mg daily) having the fewest adverse effects. The lowest possible doses should be tried first with careful monitoring of any antipsychotic.
- **Adverse effects of drugs** are 2-3 times more common in older adults than younger adults, often related to polypharmacy.
- **Drug and nutrient interactions** may impact nutrition by impairing appetite. Interactions may also alter the pharmacokinetics of nutrients or drugs, interfering with absorption, distribution, metabolism, and elimination.

PEDIATRIC PHARMACOLOGY

There are a number of **pediatric pharmacology** concerns. Pediatric doses are calculated according to the child's **weight** in kilograms, but other factors may affect dosage. Weight is estimated by age (although actual weight is safer):

- 50th percentile weight (kg) = (Age × 2) + 9.

Only **pediatric medications** should be prescribed if possible. Adult pills, for example, should not be cut for use for a child as even small variations in dosage may have adverse effects. Dosage should always be checked. Drug therapy in children may sometimes require adult dosages due to children's increased ability to quickly metabolize the medications. Children may also exhibit unusual responses or side effects to drugs compared to adults and should be very closely evaluated and frequently assessed.

SAFELY TAKING PRESCRIPTION MEDICATIONS

Patient education is vital to the success and safety of taking **prescription medications**. Patient education should include both the generic and brand name of the drug, indications for use, expected actions of the drug, dosage, route and duration of effects, what to do when a dose is missed, any associated precautions (i.e., operating machinery or diet restrictions), any associated side effects, and when to call the prescribing medical practitioner or seek help. Patients should also be educated on ways to help decrease side effects. They should be given **written information** including drug name, dosage, action, side effects, purpose, and any other pertinent information about the specific medication. All patient education should be **documented**, including a patient's understanding of the information, evaluation of patient's ability to administer the medication, and ability to obtain the medication.

POLYPHARMACY

Mental health patients are at risk for **polypharmacy**, taking too many drugs, because of taking the same drug under generic and brand names, taking drugs for 1 condition but contraindicated for another, and taking drugs that are not compatible. **Reasons** for polypharmacy include multiple prescriptions from different doctors; forgetfulness; confusion; failure to report current medications; the use of supplemental, over-the-counter, and herbal preparations in addition to prescribed medications; and failure of healthcare providers to adequately educate the patient. Patients should be encouraged to keep a list of all current medications (prescribed and otherwise) and to bring all medications with him/her to appointments. If family members are present, they should be enlisted in ensuring the patient avoids polypharmacy. Healthcare providers must take the time to discuss medications with the patient to ensure that the patient understands and must ask directly if the patient is taking any other medications. Helping the patient to make lifestyle changes, such as dieting or quitting smoking, may reduce the need for medications.

ANAPHYLAXIS SYNDROME

Anaphylaxis syndrome is a sudden acute systemic immunoglobulin E (IgE) or non-immunoglobulin E (non-IgE) inflammatory response affecting the cardiopulmonary and other systems.

- **IgE-mediated response** (anaphylactic shock) is an antibody-antigen reaction against an allergen, such as milk, peanuts, latex, insect bites, drugs, or fish. This is the most common type.
- **Non-IgE-mediated response** (anaphylactoid reaction) is a systemic reaction to infection, exercise, radio contrast material, or other triggers. While the response is almost identical to the other type, it does not involve IgE.

Typically, with IgE-mediated response, an **antigen** triggers release of substances, such as histamine and prostaglandins, which affect the skin, cardiopulmonary, and gastrointestinal systems. Histamine causes initial erythema and edema by inducing vasodilation. Each time the person has contact with the antigen, more **antibodies** form in response, and allergic reactions worsen. Anaphylactic shock related to anesthesia is rare, although anaphylactoid reactions may occur with opioids, hypnotics, and muscle relaxants. Antibiotics (penicillin, sulfonamides, cephalosporins) and latex allergy cause most medication/treatment related anaphylaxis.

DRUG INTERACTIONS

Drug interactions occur when 1 drug interferes with the activity of another in either the pharmacodynamics or pharmacokinetics:

- With **pharmacodynamic interaction,** both drugs may interact at receptor sites causing a change that result in an adverse effect or that interferes with a positive effect.
- With **pharmacokinetic interaction,** the ability of the drug to be absorbed and cleared is altered, so there may be delayed effects, changes in effects, or toxicity. Interactions may include problems in a number of areas. Absorption may be increased or (more commonly) decreased, usually related to the effects within the gastrointestinal system. Distribution of drugs may be affected, often because of changes in protein binding. Metabolism may be altered, often causing changes in drug concentration. Biotransformation of the drug must take place, usually in the liver and gastrointestinal system, but drug interactions can impair this process. Clearance interactions may interfere with the body's ability to eliminate a drug, usually resulting in increased concentration of the drug.

HERBAL REMEDIES AND DIETARY SUPPLEMENTS

There are literally thousands of **herbal remedies and dietary supplements** and myriad claims of success in treating or preventing disease, despite there being very little scientific evidence to support most claims. Many doctors recommend 1 daily **multivitamin** to ensure adequate vitamin intake and fish oil concentrate to reduce cholesterol, but patients often take high doses of herbal remedies and dietary supplements. This poses a number of problems. High doses of some vitamins can cause **toxicity**:

- **Vitamin A**: Headaches, loss of hair, liver damage, bone disorders, and birth defects.
- **Vitamin C**: Diarrhea and gastrointestinal upset.
- **Vitamin D**: Kidney stones, muscle weakness, and bleeding.
- **Vitamin E**: Inhibits action of vitamin K.
- **Niacin**: Liver damage, gastric ulcers, and increased serum glucose.
- **Vitamin B$_6$**: Neurological damage.

Herbal remedies often contain small amounts of **agents** found in drugs, so they can cause drug reactions and interactions. Also, patients often fail to inform their physicians when they are using alternative treatments.

St. John's Wort

The use of complementary and alternative medicine for the treatment of depression is very common. One of the most widely utilized and studied herbal therapies for the treatment of depression is **St. John's wort** or hypericum. This particular herb is widely utilized to treat depression symptoms in both the United States and in European countries. It has shown some effectiveness in treating mild to moderate depression, anxiety disorder, insomnia or seasonal affective disorder. Medical providers should be aware if the patient is taking this herb due to its **contraindications** with many commonly prescribed medications, such as, birth control pills, statins used to treat hyperlipidemia, protease inhibitors, antineoplastics, selective serotonin reuptake inhibitors (SSRIs), anticonvulsants, theophylline, and anticoagulants (such as warfarin).

Stimulants

Stimulants are primarily used to treat **attention-deficit/hyperactivity disorder (ADHD)** in children and **narcolepsy** in adults. Commonly used stimulants include methylphenidate (Ritalin®, Concerta®), dextro methylphenidate (Focalin®), dextroamphetamine (Dexedrine®), dextroamphetamine and amphetamine combinations (Adderall®). Magnesium pemoline (Cylert®) is used as a second- or third-line treatment because of liver toxicity. If 3 different stimulants fail to work, Wellbutrin® (bupropion), desipramine, or imipramine may be effective. Stimulants act on the central nervous system to heighten attentiveness and impulse control. Stimulant use should be accompanied by **behavioral therapy** for the child and **training** for the parents for 8 to 12 weeks. Stimulants are generally well-tolerated, though as many as 10% of patients may experience side effects, including abdominal pain, diminished appetite, nausea, vomiting, anorexia, headache, dizziness, insomnia, nervousness, changes in mood, social withdrawal, psychotic hallucinations, manic symptoms, depression, irritability, fatigue, nervous habits, and tics. Though stimulants have few drug-drug interactions, 2 are life-threatening: monoamine oxidase (MAO) inhibitors and furazolidone. Additionally, stimulants may interact with clonidine. Lowering dosage may relieve side effects.

Alzheimer's Disease Drugs

Treatment for **Alzheimer's disease** is aimed at slowing the progression of the disease and ensuring patient safety. Two types of drugs are approved by the Food and Drug Administration (FDA), but many clinical trials are taking place. In some cases, 2 drugs (such as Aricept® and Namenda®) may be given. Patients must take medication daily and be monitored carefully, as some drugs may worsen symptoms in some patients so different drugs may need to be tried.

Class of Drug	Drug and Indication	Adverse Effects
Cholinesterase inhibitors (Prevents breakdown of acetylcholine, needed for learning and memory)	Donepezil (Aricept®): All stages of Alzheimer's. Rivastigmine (Exelon®): Mild to moderate disease. Galantamine (Razadyne®): Mild to moderate disease.	Nausea, vomiting, loss of appetite, and frequent bowel movements.
	Tacrine (Cognex®): Mild to moderate disease. (Rarely used)	Nausea, vomiting, and possible damage to the liver.
Memantine (Targets glutamate, involved in learning and memory)	Namenda®: Moderate to severe disease.	Headache, confusion, dizziness, and constipation.

SSRIs

Selective serotonin reuptake inhibitors (SSRIs) are antidepressant medications that block reuptake of serotonin (neurotransmitter) in the brain, increasing the extracellular level of the neurotransmitter and improving transmission. **Neurotransmitters** allow neurons to communicate with "messages" passed from a presynaptic cell (sender) in one neuron to a post-synaptic receptor (receiver) in the other. The exact means by which SSRIs relieve depression is not clear. All SSRIs have similar action but may have different chemical properties that cause various side effects, so some people tolerate one better than others. Side effects include nausea, weight gain, sexual dysfunction, excitation, agitation, insomnia, drowsiness, increased perspiration, headache, and diarrhea. In rare cases, **serotonin syndrome** may occur from high levels of serotonin from overdose or combination with monoamine oxidase (MAO) inhibitors, so SSRIs must not be taken within 2 weeks of each other. Symptoms include severe anxiety and agitation, hallucinations, confusion, blood pressure swings, fever, tachycardia, seizures, and coma. SSRIs are not addictive but abrupt cessation may trigger **discontinuation syndrome** (flu-like symptoms).

There are a number of selective serotonin reuptake inhibitors (SSRIs) available for treatment of depression and anxiety.

CELEXA®

Citalopram (Celexa®) is chemically unrelated to other SSRIs and is specifically used to treat **acute depression** for 6-8 weeks with antidepressive results up to 24 weeks. Celexa® administered in the third trimester has been associated with neonatal complications, so the medication should be tapered during the third trimester if possible. Common side effects include dry mouth (20%), increased perspiration, tremor, nausea, somnolence, insomnia, ejaculation disorder (occurring in 6%), and decreased libido and impotence (primarily affecting males). Celexa® is associated with slight weight loss rather than weight gain. Celexa® should not be taken with triptans, linezolid, St. John's Wort, lithium, other SSRIs or central nervous system drugs. Concurrent use of nonsteroidal anti-inflammatory drugs (NSAIDs) and aspirin may increase risk of gastrointestinal bleeding. Celexa® increases the risk of suicidal thinking and behavior from childhood to young adulthood (age 24). Celexa® should not be used to treat depressive episodes of bipolar disease.

LEXAPRO® AND PROZAC®

Escitalopram (Lexapro®) and **fluoxetine** (Prozac®) are selective serotonin reuptake inhibitors (SSRIs) used for the treatment of **major depression** and **generalized anxiety disorder (GAD)**, which includes severe anxiety and apprehension for ≥6 months. They demonstrated effectiveness for depression with 8 weeks of acute treatment and maintenance for 36 weeks, but efficacy beyond 8 weeks for GAD has not been studied. Lexapro® and Prozac® administered in the third trimester has been associated with neonatal complications. Side effects, cautions, and interactions are similar to Celexa® and other SSRIs, but incidence of side effects is somewhat different. The most common side effects are nausea (15-18%), somnolence (6-13%), insomnia (9-12%), but ejaculation disorders are more common (9-14%) with impotence and anorgasmia (females) (2-6%) also reported. Side effects vary depending on whether treatment is given for depression or GAD. Lexapro® is not associated with weight gain, but Prozac® is. Lexapro® may increase suicidal thoughts and behavior in children through young adults (≤24) while Prozac® affects both children and all adults.

SERTRALINE (ZOLOFT®)

Sertraline (Zoloft®) is a **selective serotonin reuptake inhibitor (SSRI)** that is used for treatment of major depression, obsessive-compulsive disorder, panic disorder, post-traumatic stress disorder, premenstrual dysphoric disorder, and social anxiety disorder. Cautions and interactions are similar to other SSRIs, and side effects are similar to Paxil®. The most common side effects include headache (25%), nausea, diarrhea (20%), somnolence, insomnia, dry mouth, decreased libido (6%), and ejaculatory failure (14%). Zoloft® may increase suicidal thoughts and actions in both children and adults, especially in children <18. Zoloft® is not approved for bipolar disorder and may exacerbate the manic stage. Zoloft® is approved for pediatric patients only for treatment of obsessive-compulsive disorder (OCD), although it has been used successfully in clinical trials. Zoloft® is associated with weight loss, which may rarely be pronounced in patients, but usually averages 1-2 pounds.

PAXIL®

Paroxetine (Paxil®) is a selective serotonin reuptake inhibitor (SSRI) that is used as a **psychotropic drug** for the treatment of major depression, obsessive-compulsive disorder (OCD), panic disorder, social anxiety disorder, generalized anxiety disorder (GAD), and post-traumatic stress disorder (PTSD); it has broader uses than some other SSRIs. Paxil® has been shown to be effective for treatment up to 1 year and is used longer for chronic conditions, such as OCD. Cautions and interactions are similar to other SSRIs, but side effects are more pronounced than with other drugs and vary depending upon the diagnosis for which treatment is given. Paxil® is approved for adult use but not for pediatrics. Paxil® may increase suicidal thoughts and actions. Weight gain is common as is headache, asthenia, nausea, dry mouth, constipation, sweating, somnolence, insomnia, and diarrhea. Ejaculatory disorders (13-28%) and decreased libido (males) (6-15%) are fairly common, with sexual dysfunction affecting females to a lesser degree.

TRICYCLIC (CYCLIC) ANTIDEPRESSANTS

Tricyclic antidepressants (named for the 3-ring chemical structure of the first of this group) inhibit the uptake of neurotransmitters, primarily norepinephrine and serotonin, and serve as antagonists to dopamine and histamine. Tricyclic antidepressants usually target 2 or 3 of these **neurotransmitters** while newer antidepressants, such as selective serotonin reuptake inhibitors (SSRIs), target only one. Tricyclic antidepressants treat depression, attention-deficit/hyperactivity disorder (ADHD), nocturnal enuresis, and pain (migraine). They are sometimes referred to as **cyclic antidepressants** because newer drugs have a 4-ring structure. Tricyclic antidepressants are lipophilic and highly protein-bound, so they absorb rapidly. They affect the limbic system, decreasing β-receptors, which are stimulated by increased levels of norepinephrine, which interferes with receptor function. They have long half-lives, which increases toxic effects with overdose, and anticholinergic (primarily muscarinic) effects. Because of this, cyclic antidepressants tend to have more side effects than newer antidepressants: dry mouth, blurring vision, cardiac abnormalities, constipation, urinary retention, and hyperthermia. Alterations in memory and cognition, drowsiness, anxiety, muscle twitches, gynecomastia, and breast enlargement may occur. They are contraindicated with monoamine oxidase (MAO) inhibitors and cimetidine.

AMITRIPTYLINE

Amitriptyline (Elavil®) is a tricyclic (cyclic) antidepressant that targets **norepinephrine, serotonin, and histamine**. It should not be taken with monoamine oxidase (MAO) inhibitors, epinephrine, or alcohol. Alcohol inhibits antidepressive action but potentiates sedation. It is used for depression, insomnia, chronic pain, and fibromyalgia. It may increase suicidal thinking, and should be used with caution for those with history of seizures, cardiac disease, thyroid disease, prostate enlargement, pregnancy, and glaucoma. It is not recommended for children under 12 years old and is not approved for bipolar disorder. It may trigger psychosis in schizophrenic patients.

IMIPRAMINE

Imipramine (Tofranil®) targets the same neurotransmitters as amitriptyline (norepinephrine, serotonin, and histamine) and is used to treat **endogenous depression** (as opposed to depression caused by external factors, such as loss of job or loved one) and **enuresis** in children. Cautions, contraindications, and side effects are similar to amitriptyline, but extreme caution should be used with those with cardiovascular disease because of serious complications.

DESIPRAMINE

Desipramine (Norpramin®), a metabolite of imipramine, is a tricyclic (cyclic) antidepressant that targets **norepinephrine** and blocks **pain signals**, so it is used for depression, attention-deficit/hyperactivity disorder (ADHD), and neuropathic pain. It may be used in adolescents but should not be used for younger children. Cautions, contraindications, and side effects are similar to other tricyclic antidepressants. It is contraindicated with monoamine oxidase (MAO) inhibitors and in the recovery period of a myocardial infarction (MI). It should be discontinued prior to elective surgery because of possible cardiac effects and hypertension.

NORTRIPTYLINE

Nortriptyline (Aventyl®, Pamelor®), similar to desipramine, targets only **norepinephrine**. It is indicated only for the use of **endogenous depression** and is not recommended for children. Cautions, contraindications, and side effects are similar to other tricyclic antidepressants. It may exacerbate psychosis in those with schizophrenia. It may be given with electroshock therapy but should be discontinued before elective surgery.

CLINICAL MAO INHIBITORS

Monoamine oxidase (MAO) inhibitors are older antidepressant medications that are used less frequently now that others are available because they have significant side effects and interactions with other medications. MAO is an **enzyme** that breaks down neurotransmitters (norepinephrine, dopamine, serotonin, tyramine, and phenylethylamine) in the central nervous system. When levels of neurotransmitters fall, this can result in depression, so MAO inhibitors block this action.

- **Selective MAO inhibitors** may target only some neurotransmitters while non-selective may target all, including other enzymes.
- **Non-selective MAO inhibitors** include phenelzine (Nardil®), isocarboxazid (Marplan®), and tranylcypromine (Parnate®).

People using MAO inhibitors must avoid foods with high levels of tyramine (cheeses, wines, pickles) as well as medications, such as decongestants, in order to prevent severe hypertension crises. Other side effects include tremors, orthostatic hypotension, urinary retention, muscle spasms, jaundice, and agitation. Reactions may occur with opioids as well, especially meperidine (Demerol®), resulting in hyperthermia, seizures, and coma. Patients do not need to stop medication prior to surgery.

LITHIUM

Lithium carbonate (Eskalith®, Lithobid®) is used to control the **manic episodes** associated with bipolar disorder. It may also sometimes be used in conjunction with antidepressants to treat depression. Lithium has properties similar to sodium and potassium and interferes with the action of **sodium** in neuromuscular cells, reducing agitation. It also interferes with the production and action of neurotransmitters and affects levels of **tryptophan** and **serotonin** in the central nervous system. It can also cause an increase in **leukocyte production**. Lithium crosses the placenta so it should not be taken during pregnancy or while nursing. Overdosing can cause severe side effects so blood levels must be routinely monitored. Side effects include hand tremors, twitching, nausea, diarrhea, seizures, confusion, and increase in urinary output. About 1 patient in 25 develops goiter from lithium-induced hypothyroidism. Non-steroidal anti-inflammatory drugs (NSAIDs), selective serotonin reuptake inhibitors (SSRIs), phenothiazines, and diuretics may cause drug interactions.

WORK-UP REQUIRED BEFORE STARTING LITHIUM

Lithium has a very narrow therapeutic window, and **toxicity** is a medical emergency that can lead to death. Lithium is cleared from the body by the kidneys and can negatively affect **thyroid function**. An initial assessment should include an evaluation of kidney function. Tests include a urinalysis (UA), blood urea nitrogen (BUN) and creatinine levels, an electrolyte panel, 24-hour urine for creatinine clearance, screening for diabetes, hypertension, and any history of diuretic medications or over use of analgesics. Thyroid function must also be evaluated. A TSH, T3, T4 and free thyroxine index should be drawn. A complete physical exam along with a complete family and patient history should be obtained. Other tests should include a 12-lead electrocardiogram (ECG), fasting blood glucose, and complete blood count (CBC).

TOXICITY

Plasma levels of lithium must be frequently monitored for **lithium toxicity**, which can lead to death. The normal therapeutic range is 0.6 and 1.4 mEq/L for adults. Plasma levels will usually decrease to an acceptable level within 48 hours after discontinuation of the medication; however, in severe cases involving acute renal failure, **dialysis** may be necessary. A complete initial assessment, ongoing assessments, frequent evaluations of lithium levels, and patient education are all an essential part of the treatment plan. A patient must be able to tell the difference between side effects and symptoms of toxicity. Symptoms of mild toxicity associated with blood levels between 1.5–2.5 mEq/L can include severe vomiting and diarrhea, increased muscle tremors and twitching, lethargy, body aches, ataxia, ringing in the ears, blurry vision, vertigo, or hyperactive deep tendon reflexes. More severe symptoms associated with blood levels >2.5 mEq/L can include elevated temperature, low urine output, hypotension, electrocardiogram (ECG) abnormalities, decreased level of consciousness, seizures, coma, or death.

DIVALPROEX

Divalproex (Depakote®), a derivative of valproic acid, has the fewest side effects, adverse reactions, and lowest potential for toxicity of all anticonvulsants used to treat **bipolar disorder**. This medication has become the **first-line medication choice** for treatment of bipolar disorder because of its low potential for toxicity and effective treatment in several subgroups of bipolar disorder. It is usually well tolerated by the patient with side effects including gastrointestinal upset, tremors, drowsiness, headache, vertigo, and ataxia. It has also been associated with increased appetite and weight gain. The appearance of unexplained bruising, petechiae, or bleeding can indicate thrombocytopenia and the drug must be stopped. The most dangerous adverse side effect to this medication is severe liver damage. Liver function tests are obtained before starting the drug, then every 1-4 weeks for 6 months, followed by routine evaluations every 3-6 months throughout treatment. This medication is contraindicated during pregnancy.

CARBAMAZEPINE

Carbamazepine (Tegretol®) is considered a **third-line medication choice for bipolar disorder**. Divalproex and lithium are usually used in treatment before this medication choice. This medication can be added for use in combination medication therapy. Side effects can include sleepiness, vertigo, ataxia, blurred or double vision, gastrointestinal upset, fatigue, or, in rare cases, rash. Carbamazepine is metabolized by the cytochrome (CYP)-450 enzyme found in the liver and can lead to dangerous interactions and decreased effectiveness of other anticonvulsants, anticoagulants (such as warfarin), or oral birth control pills. Carbamazepine can lead to agranulocytosis, which is a decrease in the white blood cell count that can lead to fatal infections.

BENZODIAZEPINES

Benzodiazepines are the most commonly prescribed medications for **anxiety**. Some of the more commonly prescribed include chlordiazepoxide, lorazepam, diazepam, flurazepam, and triazolam. Benzodiazepines act to enhance the neurotransmitter **gamma-aminobutyric acid (GABA)**. This neurotransmitter inhibits the firing rate of neurons and therefore leads to a decline in anxiety symptoms. Indications for their use can include anxiety, insomnia disorders, alcohol withdrawal, seizure control, skeletal muscle relation, or agitation. They can also be utilized to reduce the anxiety symptoms pre-operatively or before any other type of medical procedure such as cardiac catheterization or colonoscopy. This class of drug is also the treatment of choice for alcohol withdrawal. Benzodiazepines are used to treat insomnia because of their sedative-hypnotic effects. When using a sedative-hypnotic to treat sleep disturbances, the medication should have rapid onset and allow the patient to wake up feeling refreshed instead of tired and groggy. When administered at bedtime, most benzodiazepines will produce a sleep-inducing effect and should be used on a short-term basis.

BENZODIAZEPINE TOXICITY

Benzodiazepine toxicity may result from accidental or intentional overdose with such drugs as Xanax®, Librium®, Valium®, Ativan®, Serax®, Versed®, and Restoril®. Mortality is usually the result of co-ingestion of other drugs. Symptoms are often non-specific neurological changes: lethargy, dizziness, alterations in consciousness, and ataxia. Respiratory depression and hypotension are rare complications. Coma and severe central nervous depression are usually caused by co-ingestions. Diagnosis is based on history and clinical exam, as benzodiazepine level does not correlate well with toxicity. Treatment includes:

- Gastric emptying (<1 hour).
- Charcoal.
- Concentrated dextrose, thiamine, and naloxone if co-ingestions suspected, especially with altered mental status.
- Monitoring for central nervous system/respiratory depression.
- Supportive care.
- Flumazenil (antagonist) 0.2 mg each minute to total 3 mg may be used in some cases but not routinely advised because of complications related to benzodiazepine dependency or co-ingestion of cyclic antidepressants. Flumazenil is contraindicated in the presence of increased intracranial pressure.

BUSPIRONE

Due to the addictive potential of benzodiazepines, the use of non-benzodiazepines to treat anxiety has increased. One of the most commonly used non-benzodiazepines is **buspirone**. This medication is highly effective in treating **anxiety** and its associated symptoms, such as insomnia, poor concentration, tension, restlessness, irritability, and fatigue. Buspirone had no addictive potential, is not useful in alcohol withdrawal or seizures or known to interact with other central nervous system depressants. Because it may take several weeks of continual use for the effects of this drug to be realized by the patient, it cannot be used on an as needed basis. Buspirone does not increase depression symptoms and therefore is useful in treating anxiety associated with depression. Side effects associated with medication can include gastrointestinal upset, dizziness, sleepiness, excitement, or headache.

FIRST-GENERATION ANTIPSYCHOTICS

There are a variety of **first-generation antipsychotics** available, though their use is becoming less prominent now that atypical antipsychotic agents are available. Some first-generation antipsychotics include: chlorpromazine (Thorazine®), thioridazine hydrochloride (Mellaril®), haloperidol (Haldol®), pimozide (Orap®), fluphenazine hydrochloride (Prolixin®), molindone hydrochloride (Moban®), and trifluoperazine hydrochloride (Stelazine®). Possible side effects include: photosensitivity, sexual dysfunction, dry mouth, dry eyes, nasal congestion, blurred vision, constipation, urinary retention, exacerbation of narrow-angle glaucoma, various cardiac effects, extrapyramidal effects, dyskinesia, sedation, cognitive dulling, amenorrhea, menstrual irregularities, hyperglycemia or hypoglycemia, increased appetite, and weight gain. Drug interactions depend on the individual drug.

SECOND-GENERATION/ATYPICAL ANTIPSYCHOTICS

Second-generation antipsychotics (SGAs), also called atypical antipsychotics, are used for bipolar disorders, schizophrenia, and psychosis and include aripiprazole (Abilify®), clozapine (Clozaril®), olanzapine (Zyprexa®), quetiapine (Seroquel®), risperidone (Risperdal®), and ziprasidone (Geodon®). Females report more side effects than males, but the recommended doses for males and females are identical. Women were underrepresented when SGAs were clinically tested because researchers feared teratogenic effects on fetuses. Side effects include constipation, increased appetite, weight gain, urinary retention, various sexual side effects, increased prolactin, menstrual irregularities, increased risk of diabetes mellitus, decreased blood pressure, dizziness, agranulocytosis, and leucopenia. Atypical antipsychotics may interact with fluvoxamine, phenytoin, carbamazepine, barbiturates, nicotine, ketoconazole, phenytoin, rifampin, and glucocorticoids. The use of atypical antipsychotic agents correlates with significant weight gain. Overweight and obese patients are likely to develop insulin resistance and glucose intolerance, which may lead to diabetes mellitus. Data show clozapine and olanzapine as the greatest offenders. Ziprasidone seems to present the lowest risk.

> **Review Video: <u>Anti-Psychotic Drugs: Clozapine, Haloperidol, Etc.</u>**
> Visit mometrix.com/academy and enter code: 369601

EXTRAPYRAMIDAL EFFECTS

The **extrapyramidal system** is a group of neural connections outside of the medulla that control movement. Extrapyramidal effects are the result of drug influence on the extrapyramidal system and include:

- **Akinesia** (inability to start movement).
- **Akathisia** (inability to stop movement).
- **Dystonia** (extreme and uncontrolled muscle contraction, torticollis, flexing, and twisting).

The most common extrapyramidal symptom caused by antipsychotic agents is **tardive dyskinesia**, in which patients are unable to control their movements, such as tics, lip smacking, and eye blinking. The term tardive refers to the delayed onset of the symptoms. Even after the discontinuation of a drug, extrapyramidal side effects may still be present. **Oculogyric crisis** is common in children, and features restlessness, staring, painful deviation or crossing of the eyes, jaw spasm, and protruding tongue. Antipsychotics also cause Parkinsonian symptoms like lead-pipe muscle rigidity, but these symptoms occur most often in elderly adults.

TREATMENT

Extrapyramidal effects drastically alter a patient's quality of life by making him/her conspicuous in public. The patient can also develop frightening **dysphagia** (difficulty swallowing) and **depression**. One must treat the symptoms in order to maintain an effective psychopharmacological therapy or risk the patient's discontinuation of the drugs due to their motor side effects. Symptom control agents of choice include:

- Anticholinergics, such as benztropine or biperiden.
- Antiviral amantadine hydrochloride, which mediate symptoms by increasing dopamine activity in the brain.
- Bromocriptine.
- Pergolide.

Adult studies have shown that vitamin E may mediate extrapyramidal symptoms, though research regarding pediatric use is limited.

TARDIVE DYSKINESIA

Tardive dyskinesia (TD) is a chronic syndrome that can develop as a result of the **long-term use of antipsychotic medications**. The elderly population is at the highest risk for development of this syndrome. There is currently no effective treatment and the best defense is early detection and prevention of symptoms. Use of the lowest effective dosage of an atypical antipsychotic is often recommended for prevention. TDs are abnormal movements of the tongue, lips, face, trunk, and extremities. Patients with schizophrenia appear especially vulnerable to developing TDs after exposure to neuroleptics, anticholinergics, toxins, and substances of abuse. If caused by medication, TDs continue in 50% of patients even if the medication is stopped. Symptoms include:

- Lip smacking or puckering.
- Tongue protrusion.
- Eyelid blinking.
- Repetitive tapping.
- Marching movement.
- Choreiform movements of the extremities and trunk.
- Occasional spasm of diaphragm or muscles involved in swallowing which can lead to choking or respiratory problems.

NEUROLEPTIC MALIGNANT SYNDROME

Neuroleptic malignant syndrome (NMS) is 1 of the most serious complicating side effects associated with use of **antipsychotic medications**. Initiating antipsychotics, haloperidol, benzamines, tricyclics, monoamine oxidase (MAO) inhibitors, and lithium too fast can cause NMS. This potentially fatal and rare condition can result with 1 single dosage of medication. The highest risk medications fall into the **high-potency category**. Symptoms occur acutely and can include high fever, tachycardia, diaphoresis, rigid muscles, shaking, incontinence, confusion and decreased level of consciousness, renal failure, and elevated creatine phosphokinase (CPK) levels. It is very important to always monitor a patient's **temperature** with use of antipsychotics. The patient may require supportive care in the form of resuscitation, mechanical ventilation, hydration, and fever reducing actions. All antipsychotic drugs must be discontinued and the patient may be treated with dantrolene or bromocriptine. Development of this side effect does not exclude the patient from future treatment with antipsychotic medications.

MELATONIN

Melatonin is a natural hormone that serves to regulate **sleep and circadian rhythms**. This dietary supplement has been investigated as a therapy and/or adjunct therapy for treating seasonal affective disorder (SAD), bipolar disorder, attention-deficit hyperactivity, jet lag, sleep disorders, and solid tumor cancers as well as for learning and memory enhancement. The dose for all but cancer is sublingual, 2.5 mg to 3.0 mg at bedtime only. The dose for cancer is 20 mg with chemotherapy. Melatonin is not regulated by the Food and Drug Administration (FDA). Therefore, all use of melatonin should be monitored closely, especially when it is used in conjunction with **psychotropic medications**. Melatonin is generally well tolerated. The only apparent side effects are potentiation of the effects of sedatives and mild headaches.

STEROID-INDUCED PSYCHOSIS

Steroid-induced psychosis occurs in about 5-6% of patients receiving steroids with higher doses (at least 40 mg prednisone or equivalent) most likely to result in symptoms. Onset, usually preceded by state of hyperexcitability, is with six to ten hours for parenteral drugs and four to 6 days for oral. Symptoms vary widely with about 40% primarily depressive but some exhibit mania, delirium and paranoid psychosis. Incidence is highest in females and most common with lupus erythematosus (about 40%) and pemphigus (about 20%).

ANTIBIOTIC-INDUCED MANIA

Antibiotic-induced mania (AKA antibiomania) is a rare onset of acute mania, which may include psychosis and paranoia, associated with administration of antibiotics. In the United States, the drugs most commonly associated with the disorder are clarithromycin and ciprofloxacin, but a wide range of other antibiotics, including isoniazid and penicillin, have been implicated. Discontinuing the medication should result in resolution of the symptoms.

SEROTONIN SYNDROME, BACLOFEN WITHDRAWAL, AND BENZODIAZEPINE WITHDRAWAL

Serotonin syndrome, baclofen withdrawal, and benzodiazepine withdrawal are explained below:

- **Serotonin syndrome**: This life-threatening reaction usually results from taking an overdose of medication that causes levels of serotonin to increase or combining two medications, such as an SSRI with a triptan. Drugs that contribute include antidepressants, opioids, psychedelics, St. John's wort, lithium, and CNS stimulants. Effects include cognitive (confusion, hallucinations), autonomic (tachycardia, nausea, diarrhea, hyperthermia), and somatic (myoclonus, tremor, hyperreflexia). Treatment includes stopping drugs, administering antagonist (cyproheptadine), and providing supportive interventions.
- **Baclofen withdrawal**: Baclofen is a central-acting muscle relaxant used for treatment of muscle spasticity. Patients may experience withdrawal symptoms when the medication is discontinued, especially after more than two to three months of use. Symptoms are worse with abrupt discontinuation and abate with readministration. Symptoms include hallucinations, delusions, confusion, nausea, autonomic dysfunction, fever, muscle rigidity, memory impairment, and seizures.
- **Benzodiazepine withdrawal**: Benzodiazepines are depressants used to relieve anxiety. Abrupt withdrawal after prolonged use may result in autonomic withdrawal symptoms (similar to baclofen) with increased agitation, muscular weakness, seizures, tremors, hypertension, and tachycardia. Treatment includes tapering of drug dosage and administration of diazepam.

COMMON INTERACTIONS WITH PROZAC

Prozac® (fluoxetine hydrochloride) is an **SSRI antidepressant** that is indicated for treatment of depression, OCD, bulimia nervosa, panic disorder, PTSD, premenstrual dysphoric disorder, and depressive disorders associated with bipolar I disorder. Prozac has many interactions that the NP must be aware of when prescribing Prozac.

- **Drug-drug interactions**: Because of multiple drug-drug interactions, when prescribing Prozac®, the NP should always check the list of interactions against the patient's list of drugs. Drug-drug interactions that increase risk of serotonin syndrome include MAO inhibitors (avoid use of Prozac within 5 weeks), amphetamines, tricyclic antidepressants, tramadol, and other SSRIs and SSNRIs. Drugs that increase CNS effects include benzodiazepine, lithium, and tricyclic antidepressants. Prozac® may potentiate the effects of beta-blockers, carbamazepine, flecainide, and vinblastine. Prozac® may alter glucose levels when used with insulin and oral antidiabetics, so dosage of these drugs may need to be adjusted.
- **Drug-herb interactions**: Serotonin syndrome may occur with St. John's wort. Patients may experience increased sedative effect with the two drugs.
- **Drug-lifestyle interactions**: Alcohol may increase CNS depression and should not be used with Prozac®.

COMMON INTERACTIONS BETWEEN PSYCHIATRIC MEDICATIONS AND THEOPHYLLINE

Theophylline is a methylxanthine used to treat bronchospasm, but it must be used with care with some **psychiatric medications**. Interactions include:

- **Lithium**: Theophylline increases the rate of renal clearance of lithium, so the dosage of lithium must be increased in order to maintain the appropriate serum level, usually by about 60%; however, because of the narrow therapeutic range of lithium, dosage should be titrated carefully and serum levels monitored frequently.
- **Benzodiazepines** (diazepam, lorazepam, flurazepam): Theophylline blocks adenosine receptors while benzodiazepines increase CNS concentration of adenosine. This results in the need for greater diazepam dosage to reach the desired effects. Because of the increased dosage, if the theophylline is discontinued, patients may experience respiratory depression.
- **St. John's wort**: This herbal drug decreases the concentration of theophylline in the plasma, so if the St. John's wort is discontinued, the patient may experience theophylline toxicity.

Development, Anatomy, and Physiology of the Brain

NEURONS

Neurons are nerve cells that transmit nerve impulses throughout the central and peripheral nervous systems for the brain to interpret. The neuron includes the cell body or soma, the dendrites, and the axons. The **soma** contains the nucleus. The **nucleus** contains the chromosomes. The **dendrite** extends from the cell body and resembles the branches of a tree. The dendrite receives chemical messages from other cells across the **synapse,** a small gap. The **axon** is a thread-like extension of the cell body, up to 3 feet long in spinal nerves. The axon transmits an electro-chemical message along its length to another cell. Axons of neurons in the **peripheral nervous system (PNS)** that deal with muscles are myelinated with fat to speed up the transmission of messages. Neurons in the PNS that deal with pain are unmyelinated because transmission does not have to be fast. Some neurons in the **central nervous system (CNS)** are myelinated by oligodendrocytes.

CENTRAL NERVOUS SYSTEM

The components of the **central nervous system (CNS)** are the brain and spinal cord. The CNS is the largest portion of the nervous system. The CNS is housed in the dorsal cavity, which includes the cranial cavity (the skull) and the spinal cavity (the vertebral column and spinal cord). The **brain** is responsible for behavior, and the **spinal cord** mediates signals traveling to and from the brain. The major sections of the brain include the brainstem, the cerebral hemispheres (comprising the frontal lobes, temporal lobes, occipital lobes, and parietal lobes), and the cerebellum. The major sections of the spinal cord include cervical nerves and vertebrae, thoracic nerves and vertebrae, lumbar nerves and vertebrae, and the sacral nerves and vertebrae. In addition to the nerves and vertebrae, the spinal column is also made up of vertebral discs, which serve to cushion the vertebrae.

CEREBRUM

The **cerebrum** comprises 2 cerebral hemispheres connected by the corpus callosum and is further divided into lobes. The cerebrum is primarily white matter composed of myelinated nerve fibers with a thin layer of gray matter called the cerebral cortex. The **frontal lobes** mediate reasoning, higher mental processes, problem solving, motor function, memory, and judgment. Broca's area in the left frontal lobe is essential to communication, both in understanding language and mediating facial nerves and expression. The **occipital lobes** control vision and recognition, and the **parietal lobes** mediate sensory function, cognition, and understanding speech. The **temporal lobes** regulate emotion, memory, hearing, and some functions of speech, and also interpret sensory experiences, visual pictures, and music. Wernicke's area is located in the left temporal lobe and is responsible for language comprehension.

DIENCEPHALON

The **diencephalon** is located above the brainstem and between the cerebral hemispheres. It comprises primarily gray matter and surrounds the third ventricle. The diencephalon contains a number of structures:

- **Thalamus**: Receives sensory input from other parts of the central nervous system (CNS) and carries them to appropriate areas of the cerebral cortex. The thalamus serves as a gateway and also an editor for sensory input (except for smell).
- **Hypothalamus**: Regulates heart rate, blood pressure, temperature, fluid and electrolyte balance, hunger, weight, stomach and intestines, and sleep and also produces substances that stimulate the pituitary gland to release hormones.
- **Optic chiasm:** The optic nerves cross in this area anterior to the pituitary gland.

42

- **Posterior pituitary gland:** Stores and secretes oxytocin and antidiuretic hormone, which are produced by the hypothalamus.
- **Mammillary bodies:** Active in memory of smells.
- **Pineal gland:** Attached to the third ventricle, produces melatonin, and mediates sleep.

LIMBIC SYSTEM

The **limbic system**, in the region of the diencephalon, is essential to regulation of emotion, hormones, mood, and pain/pleasure sensations. The limbic system is comprised of several structures, including:

- **Amygdala**: An almond-shaped grouping of nuclei responsible for mediating arousal, emotion and fear responses, and hormones.
- **Cingulate gyrus:** The structure responsible for matching sensory input with emotional response.
- **Hippocampus:** A group of neurons responsible for organizing and processing memories, spatial relationships, and emotional regulation.
- **Hypothalamus:** A structure that is involved in almost all body processes, including autonomic functions, emotions, homeostasis, endocrine and sleep regulation, and others.
- **Thalamus:** A group of cells that mediates motor function, and receives, processes, and relays sensory signals.

CEREBELLUM AND BASAL GANGLIA

The **cerebellum**, below the occipital lobes, comprises 2 hemispheres connected by the vermis. The cerebellum is primarily white matter with a thin covering of gray matter (cerebellar cortex). Three nerve tracts in the cerebellum carry sensory information from the spinal cord to the rest of the central nervous system. The cerebellum processes information about actual body position and desired position and sends motor impulses based on the information to facilitate balance and coordinate movement.

The **basal ganglia** (masses of gray matter in the cerebral hemispheres) mediate voluntary movement and coordination and play a role in cognition. The basal ganglia are located in the telencephalon region of the brain, and the corpus striatum, subthalamic nucleus, substantia nigra are all components of the basal ganglia. The corpus striatum (caudate nucleus and lenticular nucleus) comprises alternating layers of white and gray matter that mediate movement and executive function. The substantia nigra regulates mood, produces the neurotransmitter dopamine, and mediates voluntary movement.

VENTRICULAR SYSTEM

The brain's **ventricular system** protects the various structures of the brain from traumatic injury while transporting cerebrospinal fluid. There are 5 structures of the ventricular system:

1. The **aqueduct of Sylvius** (a cerebrospinal fluid channel between the third and fourth ventricles).
2. **Choroid plexus** (produces cerebrospinal fluid and acts as a buffer between the fluid and blood).
3. **Third ventricle** (another channel for cerebrospinal fluid).
4. **Fourth ventricle** (between the pons and medulla, acts as the primary channel for fluid to the spinal cord).
5. **Lateral ventricle** (the final channel for cerebrospinal fluid).

BRAINSTEM

The brainstem (connecting the spinal cord and the cerebrum) comprises masses of gray matter and nerve fibers, is located at the base of the brain, and controls most autonomic functions, including breathing, arousal, digestion, and heart rate. The brainstem contains the following structures:

- **Midbrain**: Connects the spinal cord to other brain regions and contains reflex centers to move the head and eyes and maintain balance.
- **Medulla oblongata:** Elongation of the spinal cord extending to the pons. Conducts impulses to and from the brain and spinal cord and contains centers to control the heart and respirations.
- **Pons**: Bulging area that is found on the underside of the brainstem. It carries impulses between the medulla oblongata and the cerebrum and also controls the rate of breathing.

SPINAL CORD

The spinal cord carries the nerves from the brain to the peripheral nervous system, contains the cerebrospinal fluid, and is covered with 3 protective membranes (meninges) that are continuous around the brain and spinal cord. The spinal cord contains a number of structures:

- **Pia mater**, the innermost layer, adheres to the spinal cord.
- **Subarachnoid space**, between the pia mater and arachnoid mater (the next layer), contains the cerebrospinal fluid. Spinal (subarachnoid) anesthesia is administered into this space.
- **Arachnoid mater** is the primary impermeable barrier preventing movement of drugs from the epidural to the subarachnoid space. It is closely adherent to the dura mater (outside layer).
- **Dura mater** is a protective fibroelastic membrane that is fairly impenetrable.
- **Epidural space** lies outside of the dura mater and contains lymphatics, fatty tissue, nerve roots, small arteries, and the epidural venous plexus. Epidural and caudal anesthesia is administered into this space. The (adult) depth ranges from 6 mm at L2 and 4-5 mm in the mid-thoracic area.

PERIPHERAL NERVOUS SYSTEM

The **peripheral nervous system (PNS)** comprises the long nerves that serve organs and limbs. The PNS is further divided into the **autonomic nervous system** and the **somatic nervous system**. Sympathetic nerves are part of the autonomic nervous system. Sympathetic nerves are found both within the central nervous system (CNS) (preganglionic) and the PNS (postganglionic), with those in the CNS communicating with those in the PNS through a series of ganglia by means of neurotransmitters (acetylcholine) at synapses. The **sympathetic nervous system** (T1-L2 or L3) activates in times of stress and is implicated in pain. The nerves innervate deep structures, viscera, and skin. **Ganglia** are paired: 3 cervical, 12 thoracic, 4 lumbar, 4 sacral, and 1 impar (at coccyx). The **parasympathetic nerves** maintain a state of homeostasis when the body is not under stress. The autonomic nervous system mediates the body's organs and maintains homeostasis. Functions of the autonomic nervous system include heart rate and function, respiration, digestion, sexual arousal, and other systems.

SOMATIC NERVOUS SYSTEM

The **somatic nervous system** comprises cranial and spinal nerves that connect the central nervous system to the skeletal muscles and skin. The somatic nervous system is the voluntarily-controlled component of the peripheral nervous system, and it receives and responds to external sensory stimuli from the skin and sensory organs. **Efferent nerves** mediate movement through stimulation of skeletal muscles, allowing the person to move. The somatic nervous system carries sensations of pain to the brain, helping the individual avoid danger, so it's part of the protective system of the body. Somatic nerves leave the spinal column as nerve roots and may form a plexus or an individual nerve. **Plexi** include cervical, brachial, lumbosacral, and sacral. **Individual nerves** include the occipital, intercostal, and suprascapular.

> **Review Video: The Nervous System**
> Visit mometrix.com/academy and enter code: 708428

PHYSIOLOGIC RESPONSE TO STRESS AND ANXIETY

The **physiologic response to stress and anxiety** occurs on a continuum from mild to severe. These responses are not controllable by the person experiencing these feelings and are mediated through the immune and autonomic nervous systems. The sympathetic nervous system turns on the physiologic response to stress and anxiety and readies the body to react. Under stress, the **hypothalamus** acts to stimulate the pituitary gland to secrete a hormone, which leads to increased cortisol levels. This increased production may lead to elevated availability of glucose for heightened cellular metabolism. In some individuals the **parasympathetic nervous system** can dominate during stress. The associated symptoms often have the opposite effect of what is seen when the **sympathetic nervous system** is in control.

> **Review Video: Autonomic Nervous System**
> Visit mometrix.com/academy and enter code: 598501

EFFECTS OF STRESS AND THE SYMPATHETIC NERVOUS SYSTEM ON CARDIOVASCULAR AND RESPIRATORY SYSTEMS

The **sympathetic nervous system** releases **epinephrine** in response to stress and anxiety. This affects the cardiovascular and respiratory systems by revving up their normal responses and readying the body to fly into action.

- In the **cardiovascular system**, the heart rate and blood pressure increase with associated feelings of palpitations. Blood is shunted away from non-vital organs, such as the stomach, intestines, and kidneys, resulting in decreased peristalsis and urine output. There is increased blood flow to necessary muscle groups to encourage a quick response time. Blood coagulation time increases.
- In the **respiratory system**, there is an increase in the rate of respirations and a decrease in the depth of respirations; breathing becomes rapid and shallow and is associated with feelings of shortness of air.

STRESS AND THE SYMPATHETIC NERVOUS SYSTEM EFFECTS

In response to stress, the **sympathetic nervous system** usually leads to a decrease in blood flow in the **gastrointestinal (GI) tract**. This decreases appetite and movement of the intestinal tract.

The **neuromuscular system** is charged up and ready to respond. Reflex time is increased, and there can be some twitching or shaking of muscles. The need for sleep is greatly reduced, leading to periods of insomnia. The facial expression may be tense and anxious, and the patient may actually pace about. The patient may have uncontrolled muscle movements, restlessness, fast speech, avoidance, or startle easily.

The **integumentary system** also responds. The skin may become flushed or itchy and there is an increase in sweat gland production. These reactions can lead to ineffective interpersonal communication or social withdrawal. Cognitive functioning can also be affected by stress and anxiety. The patient might appear distracted or unable to concentrate, forgetful, confused, or make errors in judgment not normally seen. The patient may also experience flashbacks or have frightening hallucinations.

SEROTONIN

Serotonin is one of the four major **neurotransmitters**. Serotonin affects a variety of mood and physical disorders, including depression, psychosis, anxiety, nausea and vomiting, migraines, and other ailments. Serotonin affects many aspects of mood and physical health, and this neurotransmitter is a mediator of mood, sleep, sexual desire, anger, and appetite. The serotonin neurotransmitter system originates in the caudal dorsal raphe nucleus and the rostral dorsal raphe nucleus. Axons of the serotonin neurons originating in these areas of the raphe nucleus terminate in various areas of the brain and central nervous system, including the spinal cord, cerebral cortex, thalamus, striatum, hypothalamus, cingulate gyrus, neocortex, hippocampus, and amygdala.

DOPAMINE

Dopamine is another one of the four major neurotransmitters. Dopamine affects a variety of mood and cognitive disorders, including bipolar disorder, attention-deficit/hyperactivity disorders, anxiety disorders, psychosis, and others. This system is primarily responsible for mediating the motor system, reward/pleasure system, and cognition. Dopamine is a **stabilizing force** in the brain, regulating the flow of impulses, but it does not cross the blood-brain barrier so all action is in the brain. Dopamine also affects endocrine function and may play a role in mediating nausea. There are 4 major **dopamine pathways** in the brain: the mesocortical pathway, mesolimbic pathway, nigrostriatal pathway, and tuberoinfundibular pathway. These pathways originate in the hypothalamus, substantia nigra, and ventral tegmentum. Parkinson's disease is characterized by inadequate production of dopamine.

ACETYLCHOLINE

Acetylcholine is another one of the four major neurotransmitters. Acetylcholine plays a role in a variety of cognitive and neurodegenerative disorders, including attention-deficit/hyperactivity disorders, Alzheimer's disease, and other dementias. Acetylcholine is active in the central and peripheral nervous systems. Acetylcholine, the neurotransmitter released by a **cholinergic synapse**, affects learning, short-term memory, arousal, and pleasure/reward systems. Moreover, the parasympathetic nervous system (the visceral nerves of the autonomic nervous system comprising part of the peripheral nervous system) is completely cholinergic, and acetylcholine transmits impulses that activate muscles. The **cholinergic neurotransmitter system** originates in the basal optic nucleus of Meynert, the medial septal nucleus, and the meso-pontine tegmental area.

NORADRENALINE

Noradrenaline is also called norepinephrine. It is also one of the four major neurotransmitters in the brain, released by the adrenal glands. Noradrenaline is primarily responsible for mediating arousal and the reward system, and is released in response to stress. This noradrenaline system originates in the locus coeruleus and lateral tegmental field, and it is able to transmit messages to both sides of the brain. Axons from neurons firing in the locus coeruleus and lateral tegmental field act on **adrenergic receptors** in the spinal cord, thalamus, hypothalamus, hippocampus, amygdala, neocortex, striatum, cingulate gyrus, and other areas. Norepinephrine plays a role in depressive disorders and attention-deficit/hyperactivity disorders, among others.

GLUTAMATE AND GABA

Glutamate and GABA (gamma-aminobutyric acid) are fast-acting neurotransmitters that are able to process received signals within just a few milliseconds. **GABA** has an inhibitory function, meaning it occupies and "stops" neurons. **Glutamate** stimulates and "turns on" neuronal action after meeting with a dendrite. Both types of neurotransmitters have the ability to quickly influence chemical signaling within the central nervous system. Thus, both glutamate and GABA are key elements in psychopharmacological treatments.

MONOAMINES AND NEUROPEPTIDES

Monoamines and neuropeptides are neurotransmitters; but, unlike glutamate and GABA, these neurotransmitters are slow acting and may take as many as several seconds to process and transmit neurotransmissions. Because of their slow onset of action, monoamines and neuropeptides are also called neuromodulators. Since a neuron can only process information as fast as the slowest signal it receives, neuromodulators control the entire pace of signal transmission. Monoamines and neuropeptides can be either excitatory or inhibitory. The type of signal they modulate and the design of the specific neurotransmitter determine function.

PITUITARY GLAND

The **pituitary gland**, part of the endocrine system but controlled by the brain, is located at the base of the brain inferior to the optic chiasm and is attached to the hypothalamus. The **posterior lobe**, primarily nerve fibers, stores and releases oxytocin and antidiuretic hormone, produced by the hypothalamus, which sends nerve impulses to the posterior pituitary to stimulate release of hormones. The **anterior lobe**, enclosed in a dense capsule and containing glandular tissue, secretes numerous hormones, including growth hormone (somatotropin), adrenocorticotropic hormone (ACTH), thyroid-stimulating hormone (TSH), follicle-stimulating hormone (FSH), luteinizing hormone (LH), and prolactin (which promotes milk production). Instead of nerve impulses, the hypothalamus produces releasing hormones that stimulate the pituitary to release specific hormones and other hormones that inhibit release of pituitary hormones.

AREAS OF THE BRAIN ASSOCIATED WITH AGGRESSION, ANGER, AND VIOLENCE

The 3 main areas of the brain associated with altered **aggression, anger, and violence** include the limbic system, frontal lobes, and the hypothalamus:

- The **limbic system** is involved with the processing of information, memory, and emotions. The area known as the amygdale is particularly involved in the expression of rage and fear. Alterations in this system may result in altered levels of anger and violence.
- The **frontal lobes** are involved with reasoning and intentional behaviors. Trauma to this area of the brain can lead to personality changes, angry emotional outbursts, or impaired decision-making abilities.
- The **hypothalamus** is involved with the body's stress-response system. This area of the brain sends messages to the pituitary gland to raise steroid levels within the body in response to stress. Malfunctions of the hypothalamus can lead to over-stimulation and abnormally elevated levels of steroids.

BRAIN WAVES

Brain waves, originating in the cerebral cortex, represent fluctuating changes in the electrical activity of the extracellular fluid in the brain. Waves may be recorded on an open exposed brain with an electrocorticogram (ECoG) or on the outside of the head with an electroencephalogram (EEG). **Wave patterns** include:

- **Alpha**: Recorded from the posterior portion head with a frequency of 3 to 18 cycles/second, alpha waves occur when the person is awake but resting with eyes closed but disappear when the person sleeps or opens the eyes.
- **Beta:** Recorded from the anterior portion of the head with a frequency of >13 cycles/second, beta waves occur during periods of mental activity or stress.
- **Theta:** Recorded from the parietal and temporal areas with a frequency of 4 to 7 cycles/second, theta waves are common in children but usually only occur in some adults during times of acute stress or during the first stages of sleep.
- **Delta:** Originating in the cerebral cortex with a frequency <4 cycles/second, *delta* waves occur during sleep.

Psychogenomics

GENE, ALLELES, GENOME, GENOTYPE, AND PHENOTYPE

Gene, Alleles, Genome, Genotype, and Phenotype Are Defined Below:

- **Genes:** The basic biological unit of inheritance. A gene is a section of deoxyribonucleic acid (DNA) that contains the equation for specific cell formation and building. Genes are found in specific sites on the chromosomes.
- **Alleles:** One or more alternate forms of a gene.
- **Genome:** The complete person's genes and alleles, containing all hereditary factors.
- **Genotype:** The sum of a person's genetic constitution and alleles. One's genotype is unique to the individual and determines the type species.
- **Phenotype:** The observable characteristics or behaviors (physical, biochemical, and physiological) of an individual. Physical characteristics include height, weight, and eye color. Likewise, the phenotype may include one's expressions, responses to stimuli, and other behaviors. Phenotype is influenced by both genetics and environment.

GENETICS AND MENTAL ILLNESS

Genetic inheritance has a profound effect on the development of some mental illness, especially schizophrenia and depression. Most psychiatric disorders are caused by a combination of factors, such as genetic makeup, peripartum stressors and influences, environmental influences, and family and social stressors. Eliciting **family history of mental illness** is a very important aspect of case management as it may bring to light genetic predisposition for illness, particularly if a first-degree relative has a disorder. An individual may have a high level of genetic risk if mental illness is prevalent in the family, or a low level of genetic risk if it is absent. If genetic risk is present, that individual is much more susceptible to developing mental illness as he/she ages, experiences life stressors, or is negatively influenced by environmental interactions.

DIATHESIS-STRESS MODEL

The **diathesis-stress model** is a theoretical psychological principal in which genes and environment interact to bring about mental illness. In other words, mental illness is a product of both nature and nurture. The diathesis-stress model theorizes that in the presence of **genetic predisposition**, **environmental stress** may trigger mental illness. The intensity of the stress and the severity of genetic predisposition may vary. For example, someone who has a weak genetic predisposition for mental illness may only develop the illness if he/she is exposed to extreme stress. On the other hand, an individual who has a strong genetic predisposition for mental illness may develop illness in the presence of a little stress. It is important to note, however, that an individual may have underlying genetic predisposition for mental illness but may never develop illness, regardless of stress.

HERITABILITY AND MENTAL ILLNESS

Heritability is the genetic contribution to **phenotype** in a specific population of individuals. This genetic contribution is affected by maternal and paternal genetic contributions and allelic and dominance variations. Heritability may be estimated by statistical means that take into account both genetic and environmental variances on a given population. Heritability may be estimated using **regression and correlation models** (comparison of close relatives, siblings, twins, parents, and offspring) or **analysis of variance** (equations and coefficients of variance). Because mental illness is often directly correlated with genetic predisposition, predicted heritability patterns may expose a genetic predisposition for illness, such as schizophrenia or chronic depression, before symptoms present. In some cases, patients may express concern about their offspring inheriting mental illness. Research indicates that genetic variations can markedly increase risk of developing mental illness in relation to stress and other environmental issues.

Advanced Physical Assessment

ASSESSMENT COMPONENTS

Upon a patient's admission to care, the assessment components include:

- **Presenting symptoms**: The NP should note the general appearance and the type of symptoms, including abnormal motor behavior such as automatisms, psychomotor retardation, and waxy flexibility as well as posture and eye contact.
- **Degree of thought organization**: The NP should evaluate both thought content and thought processes and note circumstantial thinking; delusions; flight of ideas; loose associations; tangential thinking; thought blocking; broadcasting; insertion; withdrawal; word salad; and ideas of reference.
- **Mood and affect**: Mood is the patients underlying emotional state while affect is the outward expression of that state. Mood may be characterized as happy, sad, angry, or anxious. Mood swings (labile mood) should be noted as well as inconsistencies between mood and affect or mood and situation. Affect is categorized as blunted (showing little expression), broad (showing a broad range of expressions), flat (showing no expression), inappropriate (expression does not match mood or situation), and restricted (showing only one type of expression).
- **Hygiene**: The NP should note the condition of the patient's skin, nails, teeth, and hair and whether the patient is clean or needs bathing. The NP may note signs of lice, such as scratching or nits, and whether clothes are clean or soiled.
- **Grooming**: The patient's grooming should include whether the patient appears unkempt. Is the hair combed and patient shaved? Completely or partially dressed? Are clothes appropriate?
- **Short/Long term memory**: The NP should ask questions that probe both short-term memory (e.g., "What did you have for lunch?") and long-term (e.g., "Who was the president before the current one?"). Additionally, questions should probe general orientation (e.g., "What state is this?", "What is your social security number?", "What is your home address?"). The NP should also assess concentration, such as by asking the patient to repeat a list of numbers backward or perform a three-part task. Assessing abstract thinking can include asking the patient to interpret a common proverb to determine if the patient understands the meaning.

FUNCTIONAL ASSESSMENT

ADLs

Functional status relates to the ability of people, especially the elderly or impaired, to perform social roles free of limitations or disabilities. Assessment should include basic **activities of daily living (ADLs)**:

- **Toileting**: The ability to adequately control urination and fecal evacuation, noting dysuria, constipation, diarrhea, the presence and degree of incontinence, as well as the use of protective materials.
- **Mobility**: The ability to transfer from bed to chair, to walk, to toilet, and to maintain balance, noting recent falls or the need for assistive devices.
- **Hygiene**: The ability to bathe, brush teeth, dress, and maintain basic standards of cleanliness both for the person and the environment.

- **Mental status**: Thinking, understanding, and memory because, by age 90, about 50% of people have some dementia.
- **Nutrition**: Basic dietary knowledge, the ability to prepare or obtain food, and adequate food and fluid intake.

PSYCHOSOCIAL AND SENSORY

Functional status assessment concerns the ability to do self-care, self-maintenance, and engage in physical activities, but other factors may prevent those who should be able to function well from doing so:

- **Psychological function:** Assess anxiety, worry, grief, and depression. Those with depression may be at increased risk of physical disability or may neglect self-care.
- **Social function:** Assess support from family or friends, the need for a caregiver, financial resources, mistreatment or abuse, the ability to drive, and the presence of advance directives.
- **Sensory function:** Assess presence of cataracts, glaucoma, myopia, presbyopia, astigmatism, macular degeneration, or eye disorders that make it difficult for people to read medication labels or do self-care. The need for audio materials or enlarged print should be assessed. Hearing is evaluated in both ears for hearing deficits and high and low frequency hearing loss as well as waxy buildup in the ear canals.

FUNCTIONAL NEUROLOGICAL SYMPTOMS

Functional neurological symptoms relate to impaired function of the neurological system that is unrelated to diagnostic evidence of damage to the neurological system and may encompass a wide range of symptoms, including limb weakness, tremors, dystonia, slurred speech, dysphagia, anxiety, poor concentration/memory, pain, sleep problems, and excessive fatigue. For example, with limb weakness, mobility and strength may be impaired, but reflexes remain intact and testing (CT, MRI) shows no abnormalities. Additionally, if the contralateral limb is exercised or stressed, the symptoms often disappear temporarily. In fact, symptoms often vary in intensity. The cause of functional neurological symptoms may be difficult to pinpoint although sometimes they occur after injury or illness, but functional neurological symptoms generally relate to impairment of transmission of impulses in the nervous system. While some symptoms may be related to malingering or psychiatric disease, in most cases this is not true although that is a common misperception. Treatment approaches vary depending on the type of symptoms.

INFORMATION OBTAINED FROM NEUROLOGICAL EXAMINATION OF BRAIN FUNCTION

Brain function can be inferred from the neurological exam:

- **General appearance**: Includes posture, affect, dysmorphic features, involuntary motor movements, and tremors. Resting tumors suggest impairment of the substantia nigra; and volitional tremors, cerebellar damage.
- **Mental status exam**: Evaluates cognitive processes, including speech and thought, and cerebellum function. Personality changes may indicate damage to frontal lobes.
- **Cranial nerve exam (I-XII)**: Evaluates sensorium (hearing, taste, smell, vision) and swallowing as well as muscles of the face and speech. Abnormalities point to possible lesions in the area of the specific nerve.
- **Motor system** (position, involuntary motor activity, muscle strength/tone): Helps to identify lesions of the upper motor neurons and lower motor neurons depending on the type of abnormalities with upper characterized by hyperreflexia and spasticity and lower by hypotonia and hyporeflexia.

- **Sensory** (sense of position, touch, pain): Helps to identify neuropathy and impaired sensations. Abnormalities may help pinpoint damage to the sensory cortex located in the parietal lobe.
- **Reflexes**: Show abnormalities of C5-C7, L3-L4, and S1.
- **Coordination and gait**: Abnormalities may be indicative of neurological disease (multiple sclerosis, Parkinson's disease) or cerebellar lesions.

NEUROPSYCHOLOGICAL TESTS

Neuropsychological tests assess the effects of brain damage or impairment on intellectual, motor, and/or emotional functioning. In adults, **impairment** may be related to various causes while in children it usually relates to congenital or perinatal conditions. Testing results may help to identify the cause for cognitive deficits and may provide information about the areas of the brain damaged and the extent of injury. In children, it may identify the cause of educational delays and learning disabilities. Patients may undergo fixed batteries of tests or individual tests. A number of different tests are used depending on the **function** to be evaluated: intelligence (general and premorbid), language (general and comprehension), memory, attention, visuospatial ability, apraxia, reasoning, and handedness. The most commonly utilized tests are the **Wechsler Adult Intelligence Scales** (WAIS, WAIS-R, and WAIS-III). WAIS-III, the current version, comprises 14 subtests and two major scales (verbal IQ and performance IQ). Other tests include the Stanford-Binet Intelligence Scale, the Halstead-Reitan Battery, and the Luria-Nebraska Neuropsychological Battery. A pediatric version of WAIS-III is available. Another pediatric assessment is the Rivermead Behavioural Memory Test.

Advanced Practice Skills

Clinical Interviewing

PATIENT'S COMFORT WHILE CONDUCTING PATIENT HISTORY

The **patient interview** is the first step in the process of treating a patient, and it is often where the most important information is obtained. Because it is such a crucial part of the overall assessment of the patient, it is important to make the patient feel **comfortable**. Making a negative impression will inhibit the ability to get a great deal of information from the patient. If possible, conduct the interview in a quiet area. If this is not a possibility, remain calm and relaxed while interviewing the patient, and take time both when asking questions and listening to the answers. If the patient is given the impression that the PMH NP is impatient or in a rush, he or she may become uncomfortable and hesitant to answer questions.

THERAPEUTIC COMMUNICATION

Therapeutic communication begins with respect for the patient/family and the assumption that all communication, verbal and non-verbal, has meaning. Listening must be done empathetically.

INTRODUCTION

Make a personal introduction and use the patient's name: "Mrs. Brown, I am Susan Williams, your nurse practitioner."

ENCOURAGEMENT

Use an open-ended opening statement: "Is there anything you'd like to discuss?"

Acknowledge comments: "Yes," and "I understand."

Allow silence and observe non-verbal behavior rather than trying to force conversation. Ask for clarification if statements are unclear.

Reflect statements back (use sparingly): Patient: "I hate this hospital." NP: "You hate this hospital?"

EMPATHY

Make observations: "You are shaking," and "You seem worried."

Recognize feelings: Patient: "I want to go home." NP: "It must be hard to be away from your home and family."

Provide information as honestly and completely as possible about condition, treatment, and procedures and respond to patient's questions and concerns.

EXPLORATION

Verbally express implied messages: Patient: "This treatment is too much trouble." NP: "You think the treatment isn't helping you?"

Explore a topic but allow the patient to terminate the discussion without further probing: "I'd like to hear how you feel about that."

ORIENTATION

Indicate reality:

- **Patient**: "Someone is screaming."
- **NP**: "That sound was an ambulance siren."

Comment on distortions without directly agreeing or disagreeing:

- **Patient**: "That nurse promised I didn't have to walk again."
- **NP**: "Really? That's surprising because the doctor ordered physical therapy twice a day."

COLLABORATION

Work together to achieve better results: "Maybe if we talk about this, we can figure out a way to make the treatment easier for you."

VALIDATION

Seek validation: "Do you feel better now?" or "Did the medication help you breathe better?"

NON-THERAPEUTIC COMMUNICATION

While using therapeutic communication is important, it is equally important to avoid interjecting **non-therapeutic communication**, which can effectively block effective communication. *Avoid the following:*

Stating meaningless clichés	"Don't worry. Everything will be fine." "Isn't it a nice day?"
Providing advice	"You should…" or "The best thing to do is…." It's better when patients ask for advice to provide facts and encourage patients to make their own decisions.
Providing inappropriate approval	This can prevent the patient from expressing true feelings or concerns. Patient: "I shouldn't cry about this." NP: "That's right. You're an adult."
Asking for explanations of behavior not directly related to patient care	Asking for explanations such as "Why are you upset?" may require analysis and explanation of feelings on the patient's part.
Agreeing rather than accepting and responding	Agreeing with patient's statements "I agree with you" or "You are right" can make it difficult for the patient to change his/her statement or opinion later.

NEGATIVE AND INAPPROPRIATE RESPONSES

Methods to promote a caring and supportive environment include avoiding **non-therapeutic communication**. *Avoid the following:*

Making negative judgments	"You should stop arguing with the nurses."
Devaluing patient's feelings	"Everyone gets upset at times."
Disagreeing directly	"That can't be true" or "I think you are wrong."
Defending against criticism	"The doctor was not being rude; he's just very busy today."

Changing the subject	This avoids dealing with uncomfortable subjects: Patient: "I'm never going to get well." NP: "Your family will be here in a few minutes."
Making inappropriate literal responses	Even as a joke, this is not appropriate, especially if the patient is confused or having difficulty expressing ideas: Patient: "There are bugs crawling under my skin." NP: "I'll get some bug spray."
Challenging to establish reality	This often increases confusion and frustration: Patient: "I'm dying!" NP: If you were dying, you wouldn't be able to yell and kick."

NON-VERBAL COMMUNICATION

Non-verbal communication can convey as much information as verbal communication, both on the NP's part and the patient's. Non-verbal communication is used for a number of purposes, such as expressing feelings and attitudes, and may be a barrier to communication or a facilitator. While there are cultural differences, interpretation of non-verbal communication can help the NP to better understand and promote communication:

- **Eye contact:** Making eye contact provides a connection and shows caring and involvement in the communication. Avoiding contact may indicate someone is not telling the truth or is uncomfortable, fearful, ashamed, or hiding something.
- **Tone**: The manner in which words are spoken (patiently, cheerfully, somberly) affects the listener, and when the message and tone do not match, it can interfere with communication. A high-pitched tone of voice may indicate nervousness or stress.
- **Touch**: Reaching out to touch an older adult's hand or pat a shoulder during communication is reassuring but hugging or excessive touching can make people feel uncomfortable. People may touch themselves (lick lips, pick at skin, scratch) if they are anxious.
- **Gestures**: Using the hands to emphasize meaning is common and may be particularly helpful during explanations, but excessive gesturing can be distracting. Some gestures alone convey message, such as a wave goodbye or pointing. Tapping of the foot, moving the legs, or fidgeting may indicate nervousness. Rubbing the hands together is sometimes a self-comforting measure. Some gestures, such as handshakes, are part of social ritual. Mixed messages, such as fidgeting but speaking with a calm voice, may indicate uncertainty or anxiety.
- **Posture**: Slumping can indicate lack of interest or withdrawal. Leaning toward the opposite person while talking indicates interest and facilitates interaction.

CULTURAL AND SPIRITUAL COMPETENCE IN COMMUNICATION

There are a number of issues related to **cultural and spiritual competence in communicating** with patients/family:

- **Eye contact:** Many cultures use eye contact differently than is common in the United States. They may avoid direct eye contact, considering it rude, or may look away to signal disapproval, or may look down to signal respect. Careful observation of the way family members use eye contact can help to determine what will be most comfortable for the patient/family.

- **Distance**: Some cultures stand close to others (<4 feet) when speaking (Middle Easterners, Hispanics) and others stand at a further distance (>4 feet) (Northern Europeans, many Americans). There is considerable difference relating to concepts of personal space among cultures. Allowing the family to approach or observing whether they tend to move closer, lean forward, or move back can help to determine a comfortable distance for communication.
- **Time**: Americans tend to be time-oriented, and expect people to be on time, but time is more flexible in many cultures, so scheduling may require flexibility.

LANGUAGE BARRIERS TO COMMUNICATION

Language barriers often compromise patient's access to care and compliance with treatment, especially if the family members are non-English speaking or have poor English skills. If the NP's practice draws from a minority population, then the NP should consider proactive steps to resolving the issue of language barriers, such as hiring bilingual staff, taking language classes, providing translated materials (i.e., treatment guidelines and pamphlets), or symbol-based signs. Many practices depend on family members, often children, to translate, but this is not a good solution as children often lack the maturity to assume this responsibility and may also lack the vocabulary or understanding to translate effectively, leading to serious misunderstandings. Interpreters should have training in **medical vocabulary**. In some cases, volunteer translators can be trained. Another solution is to pool translation resources among a number of practices so that costs are manageable.

LITERACY ASSESSMENT

A **literacy assessment** should be part of the initial interview with the patient. Basic information can be gleaned by having the patient fill out a simple form about history and educational background, if possible, as this demonstrates the patient's ability to read basic questions and provides literacy information. The NP should pay close attention to the patient's **vocabulary and syntax** as this correlates with literacy, although those with learning disabilities may be able to express themselves well but still have difficulty reading. The NP must use language that the patient understands, so assessing **health literacy** is equally important. The NP can begin by asking patients what they know about their illnesses. Even with well-educated patients, the NP should use common terms rather than medical terms whenever possible as patients may not tell the NP if they don't understand.

Health Promotion and Disease Prevention

HEALTH BELIEF MODEL

The **Health Belief Model** (HBM) is a model used to predict health behavior with the understanding that people take a health action to avoid negative consequences if the person expects that the negative outcome can be avoided and that he/she is able to do the action. The HBM, as modified, is based on 6 basic perceptions:

- Susceptibility: Belief that the person may get a negative condition.
- Severity: Understanding of how serious a condition is.
- Benefit: Belief that the action will reduce risk of getting the condition.
- Barriers: Direct and psychological costs involved in taking action.
- Action cues: Strategies used to encourage action, such as education.
- Self-efficacy: Confidence in the ability to take action and achieve positive results.

This model attempts to encourage people to make changes or take action (such as stopping smoking) in order to avoid negative consequences, so this model—when used for education—focuses on the negative consequences (such as quitting smoking to avoid cardiovascular and pulmonary disease).

THEORY OF REASONED ACTION

The **Theory of Reasoned Action**, developed in 1975 by Fishbein and Ajzen, is based on the idea that the actions people take voluntarily can be predicted according to their personal attitude toward the action and their perception of how others will view their doing the action. There are three basic concepts to the theory:

- **Attitudes**: These are all of the attitudes about an action, and they may be weighted (some more important than others).
- **Subjective norms:** People are influenced by those in their social realm (family, friends) and their attitudes toward particular actions. The influence may be weighted. For example, the attitude of a spouse may carry more weight than the attitude of a neighbor.
- **Behavioral intention:** The intention to take action is based on weighing attitudes and subjective norms (opinions of others), resulting in a choice to either take an action or avoid the action.

SOCIAL COGNITIVE THEORY

The **Social Cognitive Theory** (Bandura) evolved from the Social Learning Theory and stresses how learning is influenced by social interaction and past experience, suggesting that environmental changes will invariably lead to changes in the individual and that people can exercise control to change behavior. Principles that affect the individual's participation in activities include:

- **Reciprocal determinism:** Behavior is influenced by the interaction of the social environment, the individual's psychological processes, and the behavior itself.
- **Behavioral capability**: Skills and knowledge that allows an individual to carry out a behavior.
- **Observational learning**: People are more likely to adopt behavior if they value the outcomes and the outcomes have functional value and if the person modeling had similarities to the learner and was admired because of status.

- **Reinforcements**: Internal/External responses that increase likelihood of repeating behavior.
- **Expectations:** Anticipation of outcomes of behavior.
- **Self-efficacy:** Confidence in the ability to carry out a behavior.

HEALTHY PEOPLE 2020

The goals of *Healthy People 2020* are to allow people to have longer healthy lives, to reduce health disparities, to create environments that promote health, and to improve the quality of life and health across all age groups. Heal*thy People 2020* has 42 topic areas, including Mental Health and Mental Disorders, which aims to utilize preventive measures and mental health services to improve mental health, particularly suicide prevention. Goals include:

- Reduce the suicide rate to 10.2/100,000 (currently 11.3/100,000), focusing on disparities by sex and age.
- Reduce suicide attempts by adolescents to 1.7/100 (currently 1.9/100), focusing on disparities in obesity, sex, school grade, race and ethnicity.
- Reduce the proportion of adolescents engaging in eating disorders to control weight to 12.9% (currently 14.3%), focusing on disparities by sex and school grade.
- Reduce the proportion of adolescents experiencing major depressive episodes to 7.5% (currently 8.3%), focusing on disparities by location, insurance status, sex, race and ethnicity, age, income, and country of birth.
- Reduce the proportion of adults experiencing major depressive episodes to 5.8% (currently 6.5%) focusing on disparities by location, age, and education.

Other goals include expanding treatment for children and adults and increasing depression screening.

TYPES OF PREVENTIVE MEASURES IN MENTAL HEALTH

Gerald Caplan's (1964) **model for prevention** in mental health includes three types of preventive measures:

- **Primary**: The focus is on helping people to cope with stress and decreasing stressors in the environment, specifically targeting at-risk groups. Examples include teaching parenting skills to parents; providing support services to the unemployed; providing food, shelter and other services to the homeless; and teaching about the harmful effects of drugs and alcohol to schoolchildren.
- **Secondary**: The focus is on identifying problems early and beginning treatment in order to shorten the duration of the disorder. Examples include follow-up for patients at risk for recurrence, staffing rape crisis centers, providing suicide hotlines, and referrals as needed.
- **Tertiary**: The focus is on preventing complications and promoting rehabilitation through teaching patients socially-appropriate behaviors. Examples include teaching the patient to manage daily living skills, monitoring effectiveness of outpatient services, and referring patients to support services.

MENTAL HEALTH PROMOTION AT THE COMMUNITY LEVEL

Mental health promotion at the community level focuses on helping people maintain optimal levels of health and wellbeing, providing preventive measures, and assessing risks and protective factors associated with mental health. **Promotion efforts** may include:

- Programs for children and adolescents, such as through mentoring or education, to help children learn coping and problem-solving skills.
- 12-step programs to help people maintain sobriety/abstinence through peer support.
- Early childhood intervention programs that help teach good parenting skills.
- Support programs for people with mental illness to help them learn skills needed to live independently.
- Sheltered workshops to provide opportunity for skill acquisition and employment for people with mental impairment.
- Anti-bullying campaigns targeting all ages.
- Programs to support the LGBT community and prevent abuse and prejudice.
- Senior citizens' programs to provide services and social activities.
- Primary, secondary, and tertiary preventive measures.
- Boys' and girls' clubs to promote social interaction in a safe environment.

SCREENING TEST CONCEPTS

Screening tests must be designed according to a number of standards to ensure accuracy in results. Concepts include:

- **Specificity**: The ability to rule-out participants that should be excluded from further testing and do not have the diagnosis for which the screen tests.
- **Sensitivity**: The ability to accurately identify those who meet the criteria established by the test, providing diagnosis of a condition.
- **Reliability**: The ability to achieve similar results from repeated testing. Thus, if a condition remains unchanged, the test should provide similar results if given at a different time.
- **Validity**: The ability to achieve accuracy in results. Concurrent validity is supported by assessment within 10 days while predictive validity is supported by outcomes observed about a year after initial testing. Validity directly relates to both specificity and sensitivity.

ANTICIPATORY GUIDANCE TO IMPROVE CARE

Anticipatory guidance is a method of educating the patient and/or family about the diagnosis, prognosis, and future care. Anticipatory guidance allows patients and their parents/guardians to formulate realistic expectations with regards to the treatment plan. Anticipatory guidelines are a catalyst for bringing forth questions and concerns regarding patient development, treatment progress, disease progression, therapy outcomes, rehabilitation or palliation, and follow-up or community care. As with all communications, the NP ensures anticipatory guidance is **clear and concise** by:

- Asking patients and/or families if they have any questions.
- Offering them a business card so they can phone with any questions they think of later.
- Giving written anticipatory guidance handouts so the patient and family have reference information available at home. Often, they will not retain verbal information due to the initial shock diagnosis and prognosis causes.

- Directing them to a reputable patient support group and arrange for the team's social worker to help them.
- Asking if they would like the chaplain to visit.

USUAL ANTICIPATORY GUIDANCE VS. TARGETED ANTICIPATORY GUIDANCE

Usual anticipatory guidance is the practice of disseminating a generic set of guidelines to a certain patient population. For example, parents of a toddler may receive pamphlets and/or physician-directed education on milestones, socialization, toilet training, and discipline that are standard issue for the institution or catchment area.

Targeted anticipatory guidance is when a healthcare provider specifically speaks to the individual questions and concerns of a patient and/or the parents/guardian. There are pros and cons to both types of guidance. For example, usual anticipatory guidance covers a larger spectrum of topics and concerns, but may not touch on the 1 troubling behavior that is of specific concern to the parent, such as tantrums or combative behavior. Targeted anticipatory guidance covers 1 concern thoroughly, but fails to provide guidance on other topics that may become concerns in the interim before their next visit.

PROVIDING ANTICIPATORY GUIDANCE

CHILDREN/FAMILIES

Providing **anticipatory guidance** to **children/families** is an important role for the NP, who is guided by knowledge about risk factors and growth and development. As the child moves from one stage of development to another, the NP should provide information first to the parents and then to the parents and child about what to expect in terms of development, both physically and emotionally, as well as how to minimize risk factors. Guidance may be related to a number of different **areas of concern**:

- Diet and nutrition, especially for those children at risk for obesity or eating disorders.
- Safety measures, including information about common types of childhood injuries.
- Sexual development and normal related changes and behaviors.
- Sports activities and exercise that is age-appropriate.
- General growth and development.
- Academic progress and advice about testing and intervention for learning disabilities.
- Peer influence.
- Drug and alcohol abuse.

EARLY ADOLESCENCE

Children during **early adolescence** (11-14) are undergoing many changes in their bodies and emotions. Relationships with family and peers may begin to change, and children may be very self-conscious and concerned that they are normal. **Anticipatory guidance** helps children to navigate changes in their lives and to negotiate changes in relationships as they seek more autonomy:

- **Physical changes**: Outline what children should expect in terms of bodily changes, such as development of secondary sexual characteristics, including normal variations, and height and weight changes.
- **Cognitive changes**: Allow children to express changes in thought patterns and awareness and discuss how that relates to developing maturity and stress the importance of maintaining academic responsibilities.
- **Socio-behavioral changes**: Ask children about peer groups and pressures at school and discuss methods to avoid gangs, tobacco, drugs, alcohol, and abusive relationships.

MIDDLE ADOLESCENCE

Middle adolescence (15-17) is a time of conflict for many young people as they strive to establish an identity separate from their parents and at the same time fit in and find acceptance with their peers. For many, this is the most difficult time of adolescence, and the NP should provide **anticipatory guidance** to the adolescent through this time, even if the adolescent appears uninterested. Adolescents want respect and often respond when treated with respect. Encouraging the adolescent to discuss issues is more productive than providing direct guidance:

- **Physical changes**: Discuss the responsibilities that come with sexual maturity, including abstinence or birth control. Demonstrate breast and testicular self-examinations.
- **Cognitive changes**: Discuss future goals including both life plans and academic plans, and also provide guidance in relation to the necessary steps the adolescent needs to take in order to meet those goals.
- **Sociobehavioral changes**: Discuss relationships and risk-taking behavior while focusing on means to increase safety.

NEUROPROTECTIVE STRATEGIES

Neuroprotective strategies are those used to prevent damage to the brain. Strategies include:

- **Substance use disorder programs**: Dual diagnosis is common, but substance abuse may worsen symptoms and interfere with recovery or maintenance, so patients should be referred to substance use disorder programs specifically intended for those with mental illness.
- **Medication choice**: Atypical antipsychotics are less likely to result in extrapyramidal adverse effects than typical but more likely to result in metabolic effects and weight gain, which may lead to cardiovascular disease and diabetes. Patients should be maintained on drugs for psychotic episodes at least one year and many may need drugs indefinitely. Patients must learn to recognize signs of relapse. Restarting medications immediately on relapse can prevent symptoms from becoming severe.
- **Cognitive behavioral therapy**: Can help patients learn to control symptoms and recognize hallucinations and delusions, allowing them to function better in society.
- **Early intervention**: The prognosis for mental disorders is better if treatment is instituted early, with the first episode, rather than delayed.
- **Support programs**: Programs to support patients in the community increase compliance with treatment.

HHS GUIDELINES FOR HELPING SMOKERS QUIT

The **US Department of Health and Human Services** guidelines for helping **smokers** quit includes the following information:

- **Ask** about and record smoking status at every visit.
- **Advise** all smokers to quit and explain health reasons why quitting is beneficial.
- **Assess** readiness to quit by questioning and if willing, provide resources. If patient is not willing, provide support and attempt to motivate the person to quit with information.
- **Assist** smokers with a plan that sets a date (within 2 weeks), removes cigarettes, enlists family and friends, reviews past attempts, and anticipates challenges during the withdrawal period. The NP must give advice about the need for abstinence and discuss the association of smoking with drinking. Medications to help control the urge to smoke (patches, gum, lozenge, prescriptions) and resources should be provided.
- **Follow-up monitoring** should be done to evaluate progress and reinforce the program.

EXERCISE

Daily **exercise** is an important component of good health practices but should be age-appropriate, and some health conditions may pose restrictions. Toddlers and young children usually get exercise by running and playing and do not need organized activities, but others benefit from **planned exercise**:

- **4-5-year-olds** may participate in dancing, skating and other supervised activities but lack coordination and judgment about safety.
- **6-12-year-olds** are still growing and muscles are short, so they do best with non-competitive sports, such as bicycling and swimming, until about age 10. Team sports should be supervised to ensure children are not straining muscles. Weight lifting may be done at 11 to build strength. Gymnastics may begin but children should be monitored for eating disorders.
- **12-18-year-olds** can participate in any sports activity unless limited by illness or disability. Exercise should be done at least 3 times weekly for 30 minutes.
- **Adults:** Exercise should be done at least 30 minutes daily or 150 minutes/week.

EMERGENCY CONTRACEPTION

Females who have had unprotected sexual intercourse, consensual or rape, are at risk for pregnancy and may desire **emergency contraception.** Emergency contraception inhibits ovulation and prevents pregnancy rather than aborting a pregnancy. Because the medications contain hormones (such as ethinyl estradiol and norgestrel or levonorgestrel) in differing amounts, this treatment is contraindicated in those with a history of thromboembolia or severe migraine headaches with neurological symptoms. The criteria for administration of emergency contraception include:

- ≤72 hours since unprotected sexual intercourse.
- Negative pelvic exam.
- Negative pregnancy test.

The regimen involves taking a first dose of 1-20 pills (depending upon the brand and concentration of hormones) and then a second dose of 1-20 pills 12 hours later. A follow-up pregnancy test should be done if the person does not menstruate within 3 weeks as the failure rate is about 1.5%. Side effects include nausea (relieved by taking medication with meals or with an antiemetic), breast tenderness, and irregular bleeding.

PREVENTION OF SEXUALLY TRANSMITTED DISEASES

The Centers for Disease Control and Prevention (**CDC**) has developed 5 strategies to prevent and control the spread of **sexually transmitted diseases (STDs)**:

- Educate those at risk about how to make changes in sexual practices to prevent infection.
- Identify symptomatic and asymptomatic infected persons who may not seek diagnosis or treatment.
- Diagnose and treat those who are infected.
- Prevent infection of sex partners through evaluation, treatment, and counseling.
- Provide pre-exposure vaccination for those at risk.

Practitioners are advised to obtain sexual histories of patients and to assess risk. The **5-P approach** to questioning is advocated. One should ask about:

- **Partners**: Gender and number.
- **Pregnancy prevention**: Birth control.
- **Protection**: Methods used.
- **Practices**: Type of sexual practices (oral, anal, vaginal) and use of condoms.
- **Past history of STDs**: High-risk behavior (promiscuity, prostitution) and disease risk (human immunodeficiency virus [HIV]/hepatitis).

The Centers for Disease Control and Prevention (**CDC**) recommends a number of specific preventive methods as part of the clinical guidelines for **prevention of sexually transmitted diseases (STDs)**:

- Abstinence/reduction in number of sex partners.
- Pre-exposure vaccination: All those evaluated for STDs should receive a hepatitis B vaccination, and men who have sex with men (MSM) and illicit drug users should receive hepatitis A vaccination.
- Male latex (or polyurethane) condoms should be used for all sexual encounters with only water-based lubricants used with latex.
- Female condoms may be used if male condom can't be used properly.
- Condoms and diaphragms should not be used with spermicides containing nonoxynol-9 (N-9) and N-9 should not be used as a lubricant for anal sex.
- Non-barrier contraceptive measures provide no protection from STDs and must not be relied on to prevent disease.
- Women should be counseled regarding emergency contraception with medication or insertion of a copper intrauterine device (IUD).

Mental Health Screening Tools

MMSE AND MINI-COG

Patients with evidence of dementia or short-term memory loss, often associated with Alzheimer's disease, should have cognition assessed. The Mini-mental state exam (MMSE) or the Mini-cog test is commonly used. Both require the patient to carry out specified tasks.

MMSE:

- Remembering and later repeating the names of 3 common objects.
- Counting backward from 100 by 7s or spelling "world" backward.
- Naming items as the examiner points to them.
- Providing the location of the examiner's office, including city, state, and street address.
- Repeating common phrases.
- Copying a picture of interlocking shapes.
- Following simple 3-part instructions, such a picking up a piece of paper, folding it in half, and placing it on the floor.

A score of ≥24/30 is considered a normal functioning level.

Mini-cog:

- Remembering and later repeating the names of 3 common objects.
- Drawing the face of a clock with all 12 numbers and the hands indicating the time specified by the examiner.

ABNORMAL INVOLUNTARY MOVEMENT SCALE

The **Abnormal Involuntary Movement Scale (AIMS)** is a tool to evaluate **tardive dyskinesia** in those taking antipsychotic medications. Before or after the exam, the patient is observed at rest (as in the waiting area) for comparison. The examination procedures include having the patient do a number of activities, such as sitting in specific positions, opening mouth, protruding tongue, standing, and walking while the NP rates a number of characteristics on a scale of 0 (none) to 4 (severe):

- Facial and oral movements.
- Extremity movements.
- Trunk movements.
- Overall severity of movements.

These are assessed, and a score of ≥2 in 2 or more movement or a score ≥3 in 1 movement is positive. Then, the overall **severity** is assessed (based on the above scores), including patient's incapacitation, and patient's awareness of abnormal movements. The last part of the exam asks about dental status (problems, dentures, etc.).

CAGE

The **CAGE** acronym is used as a quick assessment tool to determine if people are drinking excessively or are problem drinkers. Moderate drinking, (1-2 drinks daily or 1 drink a day for older adults), unless contraindicated by health concerns, is usually not harmful to people, but drinking more than that can lead to serious psychosocial and physical problems. One drink is defined as 12 ounces of beer/wine cooler, 5 ounces of wine, or 1.5 ounces of liquor.

C	Cutting down	Do you think about trying to cut down on drinking?
A	Annoyed at criticism	Are people starting to criticize your drinking?
G	Guilty feeling	Do you feel guilty or try to hide your drinking?
E	Eye opener	Do you increasingly need a drink earlier in the day?

"Yes" on 1 question suggests the possibility of a drinking problem while "yes" on ≥2 indicates a drinking problem, and the patient should be provided information about reducing drinking and appropriate referrals made.

Confusion Assessment Method

The **Confusion Assessment Method** is used to assess the **development of delirium** and is intended for those without psychiatric training. The tool covers 9 factors. Some factors have a range of possibilities and others are rated only as to whether the characteristic is present, not present, uncertain, or not applicable. The tool provides room to describe abnormal behavior. Factors indicative of delirium include:

- **Onset**: Acute change in mental status.
- **Attention**: Inattentive, stable, or fluctuating.
- **Thinking**: Disorganized, rambling conversation, switching topics, or illogical.
- **Level of consciousness:** Altered, ranging from alert to coma.
- **Orientation**: Disoriented (person, place, time).
- **Memory**: Impaired.
- **Perceptual disturbances:** Hallucinations, illusions.
- **Psychomotor abnormalities:** Agitation (tapping, picking, moving) or retardation (staring, not moving).
- **Sleep-wake cycle:** Awake at night and sleepy in the daytime.

The tool indicates delirium if there is an acute onset with fluctuating inattention and disorganized thinking or altered level of consciousness.

GERIATRIC DEPRESSION SCALE

The **Geriatric Depression Scale (GDS)** is a self-assessment tool to identify older adults with depression. The test can be used with those with normal cognition and those with mild to moderate impairment. The test poses 15 questions to which patients answer "yes" or "no" and a point is assigned for each answer that indicates depression. A score of **>5 points** is indicative of depression:

1. Are you basically satisfied with your life?
2. Have you dropped many of your activities and interests?
3. Do you feel your life is empty?
4. Do you often get bored?
5. Are you in good spirits most of the time?
6. Are you afraid that something bad is going to happen to you?
7. Do you feel happy most of the time?
8. Do you often feel helpless?
9. Do you prefer to stay at home rather than going out and doing new things?
10. Do you feel you have more problems with memory than most?
11. Do you think it is wonderful to be alive now?
12. Do you feel pretty worthless the way you are now?
13. Do you feel full of energy?
14. Do you feel that your situation is hopeless?
15. Do you think that most people are better off than you are?

TRAIL MAKING TEST

The **Trail Making Test** (Parts A and B) assesses brain function and indicates increasing dementia. It is useful for detecting early Alzheimer's disease, and those who do poorly on part B often need assistance with activities of daily living (ADLs). The patient is given a demonstration of each part before beginning:

- **Part A** has 25 sequentially-numbered scattered circles across the page, and the patient is advised to use a pencil/pen to draw a continuous line to connect in ascending order the circles (starting with 1 and ending with 25).
- **Part B** is slightly more complex and has circles with numbers (1 to 12) and circles with letters (A to L) scattered about the page. The patient is advised to draw a continuous line alternating between numbers and letters in ascending order (1-A-2-B....).

The test is scored according to the number of seconds required for completion:

- **A**: 29 seconds is average, and >78 indicates deficiency.
- **B**: 75 seconds is average and >273 seconds indicates deficiency.

DIGIT REPETITION TEST

The **Digit Repetition Test** is used to assess **attention**. The patient is told to listen to numbers and then repeat them. The NP starts with 2 random single-digit numbers. If the patient gets this sequence correct, the NP then states 3 numbers and continues to add 1 number each time until the patient is unable to repeat the numbers correctly. People with normal intelligence (without intellectual disability or expressive aphasia) can usually repeat 5 to 7 numbers, so scores ≤5 indicate impaired attention.

TIME AND CHANGE TEST

The **Time and Change Test** assesses **dementia** in adults and is effective in diverse populations. Patients are shown a clock face set at 11:10 and have 1 minute to make 2 attempts at stating the correct time. The patient is then given change (7 dimes, 7 nickels, and 3 quarters) and asked to give the NP $1.00 from the coins. The patient has 2 minutes and 2 tries to make the correct change. Failing either or both tests is indicative of dementia.

CLINICAL GLOBAL IMPRESSIONS SCALE

Clinicians use the **Clinical Global Impressions (CGI)** scale to compare ratings between patients he/she has already seen, usually for research studies. The CGI scale asks the clinician to rate the **severity of illness** on a scale of 0-7, in comparison to his/her "total clinical experience." Zero corresponds to "not assessed." Seven corresponds to "among the most extremely ill patients." The scale allows the clinician to rate the change or improvement seen after commencing a study drug. Additionally, an efficacy section of the CGI scale asks the practitioner to rate the **therapeutic effects of drug treatments**. The National Institutes of Health released a more consistent, revised scale in 1997 for bipolar disorder to allow clinicians to separate out side effects of drug treatment from actual improvement.

BRIEF PSYCHIATRIC RATING SCALE FOR CHILDREN

The **Brief Psychiatric Rating Scale for Children (BPRS-C)** is designed to **identify** presenting symptoms and annotate the **severity** of each symptom, on a scale ranging from "not present" to "extremely severe." BPRS-C is used to diagnose psychiatric disorders for both children and adolescents through an interview with the child and parent(s). Symptoms evaluated on the scale include behavioral symptoms, such as uncooperativeness and hostility; mood symptoms, such as depressive mood and anxiety; sensory symptoms, such as hallucinations, delusions, and speech characteristics; symptoms of awareness and alertness, such as disorientation, hyperactivity, distractibility, and others; and symptoms of affect, such as emotional withdrawal and blunted affect. The BPRS-C assessment tool is a cursory look at many symptoms typically displayed with mental disorders.

CHILDREN'S DEPRESSION RATING SCALE-REVISED

The **Children's Depression Rating Scale-Revised (CDRS-R)** evaluates a child for **depressive disorders** and monitors **treatment response**. CDRS-R includes 17 items, 14 of which are assessed during an interview, and 3 of which are assessed by the clinician's interpretation of the patient's non-verbal cues. The CDRS-R is designed specifically for patients aged 6 through 12 but may also be used during an interview with the patient's parents, caregivers, and teachers. The items included in the interview include the following: schoolwork; capacity to have fun; social withdrawal; sleep; appetite or eating patterns; excessive fatigue; physical complaints; irritability; guilt; self-esteem; depressed feelings; morbid ideation; suicidal ideation; weeping; depressed affect; tempo of speech; and hypoactivity.

SNAP-IV-C TEACHER AND PARENT RATING SCALE

The **SNAP-IV-C Teacher and Parent Rating Scale** is the revised version of the 1983 questionnaire by Swanson, Nolan, and Pelham. Clinicians ask parents and teachers to use SNAP-IV-C when attention-deficit/hyperactivity disorder (**ADHD**) or oppositional defiant disorder (**ODD**) is suspected. SNAP-IV-C allows parents and teachers to assess the child's propensity for moods and behaviors on a scale ranging from "not at all" to "very much." SNAP-IV-C includes 90 questions, which may help the clinician arrive at a diagnosis. Questions and topics include: the child's attentiveness; organization; physical and verbal activity; mood and temper (to include his/her ability to control the extremes of either); disruptiveness; attitudes towards authority, peers, and property; ability to concentrate; sleep patterns; self-esteem; anxiety; and ability to focus. Parent and teacher ratings tend to vary according to gender and poverty status; only teacher scores tend to vary by race.

HAMILTON ANXIETY SCALE

The **Hamilton Anxiety Scale (HAS or HAMA)** is utilized to evaluate the **anxiety-related symptomatology** that may present in adults as well as children. HAS provides an evaluation of overall anxiety and its degree of severity. This includes **somatic anxiety** (physical complaints) and **psychic anxiety** (mental agitation and distress). This scale consists of 14 items based on anxiety-produced symptoms. Each item is ranked from 0 to 4 with zero having no symptoms present and 4 having severe symptoms present. This scale is frequently utilized in psychotropic drug evaluations. If performed before a particular medication has been started and then again at later visits, the HAS can be helpful in adjusting medication dosages based in part on the individual's score. It is often utilized as an outcome measure in clinical trials.

YALE-BROWN OBSESSIVE-COMPULSIVE SCALE

The **Yale-Brown Obsessive-Compulsive Scale (Y-BOCS)** is a useful tool for identifying and diagnosing **obsessive-compulsive disorders**. Y-BOCS aims to identify obsessions, including: aggressive; contamination; sexual; hoarding/saving; religious; need for symmetry; somatic; and miscellaneous, such as cleaning/washing, checking, repeating, and counting. Y-BOCS asks the patient to rate the time he/she spends on obsessions and compulsions during the week prior to the clinician's interview. It asks the patient how much control he/she has over the compulsion/obsession, and how much distress it causes him/her. Y-BOCS has questions about resistance and interference. The clinician can ask for clarification and if the patient volunteers information, it is included in the assessment. The final rating is based on the clinician's judgment.

WORLD HEALTH ORGANIZATION DISABILITY ASSESSMENT SCHEDULE 2.0

The **World Health Organization Disability Assessment Schedule 2.0 (WHODAS 2.0)**, is the DSM-5 recommended tool for assessing **global impairment and functioning**. It is based on ICD and ICF classifications. In previous versions of the DSM, global disability was assessed by the Global Assessment of Functioning (GAF) scale. WHODAS comes as a self-report tool with either 12 or 36 questions, taking around 7-15 minutes to administer. These questions help to assess the patient's performance in 6 domains over the last 30 days. The **six domains** are: cognition, participation, mobility, self-care, life activities, and interacting with other people. Using the questionnaire, the tool produces a score that represents the patient's global disability. Pros of the tool include that it is reliable and valid, even across cultures. Cons include that due to the self-report nature of the tool, there is no way to check the validity of the patient's responses to the questions.

BECK DEPRESSION INVENTORY

The **Beck Depression Inventory (BDI)** is a widely utilized, self-reported, multiple-choice questionnaire consisting of 21 items, which measures the **degree of depression**. This tool is designed for use in adults between the ages of 17 to 80 years. BDI evaluates physical symptoms, such as weight loss, loss of sleep, loss of interest in sex, and fatigue, along with attitudinal symptoms, such as irritability, guilt, and hopelessness. The items rank in 4 possible answer choices, based on an increasing severity of symptoms. The test is scored with the answers ranging in value from 0 to 3. The total score is the utilized to determine the degree of depression. The usual ranges include 0-9 (no signs of depression), 10-18 (mild depression), 19-29 (moderate depression), and 30-63 (severe depression).

MENTAL HEALTH SCREEN TOOL PHQ-9

Patient Health Questionaire-9 (PHQ-9) is used to determine the severity of depression and focuses on answers to questions related to the previous 2 weeks. The **questions** are as follows:

1. Little interest/pleasure in activities?
2. Feelings of depression or hopelessness?
3. Sleeping difficulties?
4. Tiredness of lack of energy?
5. Poor appetite or excessive eating?
6. Feelings of being a failure or letting down self/others?
7. Difficulty concentrating?
8. Speaking/moving slowly or fidgeting?
9. Suicidal ideation?

Responses are scored as 0 (not at all), 1 (several days), 2 (more than half of days), or 3 (nearly every day). Scores and assessment:

- **0-4 minimal or no depression**. Monitor but likely does not need treatment.
- **5-9 mild depression**. May need treatment.
- **10-15 moderate depression**. May need treatment.,
- **15-19 moderately severe depression**. Treatment required.
- **20-27 severe depression**. Treatment required.

Suicide risk assessment should be carried out for any patients indicating suicidal ideation.

MENTAL HEALTH SCREEN TOOLS GAD-7 AND VANDERBILT ADHD

General Anxiety Disorder-7 (GAD-7) is used to assess the severity of a patient's anxiety and focuses on the previous 2 weeks. The **questions** are as follows:

1. Feeling nervous, anxious, on edge?
2. Unable to stop/control worrying?
3. Worrying excessively about different things?
4. Having trouble relaxing?
5. Being excessively restless?
6. Easily annoyed/irritated?
7. Fearful something terrible will occur?

Responses are scored as 0 (not at all), 1 (several days), 2 (more than half of days), or 3 (nearly every day). Scores and assessment:

- **5-9 mild anxiety**, requires monitoring.
- **10-14 moderate anxiety**, requires further diagnostic tests, including MMSE and referral to professional.
- **15+ severe anxiety**, requires active treatment.

Vanderbilt ADHD is used to assess whether a child has attention deficit hyperactivity disorder. The tool has 3 parts: (1) assessment by a parent, (2) assessment by a teacher, and (3) followup assessment by a parent. The parental assessment evaluates 47 symptoms that may be associated with ADHD and 8 performance measures. The teacher assessment evaluates 35 symptoms, 3 academic performances (reading, math, written expression), and 5 classroom performance behaviors. The followup parental assessment evaluates 18 symptoms, 8 performance measures, and 12 possible side effects.

Mental Health Screen Tool COWS

The **Clinical Opiate Withdrawal Scale (COWS)** is used to evaluate the severity of opiate withdrawal and the patient's level of drug dependence. Eleven items are assessed by the clinician based on observations of the patient and include:

- Resting pulse rate
- Sweating/Chills/flushing
- Restlessness
- Pupil size (normal, pinpoint, dilated)
- Bone/Joint/Muscle aches
- Runny nose/Tearing
- GI upset
- Tremors (outstretched hands
- Yawning
- Anxiety, irritability
- Gooseflesh

Each item is scored from 0 (normal) to 4 or 5, with the score higher with increased symptoms.

Scores:

- 5-12 mild opiate withdrawal
- 13-24 moderate opiate withdrawal
- 25-36 moderately severe opiate withdrawal
- 36+ severe opiate withdrawal

Drug Screening

A **drug screen** is used to determine use of illicit drugs. Testing varies according to the type of drug used, duration of use, and time of use. Different types of screens include:

- **Serum**: Most drugs can be detected within 24 hours and for up to 3-5 days, but this varies.
- **Saliva**: Similar to serum, drugs can usually be detected within 1 to 3 hours of use and for 2 or 3 days afterward.
- **Perspiration**: The person wears a special patch for up to 2 weeks to evaluate chronic drug use.
- **Urine**: Drugs show up in the urine in about 6 to 8 hours, but tests can be inaccurate if people dilute urine by drinking 1 to 2 liters of fluids or add adulterants that change the chemical makeup of the urine.
- **Hair**: Drugs and alcohol can usually be detected in hair within about 2 weeks of use and remain for about 90 days.

Psychiatric Emergency Management

VIOLENCE AND AGGRESSION

Violence and aggression are commonly seen in the psychiatric and mental health population. The NP must be aware of signs of impending violence or aggression in order to intervene.

- **Violence** is a physical act perpetrated against an inanimate object, animal, or other person with the intent to cause harm. Violence often results from anger, frustration, or fear and occurs because the perpetrators believe that they are threatened or that their opinion is right and the victim is wrong. Violence may occur suddenly without warning or following aggressive behavior. Violence can result in death or severe injury if the patient attacks a fellow patient or staff member.
- **Aggression** is the communication of a threat or intended act of violence and will often occur before an act of violence. This communication can occur verbally or non-verbally. Gestures, shouting, speaking increasingly loudly, invasion of personal space, or prolonged eye contact are examples of aggression requiring the patient be redirected or removed from the situation.

EMERGENCY PSYCHIATRIC STABILIZATION

Emergency psychiatric stabilization is required when patients pose a threat to themselves (suicidal ideation) or others (threats or acts of violence). Conditions that most commonly result in the need for psychiatric stabilization include bipolar disease, severe depression, substance abuse, schizophrenia, and personality disorders. The purpose of stabilization is to prevent injury to the patient or others. Risk factors include disheveled appearance, disorganized behavior, thought distortion, overt threats, and verbal and behavioral agitation. The healthcare provider should remain calm, speak reassuringly, and avoid sudden movements. Emergency stabilization includes:

- **Agitation/Violence**: Verbal intervention, benzodiazepine (droperidol, lorazepam, haloperidol), atypical antipsychotics (risperidone, olanzapine), or high-potency conventional antipsychotics.
- **Suicidal ideation**: Determination of risk, close observation, antidepressants.
- **Substance abuse**: Patients should have referral for ongoing treatment.
  - *Opioids*: Antagonist, such as naloxone, observation, symptomatic support.
  - *Stimulants*: Benzodiazepine.
  - *Alcohol*: Supportive treatment, benzodiazepine. or high-potency conventional antipsychotic.
  - *Hallucinogen*: Benzodiazepines.

COERCED TREATMENT

Coerced treatment should be avoided if at all possible. However, many times patients who are suffering from mental illness may refuse medications or other treatments. These patients may be suffering from delirium, dementia, or psychosis. Patients who are admitted on a voluntary basis and are not violent towards themselves or others can legally refuse any treatment or medication. However, with patients that have been committed, certain criteria can justify coerced treatment. These **criteria** include the following:

- The patient is dangerous to themselves or others.
- Those administering treatment truly believe that the treatment has a good chance of helping the patient.
- The patient has been determined to be incompetent to make informed decisions.

Many times, a positive therapeutic relationship between the NP and the patient can help avoid the refusal of treatments. Patients may be willing to take medications in a different form, mixed in food, or at a different time.

CRISIS MANAGEMENT

Modern **crisis theory** originated with Dr. Erich Lindemann in the 1940s when he observed similar responses in survivors of the Cocoanut Grove fire that killed almost 500 people. He later established a mental health program with Dr. Gerald Caplan, who outlined the basis of crisis theory. Caplan believed that a **crisis** occurs when **changes** alter one's personal view of self and relationships with others. Caplan divided crises into those that were **developmental** and **accidental** (also referred to as situational). He further demonstrated that those who immediately had psychiatric help to deal with crises experienced better outcomes. Erik Erickson built on this concept of developmental crises by outlining the developmental stages through the lifetime, with each stage constituting a type of developmental crisis because failure to accomplish the goals at each stage can result in negative consequences.

CHARACTERISTICS OF A CRISIS

A **crisis** occurs when a person is faced with a highly stressful event and the usual problem solving and coping skills fail to be effective in resolving the situation. This even usually leads to increased levels of anxiety and can bring about a physical and psychological response. The problem is usually an **acute event** (such as a death in the family, loss of employment, or divorce) that can be identified. It may have occurred a few weeks or even months before or immediately prior to the crisis and can be an actual event or a potential event. The **crisis state** usually lasts less than 6 weeks with the individual then becoming able to utilize problem-solving skills to cope effectively. A person in crisis does not always have a mental disorder; however, during the acute crisis, social functioning and decision-making abilities may be impaired. There are basically 2 different types of crises: **developmental or maturational** crises and **situational** crises.

DEVELOPMENTAL CRISIS

A **developmental crisis** can occur during maturation when an individual must take on a new life role. This crisis can be a normal part of the developmental process. A youth may need to face the crisis and resolve it to be able to move on to the next developmental stage. A developmental crisis may occur during the process of moving from adolescence to adulthood. Situations that could lead to developmental crisis include graduating from school, going away to college, or moving away from the parents' home. These situations would cause the individual to face a maturing event that requires the development of new coping skills.

SITUATIONAL CRISIS

A **situational crisis** can occur at any time in life. There is usually an event or problem that occurs and leads to a **disruption in normal psychological functioning**. These types of events are often unplanned and can occur with or without warning. Some examples that may lead to a situational crisis include the death of a loved one, divorce, unplanned or unwanted pregnancy, onset or change in a physical disease process, job loss, or being the victim of a violent act. The patient may feel completely overwhelmed, helpless, and unable to think clearly or act appropriately, causing feelings of shame and guilt. Some may experience denial. Events that affect an entire community can also cause **individual and community situational crisis**. Terrorist attacks or weather-related disasters, such as floods or tornadoes, are examples of events that can affect an entire community.

CRISIS INTERVENTION

The first step in **crisis intervention** is a thorough evaluation and assessment of the problem and the triggering event as well as assessment of risks, such as suicide. A plan should be devised in collaboration with the patient, taking resources into consideration. **Steps in intervention** include:

- Helping the patient to gain understanding about the cause of the crisis.
- Encouraging the patient to freely express thoughts and feelings.
- Teaching the patient different coping mechanisms and adaptive behaviors.
- Encouraging social interaction.

Crisis intervention usually requires 4 to 6 weeks. Social and cultural influences can greatly affect the ability and ways in which people deal with and work through crisis. People may have preconceived ideas and beliefs about asking for and accepting assistance from others. It is very important to consider the age of the individual when assessing the need for particular crisis interventions. The needs of an elderly adult will be different than the needs of a child.

Psychoeducation

GOALS OF MENTAL HEALTH EDUCATION

Mental health education is the imparting of mental health knowledge to clients and their families. According to Walker and Price-Hoskins (1992), the **goals** of mental health education include:

- Offering information about the illness and appropriate interventions.
- Helping people recognize symptoms.
- Teaching people when and how to intervene for themselves.
- Offering relief from guilt and blame.
- Clarifying family expectations.
- Instilling confidence that change can occur.
- Developing perspective and balance.

Methods used for education include lecture, discussion, modeling, observation, experiential (role playing and behavioral rehearsal), coaching, audiovisual presentations, and self-instruction (such as keeping a diary). Guidelines for teaching adult learners include: assessing the client's knowledge base; increasing the awareness for self-learning; encouraging self-direction; encouraging the application of what has been learned; using modes of learning most useful to client; and repeating, changing, and combining teaching methods and modes as needed.

READINESS TO LEARN

The patient's/family's **readiness to learn** should be assessed because if they are not ready, instruction is of little value. Often readiness is indicated when the patient/family asks questions or shows an interest in procedures. There are a number of factors related to readiness to learn:

- **Physical factors:** There are a number of physical factors than can affect ability. Manual dexterity may be required to complete a task, and this varies by age and condition. Hearing or vision deficits may impact ability. Complex tasks may be too difficult for some because of weakness or cognitive impairment, and modifications of the environment may be needed. Health status, age, and gender may all impact the ability to learn.
- **Experience**: People's experience with learning can vary widely and is affected by their ability to cope with changes, their personal goals, motivation to learn, and cultural background. People may have widely divergent ideas about what constitutes illness and/or treatment. Lack of English skills may make learning difficult and prevent people from asking questions.
- **Mental/emotional status:** The support system and motivation may impact readiness. Anxiety, fear, or depression about the patient's condition can make learning very difficult because the patient/family cannot focus on learning, so the NP must spend time to reassure the patient/family and wait until they are emotionally more receptive.
- **Knowledge/education:** The knowledge base of the patient/family, their cognitive ability, and their learning styles all affect their readiness to learn. The NP should always begin by assessing what knowledge the patient/family already have about their disease, condition, or treatment and then build from that base. People with little medical experience may lack knowledge of basic medical terminology, interfering with their ability and readiness to learn.

APPROACHES TO TEACHING

There are many **approaches to teaching**, and the NP may need to prepare, present, and coordinate a wide range of educational workshops, lectures, discussions, and one-on-one instructions on any chosen topic. All of the following types of classes will be needed, depending upon the purpose and material:

- **Educational workshops** are usually conducted with small groups, allowing for maximal participation, and are especially good for demonstrations and practice sessions.
- **Lectures** are often used for more academic or detailed information that may include questions and answers, but limit discussion. An effective lecture should include some audiovisual support.
- **Discussions** are best with small groups so that people can actively participate. This is a good for problem solving.
- **One-on-one instruction** is especially helpful for targeted instruction in procedures for individuals.
- **Computer/Internet modules** are good for independent learners.

Participants should be asked to evaluate the presentations in the forms of surveys or suggestions, but ultimately the program is evaluated in terms of patient outcomes.

READABILITY

Studies have indicated that learning is more effective if oral presentations and/or demonstrations are supplemented with reading materials, such as handouts. **Readability** (the grade level of material) is a concern because many patients and families may have limited English skills or low literacy, and it can be difficult for the NP to assess people's reading level. The average American reads effectively at the sixth to eighth grade level (regardless of education achieved), but many health education materials have a much higher readability level. Additionally, research indicates that even people with much higher reading skills learn medical and health information most effectively when the material is presented at the sixth to eighth grade readability level. Therefore, patient education materials (and consent forms) should not be written at higher than **sixth to eighth grade level**. Readability index calculators are available on the Internet to give an approximation of grade level and difficulty for those preparing materials without expertise in teaching reading.

BLOOM'S TAXONOMY AND 3 TYPES OF LEARNING

Bloom's taxonomy outlines behaviors that are necessary for learning, and this can apply to health care. The theory describes 3 types of learning:

- **Cognitive:** (Learning and gaining intellectual skills to master 6 categories of effective learning.)
  - Knowledge. Comprehension. Application.
  - Analysis. Synthesis. Evaluation.
- **Affective:** (Recognizing 5 categories of feelings and values from simple to complex. This is slower to achieve than cognitive learning.)
  - Receiving phenomena: Accepting the need to learn.
  - Responding to phenomena: Taking active part in care.
  - Valuing: Understanding value of becoming independent in care.
  - Organizing values: Understanding how surgery/treatment has improved life.
  - Internalizing values: Accepting condition as part of life, being consistent and self-reliant.

- **Psychomotor:** (Mastering 6 motor skills necessary for independence. This follows a progression from simple to complex.)
  - o Perception: Uses sensory information to learn tasks.
  - o Set: Shows willingness to perform tasks. Guided response: Follows directions. Mechanism: Does specific tasks.
  - o Complex overt response: Displays competence in self-care.
  - o Adaptation: Modifies procedures as needed.
  - o Origination: Creatively deals with problems.

LEARNING STYLES

Not all people are aware of their **preferred learning style.** A range of age-appropriate teaching materials/methods that relates to all 3 learning preferences should be available. Part of assessment for teaching involves choosing the right approach based on observation and feedback. Often presenting learners with different options gives a clue to their preferred learning style. Some people have a combined learning style:

Visual Learners	Learn best by seeing and reading: Provide written directions, picture guides, or demonstrate procedures. Use charts and diagrams. Provide photos, videos.
Auditory Learners	Learn best by listening and talking: Explain procedures while demonstrating and have learner repeat. Plan extra time to discuss and answer questions. Provide audiotapes.
Kinesthetic Learners	Learn best by handling, doing, and practicing: Provide hands-on experience throughout teaching. Encourage handling of supplies/equipment. Allow learner to demonstrate. Minimize instructions and allow person to explore equipment and procedures.

TEACHING AND LEARNING FOR CHILDREN AGES 6 TO 11

From **ages 6 to 11**, children vary widely in physical maturity, but they have increasing control of fine and gross motor skills, are receptive to learning, can question, and reason. Thinking remains literal rather than abstract. Concentration improves with age, and older children have a better understanding of their body and body systems. They are used to structured education. Children interact with peers and fear being different or ill. Teaching is aimed at the child with the parents as support (especially in later childhood). Some **techniques** commonly used to teach children include:

- Allow children to assume responsibility for much of their care.
- Limit teaching to about 30 minutes and allow time for the child to absorb and study material.
- Provide age-specific materials, such as Kid Cards (medicine information cards).
- Use a variety of teaching materials, including pictures, diagrams, and illustrations.
- Use analogies (A CT is like a giant camera).
- Use one-on-one or group instruction as appropriate.
- Tell children about treatments/procedures in advance.
- Provide support and encourage questions and participation.

KID CARDS

One of the challenges to facilitating learning in children is to teach them about their medications. **Kid Cards** are medicine information cards that present important details about the medication in language that is age-appropriate and often with pictures or illustrations. Information on a Kid Card may include:

- Methylphenidate
- This medicine is also called Ritalin LA®.
- Why am I taking Ritalin?
- You have to take this medicine so you can think better.
- It helps you to relax and listen better to others.
- How do I take Ritalin?
- It is a capsule (about the size of a peanut M&M).
- You need to take 1 capsule each morning with breakfast. You can open the capsule and sprinkle the medicine on applesauce, but don't chew up the capsule.
- What might happen if I take Ritalin?
- Most kids don't have any bad effects from taking Ritalin.
- If you get a rash, start itching, have stomach pain, feel nervous, can't sleep, feel "funny," or have a headache, tell your mom right away so she can call the doctor.

USING PLAY TO FACILITATE LEARNING

Play can be a useful tool to help children deal with physical and emotional problems related to their illness. Allowing children to **play with medical equipment under supervision** can allay some of their fears and help them to understand. **Needle play**, in which the child gives "shots" to a doll (with safe plastic syringes) can help them to express feelings about blood draws or injections. Providing **dolls and puppets** and engaging in play may encourage the child to express anxiety and fear through "talking" for the toy. There are a number of specialty dolls, such as dolls with removable parts to show internal organs and Shadow Buddies®, which are dolls that are commercially available (custom-made) to show the effects of different illnesses or surgeries. For example, a doll with thinning hair may show the effects of chemotherapy. Other dolls have stomas and colostomy bags. Drawing also may encourage the child to express feelings.

TEACHING AND LEARNING FOR ADOLESCENTS

Adolescents vary widely in both physical and emotional maturity; they have good reasoning and abstract thinking skills, understand cause and effect, and have good motor skills, but may engage in risk-taking behaviors and may have difficulty dealing with illness and poor compliance with treatments. They are very conscious of their body image and have a strong need to belong to a peer group, often rebelling against authority. They wish to be independent and need privacy and confidentiality. Teaching is aimed at allowing the adolescent to be independent in care:

- Use one-on-one (for confidential teaching) or peer group instruction/discussion as appropriate.
- Supplement instruction with audiovisual materials, computer-generated instruction, models, diagrams, illustrations, and written instructions, focusing on learning style and learning preferences.
- Allow the adolescent to maintain as much control over learning as possible.
- Provide options from which the adolescent can choose.

Mometrix

- Be patient, respectful, and tactful.
- Provide reasons for everything.
- Avoid conflict and direct confrontation, but suggest alternatives.

TEACHING STRATEGIES FOR ADULT LEARNERS

Adults have a wealth of life and/or employment experiences. Their attitudes toward education may vary considerably. There are, however, some **principles of adult learning** and typical characteristics of adult learners that an instructor should consider when planning strategies for teaching parents, families, or staff:

Practical and Goal-Oriented	Provide overviews or summaries and examples.
	Use collaborative discussions with problem-solving exercises.
	Remain organized with the goal in mind.
Self-Directed	Provide active involvement, asking for input.
	Allow different options toward achieving the goal.
	Give them responsibilities.
Knowledgeable	Show respect for their life experiences/education.
	Validate their knowledge and ask for feedback.
	Relate new material to information with which they are familiar.
Relevancy-Oriented	Explain how information will be applied.
	Clearly identify objectives.
Motivated	Provide certificates of achievement or some type of recognition for achievement

TEACHING OLDER ADULTS

There are a number of strategies that facilitate **teaching older adults**:

- Spend a little time getting to know the patient so that he/she is more relaxed and receptive to learning.
- Determine what information is critical for the patient to learn and what is non-essential.
- Evaluate the patient's learning style and previous knowledge about the topic.
- Plan for ample time for each session of instruction and plan the probable number of sessions to determine how much instruction is needed for each session. Ensure that sessions are presented in a closely-spaced manner to reinforce learning.
- Provide the patient ample time to practice.
- Allow the patient to guide the pace of the session as much as possible and encourage feedback.
- Prepare age-appropriate handouts at accessible reading level and with large-size font.
- Provide materials (pencil, paper) in case the patient wants to make notes.
- Be supportive, patient, and enthusiastic.

PSYCHOEDUCATION FOR BIPOLAR DISORDER AND SCHIZOPHRENIA

Psychoeducation, often part of cognitive behavioral therapy, involves teaching patients about their disease to help them manage symptoms and behavior. Psychoeducation should be specific to the disease state:

- **Bipolar disorder:** Patients are taught to understand the patterns of their disease and the triggers of mood changes so they can seek appropriate medical help. Additionally, they are taught to use self-monitoring tools (i.e., a daily record) to determine patterns of activity (i.e., sleeping) so they can maintain a consistent schedule of eating, sleeping, and engaging in physical activities as consistency tends to reduce unstable mood swings.
- **Schizophrenia:** Patients must be taught about their disease and the effects of medications. Because medication may not eliminate all symptoms, such as hearing voices, patients are taught methods to test reality to determine if their perceptions are correct.

Recovery and Resilience Promotion

RESILIENCY IN THE ROAD TO RECOVERY

Resiliency is the ability to cope with risk factors and tragedies, such as poverty and disasters, and to remain emotionally healthy. Resiliency is a critical element in recovery. One of the current trends is to aid patients in developing resiliency by providing a safe and supportive environment. Promoting resiliency also includes identifying problems early and taking steps to deal with them before they become ingrained as well as providing aid for severe or long-term problems. Holding patients to high expectation and supporting them in attaining goals helps to build self-confidence and coping skills. Patients who are resilient have the ability to regulate their emotions and to avoid self-defeating thoughts and actions. Resilience does not mean that patients remain unaffected by stressful events but rather than they are able to recognize that which is causing stress and find ways to deal with it and learn. Researchers have found that experience in coping with stress helps people to deal with later stressful events.

SAMHSA'S RECOVERY TO PRACTICE

SAMHSA's Recovery to Practice program promotes expanding recovery-oriented mental health care and provides educational and training materials, such as webinars and other resources, with curricula developed by a number of different mental health organizations, including the APA, APNA, AACP, INAPS, CSWE, and NAADAC. Recovery to Practice is based on **4 dimensions** (home, health, community, and purpose), and **10 principles**: hope, person-driven, many pathways, holistic, peer support, relational, culture, addresses trauma, strength/responsibility, and respect. Recovery to practice is centered on the **needs of the patient** who should be an active participant along with clinicians, psychiatrist, case manager, and rehabilitation staff in setting goals and working toward recovery. Recovery to practice stresses the importance of community resources and encourages patients to build their own network of support. Recovery-oriented care is person-centered and individualized but includes the family and allies as well as community resources and peer recovery support programs and is responsive to culture and personal beliefs.

CASE MANAGEMENT

One model for managing patient care is to use a **case manager**. The case manager is responsible for identifying needs of the patient, finding resources, linking the patient with needed services both within a mental health facility and in the community, and monitoring the patient. Within an acute, sub-acute, or skilled nursing facility, the case manager may chair the **interdisciplinary team** to ensure that the needs of the patient are communicated and that all members of the team are focused on similar goals. As the patient moves back into the community, the case manager needs to consider the **social support services** (home health care, transportation, meals-on-wheels, etc.) that are needed for the person to remain as independent as possible and to function safely. The case manager supervises and manages all aspects of care to ensure continuity.

CONTINUUM OF CARE

The **continuum of care** can move from inpatient treatments to various outpatient treatments and support systems, including in-home family treatment. Treatment may begin with acute crisis intervention and stabilization in the hospital setting, may then move to partial hospitalization allowing for the patient to leave for periods of time or go home at night, and finally to return home fulltime. This allows for varying levels of intensity throughout the patient treatment program and allows for treatment to be coordinated in many different environmental settings, care levels, by different healthcare providers, and by a variety of different services. This continuum of care occurs over a long period of time and includes the involvement of many different services. Its purpose is to meet the comprehensive needs of the patient through the coordination of interdisciplinary care and

81

services. Outpatient treatment programs as well as supportive employment programs also participate in the provision of the continuum of care.

DISCHARGE PLANNING

Discharge planning should begin on admission and must be a joint effort so that the **transfer and discharge documents** provide the information that the individual or staff at transfer facilities/home need. Information should include:

- Contact telephone numbers, e-mail addresses, and street addresses for the NP (to contact patient for discharge surveillance) and patient or transfer facility staff (to contact the NP if problems arise).
- Information sheets outlining signs for all risk factors, especially if patient is discharged to their home without nursing care.
- Follow-up appointment dates, with physicians, labs, or the NP.
- Specific directions for medication or treatments, including side effects.
- Information about 12-step/self-help/community-assistance programs.

Patients who are **homeless** require further assistance with discharge, as compliance with treatment and follow-up appointments is poor in the homeless population. Homeless patients should receive:

- Lists of safe shelters and places they can go to bathe, eat, and get mail.
- Assistance in applying for welfare assistance or Social Security.

NEED FOR ADEQUATE HOUSING

The need for **adequate housing** is an ongoing problem with psychiatric patients. Many of these patients are **homeless** and once released from inpatient care services do not have anywhere to live and may be estranged from family, leaving them with no support system. A **safe and affordable option** is vital to the success of their treatment. Many mental health patients have a relapse of their mental illness, suffer medical illness, incarceration, or abuse by others. The most common housing available includes group homes, such as personal care homes or board-and-care homes, therapeutic foster care, and supervised apartments. Many of these provide some type of rehabilitation and/or support services such as group therapy, job training, and counseling to help the patient make the transition from the treatment facility to the home environment and to learn to manage self-care.

THERAPEUTIC FOSTER CARE HOMES

Therapeutic foster care provides for the patient in a home setting with a family that is trained to care for high-need patients. This training includes medication education, crisis management, and disease education. The foster family supervises all aspects of the patient's care and incorporates the patient into the structure of the home. Many times, the patient will share household work and may attend daytime care programs. This level of care is available for both children and adults.

SUPERVISED APARTMENTS

Supervised apartments provide residents with individual apartments. Residents may either live alone or share the apartment with a roommate. They are responsible for the upkeep of the apartment and are independent in their self-care needs. The apartment is supervised by staff members that regularly check on the residents to ensure that they are doing well and following prescribed medication regimes.

PERSONAL CARE HOMES

Personal care homes, also called residential care facilities, are located in homes in residential communities. These homes can usually provide supervised care for up to approximately 10 individuals, depending on licensure. Services often include: supervising medication regimens, providing for transportation needs, serving meals, and assisting with activities of daily living. Many of the residents are elderly or suffer mild intellectual disability or psychiatric illness.

BOARD-AND-CARE HOMES

Board-and-care homes are similar to personal care homes; however, there is little assistance with activities of daily living although meals are usually provided. Many of the residents can provide their own self-care with little supervision. Board-and-care homes are usually larger in size and accommodate up to 150 individuals. Both types of residential services are licensed by the state.

Risk Assessment

A **risk assessment** evaluates the patient's condition and situation for the presence of certain **risk factors**. These risks can be influenced by age, ethnicity, spiritual or social beliefs and can include risk for suicide, harming others, exacerbation of symptoms, development of new mental health issues, falls, seizures, or allergic reactions. This assessment should occur within the first hour of their arrival and then continue as an ongoing process. The patient's specific risks should be prioritized, documented, and then nursing interventions should be put into place to protect the patient or others. Two of the most important areas to evaluate are the patient's risk for **self-harm** or **harm to others**. The staff member performing the assessment should very closely evaluate for any descriptions or thoughts the patient may have concerning these risks. Direct questioning on these subjects should be performed and documented. If the patient admits having these thoughts or ideas, the patient must be placed in close monitoring for either suicidal or assaultive precautions per facility protocol.

RISK FACTORS FOR EMOTIONAL AND MENTAL DISORDERS IN CHILDREN AND ADOLESCENTS

Psychiatric illness occurs in about 10% of children before age 18, although only about 20% receive treatment. Risk factors for **emotional and mental disorders** in children and adolescents include:

- Exposure to environmental toxins, such as high levels of lead.
- Living in poverty or crowded inner-city locations.
- Exposure to violence, such as witnessing or being the victim of physical or sexual abuse, drive-by shootings, muggings, etc.
- A child of a parent who with a substance use disorder or who is mentally ill.
- Children of a teenage parent.
- Children with a chronic disease or a disability.
- Children exposed to prolonged separation from parent(s).
- Children with multiple separations from parent(s).
- Children who experience frequent changes in primary caretakers.
- Homelessness.
- Children who experience the loss of significant others through death, divorce, or broken relationships.

BIOLOGICAL RISK FACTORS FOR MENTAL ILLNESS

Biological factors affect one's predisposition for **mental illness**. In addition to genetics, maternal and fetal health during pregnancy and exposure to environmental toxins before the age of 6 can affect mental health. Peripartum concerns, including poor nutrition, maternal stress, drug use, and poor living conditions may contribute to biological risk for mental illness. Intellectual disability and physical retardation, developmental deficits, and deformities may also increase the risk for mental illness. Tumors, trauma, and degenerative processes of the brain may cause structural or chemical changes within the brain that result in mental disorders. Biological factors can interact with other influences, such as a family history of violence, drug or alcohol abuse, schizophrenia, or non-compliance with medication regimens.

RISK FACTORS FOR MALNUTRITION

There are a number of **risk factors for malnutrition**:

- **Hypermetabolism** resulting from various diseases, such as acquired immune deficiency syndrome (AIDS), and trauma, stress, or infection.
- **Weight loss,** especially sudden or loss of 10% of normal weight over a 3-month period.
- **Low body weight**, defined as <90% of ideal body weight for age.
- **Low Body Mass Index** (BMI), defined as <18.5.
- **Immunosuppressive drugs**, which interfere with absorption of nutrients.
- **Malabsorption of nutrients** caused by diseases, such as chronic failure of kidneys or liver.
- **Changes in appetite** that decrease intake of nutrients.
- **Food intolerances**, such as lactose intolerance, resulting from lack of enzymes needed to completely digest food so it can be absorbed into the blood stream from the small intestine.
- **Dietary restrictions,** such as limited intake of protein with kidney failure.
- **Functional limitations,** such as inability to feed oneself.
- Lack of teeth or dentures, limiting intake.
- **Alterations of taste or smell** that render food unpalatable.

RISK FACTORS FOR TARDIVE DYSKINESIA

Tardive dyskinesia (TD) is caused by typical antipsychotics and affects overall about 20% of patients receiving these drugs; however, older adults (>50) are more severely impacted with rates of 50 to 70% in those receiving antipsychotic drugs. Females are more likely to suffer TD than males. Other **risk factors** include:

- Depression and other affective disorders.
- Brain injury.
- Prolonged treatment and/or excessively high doses (prevalence increases about 5% per year of treatment).
- Standard antipsychotics (such as haloperidol).

Symptoms usually begin after 6 months of treatment or withdrawal of medication and include abnormal movements, such as lip smacking and blinking, muscle twitching, hair pulling, and protruding tongue. Symptoms are often irreversible but if associated with reduction or withdrawal of medication, usually resolve within 3 months.

RISK FACTORS FOR FALLING

There are both physical and psychological deficits or abnormalities that can contribute to a patient's **fall risk**. **Physical factors** include weakness, lower extremity abnormalities that could negatively affect gait or ability to bear weight, diarrhea or urinary urgency or frequency, or altered mental status due to medications, electrolyte imbalances, infection, or hypoxia. **Psychological alterations** that can increase the patient's fall risk can include dementia, delirium, other confusional states, paranoia, or suicidal ideations. **Environmental factors** can also increase risk for a fall. These factors may include: lack of adequate lighting, lack of adequate footwear, bed raised to a high position, unfamiliar environment, call bell not within easy reach, or use of restraints. All of these factors should be evaluated to provide the safest environment possible to prevent patient injury.

RISK FACTORS FOR ANGER, AGGRESSION, AND VIOLENCE

Psychological aspects of increased **anger, aggression, and violence** can be associated with uncontrollable instinctual urges or as a result of the person's particular life experiences. Exposure to violence, altered mother/child bonding, altered socialization skills, or reinforcement of aggressive behavior by achievement of a goal can all lead to increased utilization of aggression and violence. Overexposure to violence through the media, entertainment, or the immediate environment can possibly lead to a desensitization of aggression and violence and lead to maladaptive behavioral responses. During an assessment, the background history of a patient can reveal many different **predictors** of future maladaptive responses associated with aggression and violence. The history may reveal violent behaviors and rage responses, increasing irritability, or loss of control. Some examples of **maladaptive background behaviors** include: cruelty to animals or children, setting fires or other destruction of property, drug or alcohol abuse, self-directed violence, such as cuts or burns on the arms, or juvenile delinquency. Many of these behaviors are evident during childhood.

RISK FACTORS FOR ACUTE AND CHRONIC PAIN

Pain affects both the physical and psychological wellbeing of the individual. It encompasses both a sensory and emotional response. A patient will cope with pain through many different behavioral responses. **Acute pain** is associated with an immediate occurring problem and is usually resolved in a few months or less. Fear, expectations, coping abilities, or cultural influences can all affect a patient's response to pain. A change in normal sleep patterns, anorexia, anxiety, or agitation can occur. **Chronic pain** is pain that lasts longer than 6 months. Chronic pain can lead to neurochemical abnormalities and depression. A complete assessment and evaluation of the pain should be performed and documented. Appropriate diagnosis and treatment plan should be in place to assist with successful treatment of pain.

NEGLECT AND LACK OF SUPERVISED CARE IN CHILDREN

While some children may not be physically or sexually abused, they may suffer from profound **neglect or lack of supervision** that places them at risk. Indicators include:

- Appearing dirty and unkempt, sometimes with infestations of lice, and wearing ill fitting, torn clothing and shoes.
- Being tired and sleepy during the daytime.
- Having excessive medical or dental problems, such as extensive dental caries.
- Missing appointments and not receiving proper immunizations.
- Being underweight for their current stage of development.

Neglect can be difficult to assess, especially if the NP is serving a homeless or very disadvantaged population. Home visits may be needed to ascertain if there is adequate food, clothing, or supervision, and this may be beyond the scope of care provided by the NP. Thus, suspicions should be reported so that a follow-up assessment of the home environment can be done.

PHYSICAL AND BEHAVIORAL SIGNS OF PHYSICAL ABUSE IN CHILDREN

Children rarely admit to being abused and, in fact, typically deny it and attempt to protect the abusing parent. Therefore, the NP must often rely on physical and behavioral signs to determine if there is cause to suspect **physical abuse**:

- **Behavioral indicators:** The child may be overly compliant or fearful with obvious changes in demeanor when a parent/caregiver is present. Some children act out with aggression toward other children or animals. Children may become depressed, suicidal, or present with sleeping or eating disorders. Behaviors may become increasingly self-destructive as the child ages.
- **Physical indicators:** The type, location, and extent of injuries can raise suspicion of abuse. Head and facial injuries and bruising are common, as are bite or burn marks. There may be hand prints or grab marks, unusual bruising, such as across the buttocks. Any bruising, swelling, or tearing of the genital area and the identification of sexually transmitted diseases are also causes for concern.

RAPE AND SEXUAL ABUSE

Rape and sexual abuse victims (both male and female) should be treated sensitively and questioned privately. Examination should include:

- **Assault history** that includes what happened, when, where, and by whom. Questioning should determine if there is a possibility of drug-induced amnesia or activities, such as douching or showering, which might have destroyed evidence.
- **Medical history** to determine if there is a risk of pregnancy and when and if the last consensual sex occurred that might interfere with laboratory findings.
- **Physical examination** should include examination of the genitals, rectum, and mouth. The body should be examined for bruising or other injuries. Toluidine dye should be applied to the perineum before insertion of a speculum into the vagina to detect small vulvar lacerations.

Forensic evidence must be collected within 72 hours and requires informed consent and the use of a rape kit. Forensic evidence includes:

- Victim samples for control.
- Assailant-identifying samples.
- Evidence of sexual activity.
- Evidence of force or coercion.

DOMESTIC VIOLENCE

According to guidelines of the Family Violence Prevention Fund, assessment for **domestic violence** should be done for all adolescent and adult patients, regardless of background or signs of abuse. While females are the most common victims, there are increasing reports of male victims of domestic violence, both in heterosexual and homosexual relationships. The person doing the assessment should be informed about domestic violence and be aware of risk factors and danger signs. The interview should be conducted in private (or with children <3 years old). The NP's office, bathrooms, and examining rooms should have information about domestic violence posted prominently. Brochures and information should be available to give to patients. Patients may present with a variety of physical complaints, such as headache, pain, palpitations, numbness, or pelvic pain. They are often depressed and may appear suicidal and may be isolated from friends and family. Victims of domestic violence often exhibit fear of spouse/partner and may report injury inconsistent with symptoms.

INJURIES CONSISTENT WITH DOMESTIC VIOLENCE

There are a number of characteristic injuries indicating **domestic violence**:

- Ruptured eardrum.
- Rectal/genital injury—burns, bites, trauma.
- Scrapes and bruises about the neck, face, head, trunk, arms.
- Cuts, bruises, and fractures of the face.

The **pattern of injuries** is also often distinctive:

- Bathing suit pattern—injuries on parts of body that are usually covered with clothing as the perpetrator abuses but hides evidence of abuse.
- Head and neck injuries (50%).

Abusive injuries (rarely attributable to accidents) are common:

- Bites, bruises, rope and cigarette burns, welts in the outline of weapons (belt marks).
- Bilateral injuries of arms/legs.

Defensive injuries are indicative of abuse:

- Back of the body injury from being attacked while crouched on the floor face down.
- Soles of the feet from kicking at perpetrator.
- Ulnar aspect of hand or palm from blocking blows.

FAMILY VIOLENCE PREVENTION FUND STEPS TO IDENTIFYING VICTIMS OF DOMESTIC VIOLENCE

The **Family Violence Prevention Fund** has issued guidelines for identifying victims of domestic violence. There are 7 steps:

1. **Inquiry:** Non-judgmental questioning should begin with asking if the person has ever been abused—physically, sexually, or psychologically.
2. **Interview:** The person may exhibit signs of anxiety or fear and may blame himself/herself or report that others believe he/she is abused. The person should be questioned if he/she is afraid for his/her life or for children.
3. **Question:** If the person reports abuse, it is critical to ask if the person is in immediate danger or if the abuser is on the premises. The interviewer should ask if the person has been threatened. The history and pattern of abuse should be questioned, and if children are involved, whether the children are abused. Note: State laws vary, and in some states, it is mandatory to report if a child was present during an act of domestic violence as this is considered child abuse. The NP must be aware of state laws regarding domestic and child abuse, and all NPs are mandatory reporters.
4. **Validate:** The interviewer should offer support and reassurance in a non-judgmental manner, telling the patient the abuse is not his/her fault.
5. **Give information:** While discussing facts about domestic violence and the tendency to escalate, the interviewer should provide brochures and information about safety planning. If the patient wants to file a complaint with the police, the interviewer should assist the person to place the call.

6. **Make referrals:** Information about state, local, and national organizations should be provided along with telephone numbers and contact numbers for domestic violence shelters.
7. **Document:** Record keeping should be legal, legible, and lengthy with complete report and description of any traumatic injuries resulting from domestic violence. A body map may be used to indicate sites of injury, especially if there are multiple bruises or injuries.

ELDER ABUSE

There are many different types of **elder abuse:** physical (such as hitting or improperly restraining), sexual, psychological, financial, and neglect. Elder abuse may be difficult to diagnose, especially if the person is cognitively impaired, but *symptoms* can include: fearfulness, disparities in reports of injuries between patient and caregiver, evidence of old or repeated injuries, poor hygiene and dental care, decubiti, malnutrition, undue concern with costs on caregiver's part, unsupportive attitude of caregiver, and caregiver's reluctance or refusal to allow patient to communicate privately with the NP. **Self-abuse** can also occur when patients are not able to adequately care for themselves. Diagnosis of elder abuse includes a careful history and physical exam, including directly questioning the patient about abuse. Treatment includes attending to injuries or physical needs, and this can vary widely, and referral to adult protective services as indicated. Reporting laws regarding elder abuse vary somewhat from one state to another, but all states have laws regarding elder abuse and 42 require **mandatory reporting** by health workers.

SUICIDE RISK ASSESSMENT

A **suicide risk assessment** should be completed and documented upon admission, with each shift change, at discharge, or any time suicidal ideation is suggested by the patient. This risk assessment should evaluate some of the following criteria: Would the patient sign a contract for safety? Is there a suicide plan? How lethal is the plan? What is the elopement risk? How often are the suicidal thoughts, and has the person attempted suicide before? Any associated symptoms of hopelessness, guilt, anger, helplessness, impulsive behaviors, nightmares, obsession with death, or altered judgment should also be assessed and documented. The higher the score is, the higher the risk for suicide. Patients who actually attempt suicide should be hospitalized and assessed for suicide risk after initial treatment. **High-risk findings** include:

- Violent suicide attempt (knives, gunshots).
- Suicide attempt with low chance of rescue.
- Ongoing psychosis or disordered thinking.
- Ongoing severe depression and feeling of helplessness.
- History of previous suicide attempts.
- Lack of social support system.

Substance Use Screening

ALCOHOL USE IN CHILDREN AND ADOLESCENTS

Alcohol is a significant problem in adolescence and even in younger children. It is the **most-commonly abused substance**. Studies have shown that about 32% of young people drink and 20% are binge drinkers. While alcohol can impair development of almost all body systems in a growing child, it is of particular concern for the effects on the neurological system and liver. Additionally, because it interferes with impulse control, adolescents who drink are often involved in violence, abuse, and at-risk sexual behavior. Drinking should be suspected if a child has memory problems, changes in behavior, poor academic progress, emotional lability, and physical changes, such as slurring of speech, general lethargy, or lack of coordination. *Intervention* includes teaching children from about age 9 about the dangers of drinking, identifying those who are drinking, identifying underlying problems, and providing programs to help teenagers stop drinking, such as counselling or Alcoholics Anonymous.

ASSESSMENT TECHNIQUES FOR ALCOHOL USE

All patients should be assessed for **alcohol use** as part of the initial history and physical exam as well as at subsequent visits, especially if there are health indications (abnormal liver function tests, falls, insomnia) or social indications (family problems, divorce, job loss). There are numerous **self-assessment screening tools** that ask the patient a number of questions about the frequency and amount of drinking as well as questions such as if he/she drinks in the morning or alone; has been arrested, has lost a job, or missed work because of drinking; feels depressed; or if he/she drinks to gain confidence. The assessment tools have a **scale indicator** that suggests a problem with certain scores. The NP should discuss the assessment and score with the patient and provide information about resources (such as Alcoholics Anonymous and alcohol rehabilitation programs) and health consequences of drinking to the patient.

DRUG USE IN CHILDREN AND ADOLESCENTS

Drug use continues to be a serious problem for children and teenagers, with some starting as young as 9 or 10, using a wide variety of drugs, including marijuana, crack, prescription drugs, cocaine, inhalants (such as glue and lighter fluid), hallucinogens, and steroids. Risk factors include aggressive behavior, poor social skills, and poor academic progress coupled with lack of parental supervision, poverty, and availability of drugs. Small children are often reacting to circumstances within the family while teenagers are responding to peer pressure from outside the family. Studies have shown that early *intervention* to teach children better self-control and coping skills is often more effective than trying to change behavior patterns that are established, so family-based programs often show positive results. Teenagers may need help with basic academic skills and social skills to improve communication. Methods of resisting drugs must be provided and reinforced. Drug recovery programs can be helpful but are often too expensive or not available for those who need them.

INDICATORS OF SUBSTANCE USE DISORDER

Many people with substance use disorders (alcohol or drugs) are reluctant to disclose this information, but there are a number of indicators that are suggestive of **substance use disorder:**

- Physical signs
  - Needle tracks on arms or legs.
  - Burns on fingers or lips.
  - Pupils abnormally dilated or constricted, watery eyes.

- o Slurring of speech, slow speech.
  - o Lack of coordination, instability of gait.
  - o Tremors.
  - o Sniffing repeatedly, nasal irritation.
  - o Persistent cough.
  - o Weight loss.
  - o Dysrhythmias.
  - o Pallor, puffiness of face.
- Other signs
  - o Odor of alcohol/marijuana on clothing or breath.
  - o Labile emotions, including mood swings, agitation, and anger.
  - o Inappropriate, impulsive, and/or risky behavior.
  - o Lying.
  - o Missing appointments.
  - o Difficulty concentrating/short term memory loss, disoriented/confused.
  - o Blackouts.
  - o Insomnia or excessive sleeping.
  - o Lack of personal hygiene.

INTERVIEWING A SUBSTANCE-ABUSING PATIENT

Issues to discuss with a **substance-abusing patient** during an initial interview include:

- Drug(s) and/or drink of choice: Amount, frequency and duration of use, route of administration, and when last used.
- The use of any other substances.
- Any history of and response to withdrawal.
- Any history of delirium tremens (DTs), seizures, blackouts, alcoholic amnesia, or past events of injury to self or others.
- Changes in mood and/or behavior.
- Sleep pattern changes.
- Eating habits and any associated changes.
- Problems with relationships, finances, legal system, occupation, school, family, medical disorders, and psychiatric disorders.
- Any family history of drug or alcohol use and mental health disorders.
- Access to substances of abuse.
- Previous substance use disorder treatments.
- Longest period of being substance-free.

Interviews with family members and/or significant others may be warranted if denial or rationalization is suspected.

Diagnosis and Treatment

Diagnostic Criteria

CRITERIA FOR PSYCHIATRIC/MENTAL HEALTH DIAGNOSES

The standard references that provide criteria for making a mental health or psychiatric diagnosis include:

- **North American Nursing Diagnosis Association** (NANDA) is an association of professional nurses developed to standardize nursing terminology. In 2002, NANDA became NANDA International. Reference: North American Nursing Diagnosis Association. (1998-2000). NANDA Nursing Diagnoses: Definitions and Classification.
- **The American Psychiatric Association** produces the Diagnostic and Statistical Manual of Mental Disorders (DSM) through the work of task forces that study current research and practice in the field of psychiatry. The DSM-5 is the most current version, released May 2013.
- **The World Health Organization** produces the International Classification of Diseases to try to provide consistent diagnosis of disease worldwide: *International Classification of Diseases, Tenth Revision, Clinical Modification (2007) (ICD-10-CM)*).

ICD AND DSM CODES

The current International Statistical Classification of Diseases and Related Health Problems (**ICD-10**) codes are used to code for all diseases, signs and symptoms, and external causes of injuries. ICD was developed by the WHO; and the version utilized in the United States since October 15, 2015, is ICD-10-CM (Clinical modification). ICD-10-PCS was developed by CMS to code for inpatient procedures (while CPT codes are used for outpatient procedures).

The Diagnostic and Statistical Manual of Mental Disorders (**DSM-5**) also codes for diagnoses but is limited to mental health disorders. DSM-5 contains full descriptions of different disorders and the criteria for diagnosis in narrative form, so it is more detailed than ICD-10, but DSM-5 directs the user to the correct ICD-10 codes because the ICD-10 code must be used for billing purposes. Thus, the codes for ICD-10 and DSM-5 are essentially the same.

REMOVAL OF THE AXIAL DIAGNOSIS SYSTEM IN THE DSM-5

The multi-axial diagnostic system of DSM-IV comprised fives **axes** (or levels), with each axis representing a characteristic of mental disorders with some third-party reimbursement requiring that patients be evaluated in all five axes:

1. Clinical disorders: Major psychiatric disorders.
2. Personality/Intellectual disabilities.
3. General medical conditions.
4. Psychosocial and environmental problems.
5. Global Assessment of Functioning Scale (GAF).

DSM-5 combines the first three axes into one category with **severity** rated along a continuum. Axes IV and V now require separate assessment with the GAF eliminated and practitioners advised to use other assessment instruments, such as WHODUS-2. Changes have occurred throughout the text. For example, "mental retardation" has been replaced with "intellectual disability" and sub-types of schizophrenia have been eliminated. Autistic-associated disorders have been combined into one category, autism spectrum disorders. New additions include binge-eating disorder, disruptive mood dysregulation disorder, hoarding disorder, and excoriation (skin picking) disorder. The bereavement exclusion from depression has been removed.

MAJOR DSM-5 CATEGORIES

The major DSM-5 categories are listed below:

- Neurodevelopmental disorders
- Schizophrenia spectrum and other psychotic disorders
- Bipolar and related disorders
- Depressive disorders
- Anxiety disorders
- Obsessive-compulsive and related disorders
- Trauma- and stressor-related disorders
- Dissociative disorders
- Somatic symptom and related disorders
- Feeding and eating Disorders
- Elimination disorders
- Sleep-wake disorders
- Sexual dysfunctions
- Gender dysphoria
- Disruptive, impulse-control, and conduct disorders
- Substance-related and addictive disorders
- Neurocognitive disorders
- Personality disorders
- Paraphilic disorders
- Other mental disorders
- Medication-induced movement disorders
- Other conditions that may be a focus of clinical attention

INTELLECTUAL DISABILITY

Intellectual disability (ID) is usually diagnosed in patients <18 years of age. Patients may have difficulty adapting to changing environments, need guidance in decision-making, and have self-care or communication deficits. Behaviors range from shy and passive to hyperactive or aggressive. Those with associated physical characteristics (Down syndrome) or problems are often diagnosed early. ID may be inherited (Tay-Sachs), toxin-related (maternal alcohol consumption), perinatal (hypoxia), environmental (lack of stimulation/neglect), or acquired (encephalitis, brain injury). Diagnosis involves performance results from standardized tests along with behavior analysis. There are 4 ID classifications based on intelligence quotient (IQ):

- **55-69 – mild** (85%): Educable to about sixth grade level. May not be diagnosed until adolescence. Usually abie to learn skills and be self-supporting but may need assistance and supervision.
- **40-54 – moderate** (10%): Trainable and may be able to work and live in sheltered environments or with supervision.
- **25-39 – severe** (3-4%): Language usually delayed and can learn only basic academic skills and perform simple tasks.
- **<25 – profound** (1-2%): Usually associated with neurological disorder with sensorimotor dysfunction. Require constant care and supervision.

COMMUNICATION DISORDERS

Communication disorders impair a person's ability to communicate with others through speech or language development. These disabilities often go unnoticed and lead to delays in social and educational development. Examples of communications disorders include:

- **Language disorder**: Impaired language development with limited vocabulary or difficulty understanding words, and/or abnormal auditory processing.
- **Speech sound disorder**: Impairment in production of speech sounds with absence or substitution of sounds, causing interference with work, school, or social communication.
- **Childhood-onset fluency disorder**: Onset is usually at 2-7 years. Sometimes associated with tics or other motor movements.
- **Social communication disorder**: difficulty in using verbal or nonverbal communication in social settings.

Because their speech may not sound as expected, patients may experience teasing or ridicule, leading to **self-esteem problems** and **social isolation**. Communication disorders may be related to intellectual disability, speech-motor deficit, hearing/sensory impairment, or environmental deprivation. Mild communication disorders may not be diagnosed until adolescence. Specialized educational training and speech therapy may help improve symptoms.

AUTISM SPECTRUM DISORDER

Autism spectrum disorder (ASD) has two components in its diagnosis: delays or abnormal functioning in social interaction/language for social communication and restricted repetitive behaviors, interests, and activities. Both of these pieces will be present in the ASD diagnosis. Severity levels are: Level 1 (requires support), Level 2 (requiring substantial support), and Level 3 (requiring very substantial support).

ASD now encompasses four disorders that were previously separate under DSM-IV: autistic disorder, Asperger's disorder, childhood integrative disorder, and pervasive developmental disorder. Patients with ASD associated with other known conditions and/or environmental factors should have the diagnosis written: autism spectrum disorder associated with (name of condition, such as Rett Syndrome).

REMOVAL OF ASPERGER'S DISORDER UNDER DSM-5

Asperger's disorder was previously part of the autism spectrum (with less severe symptoms). This diagnosis which was once considered one of four separate disorders under autism but has been removed under DSM-5. Patients who previously had a DSM-IV diagnosis of Asperger's disorder will now most often meet criteria for either autism spectrum disorder or social (pragmatic) communication disorder. The disorders are similar, but when working through a differential diagnosis, ASD will have as a defining characteristic restricted, repetitive behaviors or interests.

RETT'S SYNDROME

Rett's syndrome is a neurological disorder with a genetic cause found almost exclusively in females. It is characterized by normal prenatal development, normal motor development in the first 5 months of life, and a normal head circumference. However, between 5-48 months of age, head growth decelerates and the loss of purposeful use of the hands, along with gait abnormalities, seizures, and intellectual disability appears.

- **Stage I** (Early onset) **Age** 6-18 mo. **Characteristics:** The infant begins to exhibit less eye contact, diminished interest in playing, and delays in motor skill development (crawling/sitting).
- **Stage II** (Rapid destruction) **Age** 1-4 yrs. **Characteristics:** Previously gained skills, such as use of hands and speech, are lost. Purposeless hand movements such as wringing, grasping or finger wriggling begin but disappear when child is asleep. Deceleration of head growth is usually evident.
- **Stage III** (Pseudo-stationary) **Age** 2-10 yrs. **Characteristics:** Apraxia and seizures are prominent. A child may show more interest in her surroundings than she did during Stage II, and her alertness, attention span, and communication skills may improve. Many girls remain in this stage for most of their lives.
- **Stage IV** (Motor deterioration) **Age** 10+ yrs. **Characteristics:** Common features include: reduced mobility, muscle weakness, rigidity spasticity, dystonia, and scoliosis. Girls who were previously able to walk may stop walking. Generally, there is no decline in cognition, communication, or hand skills. Repetitive hand movements may decrease, and eye gaze usually improves.

Rett's was previously considered one of five autism related disorders but a genetic cause for Rett's was discovered in 1999, and it was removed during the DSM-5 update.

ADHD

Attention-deficit/hyperactivity disorder (ADHD) is commonly diagnosed in pre-school or school-aged children, although some are diagnosed as adults. It is more common in males than females. The person may have constant inattentiveness, display unruly conduct, and exhibit antisocial behaviors. ADHD is characterized by hyperactivity-impulsiveness and inattention, with some primarily hyperactive-impulsive, some inattentive, and some combined. ADHD may be delayed in its diagnosis. Behaviors may persist through adolescence and appear in some form into adulthood with less impulsivity as the child ages. Diagnostic criteria include:

- ≥6 symptoms of inattention or ≥6 symptoms of hyperactivity-impulsivity, inappropriate for developmental level persisting for ≥6 months.
- Several symptoms present prior to age 12.
- Symptoms present in ≥2 settings (home, school, work, play).
- Significant impairment socially, academically, and/or occupationally.
- Not exclusively related to other disorder (schizophrenia, mood disorder).

Treatment for ADHD is long-term and involves both the patient and the family. Treatment may include pharmacotherapy, psychotherapy, behavioral therapy, social skills training, or support services.

LEARNING DISORDERS

Children with **learning disorders** often fall substantially behind their peers in regards to expected skill and academic achievement levels. These disorders are often classified into verbal and non-verbal groups that include reading, writing, and mathematics.

- **Dyslexia**, a reading disorder, is not defined by reduced intelligence. It has both genetic and environmental components and is a deficit involving the processing of the sounds involved in speech.
- **Mathematic disorders** appear to involve a dysfunction of the right hemisphere of the brain.
- **Medical conditions**, such as Turner's syndrome or seizure disorders, can lead to right hemispheric dysfunction.

Diagnosis of these disorders is often not made until the child reaches school and experiences a decreased performance. This group can often have low self-esteem and may need support to assist with these issues. Specialized educational training can improve functioning.

MOTOR DISORDERS

Motor disorders are a type of neurodevelopmental disorder. Motor disorders can be classified as developmental coordination disorders, stereotypic movement disorders, and tic disorders. Tic disorders are further classified as Tourette's disorder, persistent motor or vocal tic disorder and provisional tic disorder.

Tics are sudden, involuntary, repetitive movements or sounds that appear out-of-context. Tics affect mostly Caucasian males and may be chronic or transient. Tics include uncontrollable blinking, grimacing, jerking, shrugging, barking, and obscene expletives. One-quarter of schoolchildren have transient tics lasting 4 weeks to 1 year. Tics are caused by blood flow problems through the basal ganglia and anterior cingulate cortex, and imbalance of dopamine, serotonin, and cyclic adenosine monophosphate (AMP). The cause is genetic in 75% of cases. Stroke, viral encephalitis, strep infection, and head trauma also cause tics. Tics often progress from the face, towards the neck and torso, to the feet. With support, many patients effectively manage tics throughout childhood, and the disorder remits in 73% of cases by adulthood. However, a childhood tic that worsens with age is likely to become a severe tic in adulthood. Ritalin, Cylert, antihistamines, amphetamines, tricyclic antidepressants, anticonvulsants, opioids, and cocaine worsen tics. Tics are often more manageable when the patient learns to effectively control their stress and anxiety.

TOURETTE'S DISORDER

Tourette's syndrome is a neurological disorder characterized by at least one vocal tic and multiple motor tics that appear simultaneously or at different times, and starting before the age of 18. Those with Tourette's disorder typically have multiple motor tics and one or more vocal tics.

Those with chronic motor or vocal tic disorder have either motor or vocal tics. Individuals with Tourette's Disorder are likely to have obsessions and compulsions, high levels of hyperactivity, impulsivity, and distractibility.

Boys are 3 times more likely to inherit it than girls, with onset usually during childhood or early adolescence. Girls with a Tourette's parent are more likely to manifest obsessive-compulsive disorder (ADHD). Tourette's children are likely to have emotional problems because their barking, echolalia (repeating others' words), and coprolalia (loud cursing) stigmatizes them at school.

Tourette's disorder is often associated with obsessive-compulsive behavior. Symptoms worsen around puberty and then may lessen.

Most successful treatments for Tourette's syndrome include **pharmacotherapy**. The antipsychotics haloperidol (Haldol) and pimozide (Orap) are successful in relieving the symptoms of Tourette's syndrome because they inhibit the flow of dopamine in the brain; their success has led many scientists to speculate that Tourette's Disorder is caused by an excess of dopamine. In some cases, psychostimulant drugs amplify the tics displayed by the individual. In these cases, a doctor may treat the hyperactivity and inattention of Tourette's with clonidine or desipramine. The former of these is a drug usually used to treat hypertension, while the latter is typically used as an antidepressant.

SCHIZOPHRENIA

Schizophrenia is a psychotic disorder characterized by personality disintegration and distortion in the perception of reality, thought processes, and social development. Criteria include:

Criteria A: The client must have at least 2 of the following symptoms:

- Hallucinations (known as a core positive symptom)
- Delusions (known as a core positive symptom)
- Disorganized speech (known as a core positive symptom)
- Severely disorganized or catatonic behavior
- Negative Symptoms (such as avolition or diminished expression)

For diagnosis the client must have at least one of the 3 core positive symptoms listed above.

Criteria B: Client's level of functioning is significantly below level prior to onset.

Criteria C: If the patient has not had successful treatment there are continual signs of schizophrenia for more than six months.

Criteria D: Depressive disorder, bipolar disorder, and schizoaffective disorder have been ruled out.

Criteria E: The symptoms cannot be attributed to another medical condition or a substance.

Criteria F: If the patient has had a communication disorder or Autism since childhood, a diagnosis of schizophrenia is only made it the patient has hallucinations or delusions.

CHILDHOOD SCHIZOPHRENIA

Schizophrenia rarely presents in children and adolescents, but it can occasionally present early. Many symptoms of schizophrenia mirror normal childhood characteristics and fantasies, so it is particularly difficult to diagnose in this age group. Symptoms of **early-onset schizophrenia** include:

- Paranoia.
- Visual and/or auditory hallucinations.
- Bizarre thoughts and beliefs.
- Impaired or confused concentration, speech, and social skills.
- Inappropriate reaction to events.
- Developmental delays.

Children with schizophrenia will have disturbances in all settings and are unlikely to show interest in making friends with others. Hallucinations and delusions must persist beyond 6 months in duration and continue past the age of 7. Early-onset schizophrenia has a very poor prognosis. The patient is high risk for suicide and symptom-related accidental death.

OLDER ADULTS

In **older adults with schizophrenia**, psychosis often reduces, but some cognitive impairment is common during all ages and is a persistent problem with chronic schizophrenia. There are about 300,000 older adult schizophrenics in the United States and about two-thirds are in nursing homes but only 15,000 in psychiatric hospitals, suggesting that cognitive impairment is the bigger problem with older adults. Schizophrenia is treated with typical antipsychotics (chlorpromazine, haloperidol, loxapine) and atypical antipsychotics (olanzapine, clozapine, risperidone), which provide better reduction in negative symptoms. All are associated with significant side effects, including tardive dyskinesia, but atypical antipsychotics have fewer side effects, and studies suggest they may be better tolerated in older adults.

Individuals typically develop schizophrenia as a **chronic condition**, with very little chance of full remission. Positive symptoms of schizophrenia tend to decrease in later life, though the negative symptoms may remain. The following factors bode well for prognosis: good premorbid adjustment; acute and late onset; female gender; presence of a precipitating event; brief duration of active-phase symptoms; insight into the illness; family history of mood disorder; no family history of schizophrenia.

POSITIVE AND NEGATIVE SYMPTOMS

Positive symptoms of schizophrenia are delusions and hallucinations. **Delusions** are false beliefs that are held despite clear evidence to the contrary. The delusions suffered by a schizophrenic usually fall into one of three categories: persecutory, in which the person believes that someone or something is out to get him or her; referential, in which the person believes that messages in the public domain (like song lyrics or newspaper articles) are specifically directed at him or her; or bizarre, in which the person imagines that something impossible has happened. The most common sensory mode for hallucinations is sound, specifically the audition of voices.

For many, the tell-tale characteristic of schizophrenia is **disorganized speech**. Disorganized speech manifests as incoherence, free associations that make little sense, and random responses to direct questions. Disorganized behavior manifests as shabby or unkempt appearance, inappropriate sexual behavior, unpredictable agitation, and catatonia and decreased motor activity.

Negative symptoms of schizophrenia are restricted range of emotions, reduced body language, lack of facial expression, lack of coherent thoughts, inability to make conversation, and avolition (the inability to set goals or to work in a rational, programmatic manner).

POSSIBLE CAUSE AND TREATMENT

For many years, the professional consensus was that schizophrenia was caused by either an excess of the neurotransmitter **dopamine** or oversensitive **dopamine receptors**. The dopamine hypothesis was supported by the fact that antipsychotic medications that block dopamine receptors had some success in treating schizophrenia, and by the fact that dopamine-elevating amphetamines amplified the frequency of delusions. The dopamine hypothesis has been somewhat undermined, however, by research that found elevated levels of norepinephrine and serotonin, as well as low levels of GABA and glutamate in schizophrenics. Some studies have shown that clozapine and other atypical antipsychotics are effective in treating schizophrenia, even though they block serotonin rather than dopamine receptors.

Treatment for schizophrenia begins with the administration of **antipsychotic medication**. Antipsychotics are very effective at diminishing the positive symptoms of schizophrenia, though their results vary from person to person. Antipsychotics have strong side effects, however, including tardive dyskinesia. Medication is more effective when it is taken in combination with psychosocial intervention. Many schizophrenics are prone to relapse if they receive a great deal of criticism from family members, so it may be a good idea to initiate family therapy in which the level of expressed emotion in the family is discussed.

CRITERIA FOR CATATONIA AND CRITERIA FOR DELUSIONAL DISORDER

Criteria for **catatonia** includes at least three of the following: Catalepsy,

Defying or refusing to acknowledge instruction, Echolalia, Echopraxia, Little to no verbal response, Grimacing, Agitation, Semi-consciousness, Waxy flexibility, Posturing, Mannerism, Stereotypy.

When writing the diagnosis of catatonia, first write the diagnosis and code of the mental disorder associated with catatonia, then write the catatonia diagnosis. For example: 295.90 schizophrenia, multiple episodes, currently in acute episode; 293.89 catatonia associated with schizophrenia.

Delusional disorder is typified by the presence of a persistent delusion. Delusion may be persecutory type, jealous type, erotomanic type (that someone is in love with delusional person), somatic type (that one has physical defect or disease), grandiose type, or mixed.

Criteria A: The client experiences at least one delusion for at least one month or longer. **Criteria B**: The client does not meet criteria for schizophrenia. **Criteria C**: Functioning is not significantly impaired, and behavior except dealing specifically with delusion is not bizarre. A non-bizarre delusion is one that could have happened. **Criteria D**: Any manic or depressive episodes are brief. **Criteria E**: The symptoms cannot be attributed to another medical condition or a substance. It should be specified if the delusions are bizarre. Severity is rated by the quantitative assessment measure.

CRITERIA FOR SCHIZOPHRENIFORM DISORDER

For a diagnosis of **schizophreniform disorder**, the following criteria must be met:

Criteria A: The client must have at least 2 of the following symptoms:

- Hallucinations (known as a core positive symptom)
- Delusions (known as a core positive symptom)
- Disorganized speech (known as a core positive symptom)
- Severely disorganized or catatonic behavior
- Negative Symptoms (such as avolition or diminished expression)

For diagnosis the client must have at least one of the 3 **core positive symptoms** listed above.

Criteria B: an illness of at least one month but less than six months duration.

Criteria C: Depressive disorder, bipolar disorder, and schizoaffective disorder have been ruled out.

Criteria D: The symptoms cannot be attributed to another medical condition or a substance.

99

BRIEF PSYCHOTIC DISORDER

Brief psychotic disorder is a delusion that has sudden onset and lasts less than one month. Brief psychotic disorder is a classification of the schizophrenia spectrum and other psychotic disorders.

Criteria A: At least one of the following symptoms: Delusions, hallucinations, disorganized speech, or catatonic behavior.

Criteria B: The symptoms last more than one day but less than one month. The client does eventually return to baseline functioning.

Criteria C: The disorder cannot be attributed to another psychotic or depressive disorder.

SCHIZOAFFECTIVE DISORDER

Schizoaffective disorder is characterized by the initial symptoms of schizophrenia (delusions, hallucinations, disorganized speech and behavior, catatonia, negative symptoms) with delusions or hallucinations for at least 2 weeks out of a one-month period.

Criteria A: The client must have at least 2 of the following symptoms:

- Hallucinations (known as a core positive symptom)
- Delusions (known as a core positive symptom)
- Disorganized speech (known as a core positive symptom)
- Severely disorganized or catatonic behavior
- Negative Symptoms (such as avolition or diminished expression)

For diagnosis the client must have at least one of the 3 **core positive symptoms** listed above.

The client will experience the above symptoms during a continuous period of illness during which there will also be a significant manic or depressive mood episode. Schizoaffective disorder is less common than schizophrenia, and symptoms are usually less severe, but social and work activities dysfunction is common. Onset is usually in early adulthood. Differential diagnoses include delirium, dementia, schizophrenia, and mood disorders with psychosis.

BIPOLAR DISORDER

Bipolar disorder is a mood disorder characterized by mania, depression, or both. Subtypes include:

- **Bipolar I:** Characterized by at least 1 manic episode, sometime following an episode of depression. This form of bipolar usually includes cycling between mania and depression with episodes of psychosis that include paranoia and hallucinations.
- **Bipolar II:** Characterized by at least 1 episode of depression and at least 1 episode of hypomania (shorter lasting and less severe than mania) with the depressive periods of longer duration than hypomanic periods.
- **Cyclothymia (Bipolar III):** Characterized by milder mood swings.
- Bipolar not otherwise specified (NOS): Mood disorder without a clear pattern.

Some people with bipolar disorder may experience rapid cycling between depression and mania, often more than 4 times in a year, with mood changes occurring rapidly (within a few hours). Additionally, some people may experience a **mixed type of bipolar disorder** in which depression and mania both occur at the same time.

Writing a Bipolar Diagnosis and Differences Between Bipolar I and II

Bipolar disorders should be **written** with current (or most recent) features, whether manic, hypomanic or major depressive episode noted. The current severity of mild, moderate or severe should also be noted as well as any applicable specifiers. Partial or full remission should be noted when applicable. Example: bipolar I disorder, current episode manic, moderate severity, with anxious distress. Bipolar specifiers:

1. With anxious distress
2. With melancholic features
3. With peripartum onset
4. With seasonal pattern
5. With psychotic features
6. With catatonia
7. With atypical features
8. With mixed features
9. With rapid cycling

Bipolar II is distinguished from **Bipolar I** by the fact that the individual has never had either a manic or a mixed episode. Males and females develop Bipolar I disorder equally, but Bipolar II is much more common for females. On average, the age of onset for the first manic episode is the early 20s.

Manic Episodes

Bipolar disorder is characterized by **manic episodes** alternating with depressive episodes that occur in varying patterns interspersed with periods of normal mood (euthymia). A manic episode is a distinct period characterized by extremely elevated mood, energy, and unusual thought patterns, causing impairment in occupational functioning and social activities for at least 1 week.

Criteria A: An episode of significantly elevated, demonstrative, or irritable mood. There are significant goal-directed behaviors, activities, and an increase in the amount of energy the patient normally has. These symptoms are present for most of the day and last at least one week.

Criteria B: During the period described in criteria A, the patient will experience 3 of the following symptoms (if the client presents with only an irritable mood 4 of the following symptoms need to be present for diagnosis):

- less need for sleep
- excessive talking
- inflated self-esteem
- easily distracted
- flight of ideas
- engages in activities that have negative consequences
- engages in either goal directed activity or purposeless activity

Criteria C: The episode causes significant impairment socially.

Criteria D: The symptoms cannot be attributed to a substance.

Among all mental disorders, Bipolar I and II disorders are the most clearly linked to **genetic factors**. Identical twins are overwhelmingly more likely to develop the disease than are fraternal twins.

CRITERIA FOR HYPOMANIC EPISODES

A **hypomanic episode** will be severe enough to be a clear departure from normal mood and functioning, but will not be severe enough to cause a marked impairment in functioning, or to require hospitalization.

Criteria A: An episode of significantly elevated, demonstrative, or irritable mood. There are significant goal-directed behaviors, activities, and an increase in the amount of energy the patient normally has. These symptoms are present for most of the day and last at 4 days.

Criteria B: During the period described in criteria A, the patient will experience 3 of the following symptoms (if the client presents with only an irritable mood 4 of the following symptoms need to be present for diagnosis):

- less need for sleep
- excessive talking
- inflated self-esteem
- easily distracted
- flight of ideas
- engages in activities that have negative consequences
- engages in either goal directed activity or purposeless activity

Criteria C: The episode causes a change in the functioning of the individual.

Criteria D: The episode causes changes noticeable by others.

Criteria E: The episode does not cause social impairments.

Criteria F: The symptoms cannot be attributed to a substance.

DEPRESSIVE EPISODES

The symptoms of the **depressive phase** of bipolar disorder are the opposite of those symptoms that occur during the manic phase; additionally, suicide is a constant concern for those suffering through the depressive phase. **Depressive episodes** include:

- Feelings of hopelessness or helplessness.
- Putting affairs in order as if leaving somewhere.
- Acting recklessly as if not caring about one's life.
- Suicidal ideation: Seeking out weapons or pills that could be used to commit suicide.
- Loss of interest in enjoyable pastimes.
- Physical and mental sluggishness.
- Appetite or weight changes.
- Sleeping too much.
- Concentration and memory problems.
- Feelings of self-loathing, shame, or guilt.
- Ruminating about death, self-harm, or suicide.

CHILDREN AND ADOLESCENTS

Bipolar disorder is increasingly diagnosed in **children and adolescents**, but symptoms may vary from those of adults and may vary as the child's brain matures. Children often present with **behavioral problems**. Symptoms, usually after age 4, include:

- Violent rages, temper, hostility.
- Preoccupation with violence.
- Depressive periods or severe sadness.
- Pronounced separation anxiety.
- Inappropriate sexualized behavior.
- Suicidal ideation.
- Food/object cravings.
- Bossing, bullying behavior.
- Risk-taking behavior and grandiose beliefs.
- Delusions, hallucinations.
- Rapid speech, thoughts.
- Sleep disorders.

About 90% of all children diagnosed with bipolar disorder continue to experience the disorder throughout adulthood. However, early treatment during adolescence opens the door for remission. The bipolar child is high-risk for school failure, and 18% commit suicide.

OLDER ADULTS

Bipolar disorder, a psychiatric affective disorder characterized by mood swings ranging from depression to mania, includes **subtypes** bipolar I, bipolar II, cyclothymia, rapid cycling, and mixed state. Co-morbid conditions include substance use disorder, thyroid disorders, suicidal tendencies, obsessive-compulsive disorder, post-traumatic stress disorder, and dementia. Those with **late onset (>50)** tend to have less severe symptoms than those with early onset. *Symptoms* include severe mania, hypomania, normal mood, mild to moderate depression and severe depression. Symptoms may be precipitated by environmental triggers, such as medications, stress, substance abuse, sleep disorders, and changes of seasons. *Treatment* includes medications (mood stabilizers, anticonvulsants, and atypical antipsychotics). Antidepressants are contraindicated. Treatment with 1 drug (mood stabilizer) is the goal for older adults because of the potential for adverse effects and drug interactions because of co-morbidities. Electroshock treatment is effective for older adults with depressive states. The half-life of drugs, such as lithium, increases because of reduced renal clearance, so lower doses and careful monitoring are often necessary.

CRITERIA FOR CYCLOTHYMIC DISORDER

Cyclothymic disorder is characterized by chronic, fluctuating mood with many hypomanic and depressive symptoms, however, not as severe as either bipolar I or bipolar II.

Criteria A: The client experiences a considerable number of hypomania symptoms without meeting all the criteria for hypomanic episodes and depressive symptoms that do not meet the criteria for major depressive episode for two years or more (can be for one year or more in <18 y/o).

Criteria B: During the above time period, the client exhibits the symptoms more than half of the time and the client is never symptom free more than two months at a time.

Criteria C: The client has not met the criteria for manic, hypomanic, or major depressive episodes.

Criteria D: The episode doesn't meet criteria for schizophrenia spectrum or other psychotic disorder.

Criteria E: The symptoms cannot be attributed to a substance.

Criteria F: The episodes cause significant impairment socially or functionally.

MAJOR DEPRESSIVE EPISODE

A **major depressive episode** is a depressed mood, profound and constant sense of hopelessness and despair, or loss of interest in all or almost all activities for a period of at least 2 weeks. Family history of depression is a major risk factor. Developmental hormone changes at puberty or hormone disruption from disease can also contribute to depression. Depression is associated with neurotransmitter dysregulation, especially serotonin and norepinephrine.

Criteria A: The client experiences 5 or more of the following symptoms during 2 consecutive weeks. These symptoms are associated with a change in the client's normal functioning. (Note: Of the presenting symptoms, either depressed mood or loss of ability to feel pleasure must be included to make this diagnosis).

- Depressed mood.
- Loss of ability to feel pleasure or have interest in normal activities.
- Decreased aptitude for thinking.
- Thoughts of death.
- Fatigue (daily).
- Inappropriate guilt/worthlessness.
- Observable motor agitation or psychomotor retardation.
- Weight change of more than or less than 5% in one month.
- Hypersomnia or Insomnia (almost daily).

Criteria B: The episode causes distress or social/functional impairment.

Criteria C: The symptoms cannot be attributed to a substance or another condition/disease.

Criteria D: The episode does not meet the criteria for schizophrenia spectrum or other psychotic disorder.

Criteria E: The client does not meet criteria for manic episode or a hypomanic episode.

SPECIFIERS FOR MAJOR DEPRESSIVE DISORDER

Major depressive disorder is diagnosed when an individual has one or more major depressive episodes without having a history of manic, hypomanic, or mixed episodes. There are a few different **specifiers** (categories of associated features) for **major depressive disorder** issued by the DSM 5:

1. With anxious distress
2. With melancholic features
3. With peripartum onset
4. With seasonal pattern
5. With psychotic features
6. With catatonia
7. With atypical features
8. With mixed features

Some studies estimate that 20% of women will have symptoms worthy of a diagnosis of major depressive disorder after giving birth. From the beginning of adolescence on, the rate of major depressive disorder is about twice as great for males as for females. Before adolescence, the rates are about the same. Most major depressive disorders occur in the mid-twenties.

POSSIBLE ETIOLOGIES

The **catecholamine hypothesis** suggests major depressive episodes are due to a deficiency of the neurotransmitter **norepinephrine**. The **indolamine hypothesis** proposes that depression is caused by inferior levels of **serotonin**. Some researchers speculate depression is caused by hormonal disturbances, like an increased level of **cortisol**. Cortisol is one of the stress hormones secreted by the adrenal cortex. Other researchers speculate there is a connection between depression and diminished new cell growth in certain regions of the brain, particularly the subgenual prefrontal cortex and hippocampus. Many antidepressant drugs seem to stimulate new growth in the hippocampus. Three major **cognitive-behavioral etiologies** have been offered for major depressive disorder:

- The **learned helplessness model** proposed by Seligman suggests afflicted individuals have been exposed to uncontrollable negative events in the past, and also have a tendency to attribute negative events to internal, stable, and global factors
- **Rehm's self-control model** suggests depression occurs in individuals who obsess over negative outcomes, set extremely high standards for themselves, blame all of their problems on internal failures, and have low rates of self-reinforcement. coupled with high rates of self-punishment
- **Beck's cognitive theory** suggests depression is the result of negative and irrational thought and beliefs about the depressive cognitive triad (the self, the world, and the future)

SYMPTOMS AND TREATMENT

Symptoms of major depressive disorder vary with **age**. For children, common symptoms are somatic complaints, irritability, and social withdrawal. Male preadolescents often display aggressive and destructive behavior. When elderly individuals develop a major depressive disorder, it manifests as memory loss, distractibility, disorientation, and other cognitive problems. Many major depressive episodes are misdiagnosed as dementia. It is very common in non-Anglo cultures for the symptoms of depression to be described in terms of **somatic content**. Latinos, often complain of jitteriness/headaches, while Asians often complain of tiredness/weakness.

The typical **treatment program** for major depressive disorder combines antidepressant drugs and psychotherapy. Three classes of antidepressant medication are commonly prescribed. **Selective serotonin reuptake inhibitors (SSRIs)** are prescribed for melancholic depressives; they have a lower incidence of serious adverse side effects than do tricyclics. **Tricyclics (TCAs)** are prescribed for classic depression, involving vegetative bodily symptoms, a worsening of symptoms in the morning, acute onset, and short duration of moderate symptoms. **Monoamine oxidase inhibitors** are prescribed as a last resort for patients who have an unorthodox depression that includes phobias, panic attacks, increased appetite, hypersomnia, and a mood that worsens as the day goes on.

DEPRESSIVE DISORDER WITH SEASONAL PATTERN

Depressive disorder with seasonal pattern, formerly called seasonal affective disorder (SAD), is a depressive disorder that afflicts people in the Northern Hemisphere from October to April. Symptoms are hypersomnia, increased appetite, weight gain, and an increased desire for carbohydrates. Research suggests this disorder is caused by circadian and seasonal increases in the level of **melatonin** production by the pineal gland from lack of sunlight. Depressive disorder with seasonal pattern patients are treated with phototherapy (exposure to full-spectrum white light for several hours each day), aerobic exercise, and SSRIs.

DYSTHYMIC DISORDER

Dysthymic Disorder criteria:

- **Criteria A**: For at least two years the client experiences for most of a day, more days than they don't experience it, a depressed mood.
- **Criteria B**: The client experiences 2 or more of the following when depressed: low self-esteem, decreased appetite or overeating, a feeling of hopelessness, fatigue, difficulty concentrating, insomnia or hypersomnia.
- **Criteria C**: During the episode the client has not had relief from symptoms for longer than 2 months at once.
- **Criteria D**: The client may have met the criteria for a major depressive disorder.
- **Criteria E**: The client does not meet criteria for cyclothymic disorder, manic episode or hypomanic episode.
- **Criteria F**: The episode does not meet the criteria for schizophrenia spectrum or other psychotic disorder.
- **Criteria G**: The symptoms cannot be attributed to a substance.
- **Criteria H**: The symptoms cause distress or impairment socially or functionally.

25-50% of patients show sleep EEG abnormalities. Women are two to three times more likely to suffer dysthymic disorder than men. 75% of patients with dysthymic disorder develop major depressive disorder in five years. First degree relatives are likely to also suffer dysthymia or major depression. Treatment programs for dysthymic disorder usually include a combination of antidepressant drugs (especially fluoxetine) and either cognitive-behavioral therapy or interpersonal therapy.

ANXIETY DISORDERS

Anxiety disorders include the following:

- **Panic disorder**—recurrent brief but intense fear in the form of panic attacks with physiological or psychological symptoms.
- **Specific Phobia**—fear of specific situations or objects
- **Generalized anxiety disorder**—chronic psychological and cognitive symptoms of distress, excessive worry lasting at least 6 months of duration.
- **Separation anxiety disorder**—excessive anxiety related to being separated from someone the client is attached to
- **Selective mutism**—unable to speak in social settings (when it would seem appropriate) though normally able to speak
- **Social anxiety disorder**—anxiety about social situations
- **Agoraphobia**—anxiety of being outside of the home or in open places

The following symptoms are common to **both anxiety and depression**:

1. Poor concentration and memory
2. Irritability
3. Fatigue
4. Insomnia
5. Feelings of hopelessness

GENERALIZED ANXIETY DISORDER

Generalized anxiety disorder (GAD) is an unrealistic apprehension and worry that persists for 6 or more months. GAD may be accompanied by tension, sweating, irritability, and hypervigilance. Symptoms include:

- **Motor tension**: Tremulousness, muscle tension.
- **Autonomic arousal**: Shortness of breath, tachycardia, dry mouth, and diarrhea.
- **Vigilance**: Insomnia and a feeling of being edgy.
- **Depression.**
- **Impaired quality of life.**

Levels of anxiety include:

- **Mild**: Slight physical arousal but retains the ability to learn well.
- **Moderate**: Physical symptoms are present.
- **Severe**: Physical symptoms interfere with day-to-day activities, difficulty concentrating, very anxious.
- **Panic**: Terrified, little-or-no ability to concentrate, shortness of breath, palpitations, fear of dying.

The treatment for GAD usually entails a multicomponent cognitive-behavioral therapy, occasionally accompanied by pharmacotherapy. SSRI antidepressants and the anxiolytic buspirone have both demonstrated success in diminishing the symptoms of GAD.

PANIC DISORDER

Panic disorder is chronic, repeated, and unexpected panic attacks, with spells of overwhelming fear, apprehension, terror, and being in danger when there is no specific cause. Episodes last from minutes to several hours and may include sense of unreality, detachment from oneself, fainting, vertigo, choking, and chest pain. Initial attacks usually occur in an anxiety-provoking situation, while successive attacks are spontaneous and unexpected. Anticipatory anxiety may exist between attacks because of fear that another may occur without warning. Those affected often report to the Emergency Department thinking that they may be having a heart attack or severe respiratory problems. Attacks must include ≥4 of the following symptoms, which may be minimal to severe:

- Palpitations or accelerated heart rate (tachycardia)
- Sweating
- Chest pain
- Nausea
- Dizziness
- Derealization
- Paresthesia (pins and needles or numbness)
- Shaking
- Shortness of breath
- Fear of losing control
- Fear of dying
- Chills or heat sensation
- Feeling of choking

The most effective treatment is **controlled in vivo exposure with response prevention**, known as flooding. **Flooding** is typically accompanied by cognitive therapy, relaxation, breathing training, and/or pharmacotherapy, with antidepressant medications.

PHOBIAS

A **phobia** is an uncontrollable, unfounded, and persistent fear of a specific object, situation, or activity that actually poses no threat. If confronted with the item causing the fear, anxiety, sweating and tachycardia may develop. In severe situations, a panic may develop. **Specific phobias** include a number of subtypes:

- **Animals**: Includes animals (such as dogs or cats) and insects (such as spiders) with onset usually during childhood.
- **Natural environment**: Includes fear of storms, water, and heights with onset usually during childhood.
- **Blood-injection-injury**: Includes fear of needles, blood.
- **Situational**: Includes fear of flying, tunnels, and bridges with onset in childhood or mid-20s.
- **Other**: Includes various phobias, such as fear of choking, falling, sounds.

Individuals with blood-injection-injury phobia have a brief increase in heart rate and blood pressure, followed by a drop in both, often ending in a brief loss of consciousness.

Social phobias are characterized by fear of social or performance activities, resulting in anxiety and/or panic attacks which cause the person to avoid triggering situations. Onset is usually during adolescence and often occurs in those with history of shyness. Duration is >6 months and may persist throughout life.

AGORAPHOBIA

Agoraphobia is fear and anxiety about being in a situation or place from which **escape** may be difficult, causing the person to avoid these places/situations. This often results in the person being unable to leave the home or to be in a crowd or line, use an elevator or types of public transportation, or be in either wide open or enclosed spaces. To meet the diagnosis of agoraphobia, the disorder must not be related to substance abuse or another condition. Other diagnostic criteria include:

- the person avoids and fears the situations
- the situation provokes fear when thought about
- there is disproportionate fear/anxiety for the actual situation
- the feelings last more than six months
- the feelings cause distress and social or occupational impairment

Since the DSM-5 update, agoraphobia can now be diagnosed irrespective of panic disorder. If the patient also meets criteria for panic disorder, both diagnoses can be given.

PHOBIAS

The two-factor theory proposed by **Mower** asserts that phobias are the result of **avoidance conditioning**, when an individual associates a neutral or controlled stimulus with an anxiety-causing, unconditioned stimulus. The phobia reinforces a strategy of avoidance because it prevents anxiety (even though the neutral stimulus was not to blame for the anxiety in the first place).

Another theory for the etiology of phobias is offered by **social learning theorists**, who state that phobic behaviors are learned by **watching avoidance strategies** used by one's parents.

As with panic disorder, **in vivo exposure** is considered the best treatment for a specific phobia. **Relaxation and breathing techniques** are also helpful in dispelling fear and controlling physical response.

As with other phobias, social phobia is best treated with exposure in combination with social skills and cognitive therapy. Antidepressants and the beta-blocker propranolol are helpful for treating social phobia.

SEPARATION ANXIETY

Separation anxiety disorder is characterized by age-inappropriate and excessive anxiety that occurs when an individual is separated or threatened with separation from his or her home or family unit. It may occur in children or adults. Symptoms include:

- Excessive distress when separated from home or attachment figures.
- Persistent fear of being alone.
- Frequent physical complaints during separation.

These symptoms typically ≥6 months and cause **functional impairment** to be diagnosed as separation anxiety disorder. The exact cause of is unknown. Environment, genotype, and family history all influence the development of separation anxiety disorder. Children with separation anxiety tend to be from loving, stable homes; many manifest the disorder after suffering some personal loss. Many children with this disorder will refuse to go to school, and claim physical ailments to avoid having to leave the home. In some cases, the child will actually develop a headache or stomachache as a result of anxiety about separation from the home or from an individual to whom they are attached. The refusal to go to school may begin as early as 5 or as late as 12. If the separation anxiety occurs after the age of 10, however, it is quite possibly the result of depression or some more severe disorder. There are various treatment plans for separation anxiety disorder, all of which recommend that the child immediately resume going to school on a normal schedule.

OBSESSIVE-COMPULSIVE AND RELATED DISORDERS

Obsessive-compulsive and related disorders include the following:

- **OCD** – disorder including frequent intrusive thoughts and urges, causing distress, that are associated with repetitive acts the patient performs in response
- **Body dysmorphic disorder** – preoccupation with perceived flaws in the appearance, believing the flaws to be abnormal in appearance
- **Trichotillomania** – hair-pulling disorder
- **Hoarding disorder** – ongoing distress when parting with possessions
- **Excoriation** – skin-picking disorder

DSM-5 includes the following **specifiers**:

- Good or fair insight
- Poor insight
- Absent or delusional insight
- Tic-related

OBSESSIVE-COMPULSIVE DISORDER (OCD)

OCD criteria:

- **Criteria A**: The client exhibits obsessions, compulsions, or both. Obsessions are continuous, repetitive thoughts, compulsions, or things imagined that are unwanted and cause distress. The client will try to suppress thoughts, ignore them, or do a compulsive behavior. Compulsions are recurrent behavior or thought the client feels obliged to perform after an obsession to decrease anxiety, however, the compulsion is usually not connected in an understandable way to an observer.
- **Criteria B**: The obsessions/compulsions take at least one hour per day and cause distress.
- **Criteria C**: The behavior is not caused by a substance.
- **Criteria D**: The behavior could not better be explained by a different mental disorder.

Note if the criteria are met with good insight (client realizes OCD beliefs are not true), poor insight (client thinks the OCD beliefs are true), or absent insight (client is delusional, truly believing OCD beliefs are true). Note if the client has ever had tic disorder.

A **sense of dread** may develop if the compulsion is resisted, and some try to ignore or suppress thoughts/behaviors. Intervention usually is not sought until emotional and/or physical exhaustion occurs in either client or a significant other. Differential diagnoses include depressive disorders, hypochondriasis, generalized anxiety disorder (GAD), Tourette's (may be a co-morbid condition), temporal lobe epilepsy, and schizophrenia.

TRAUMA- AND STRESSOR-RELATED DISORDERS

Disinhibited social engagement disorder: Child has decreased hesitations regarding interacting with unfamiliar adults. Does not question leaving normal caregiver to go off with a stranger.

Posttraumatic stress disorder: Persistently re-experiencing a severe trauma for more than one month. Individual exhibits arousal-anxiety symptoms, and avoidance of things associated with the trauma or numbness.

Acute stress disorder: Anxiety and dissociative symptoms develop within one month of experiencing a trauma.

Adjustment disorder: The client has behavior/emotional changes occurring within 3 months of a stressor. These changes cause distress for the client and are disproportional to the actual stressor.

REACTIVE ATTACHMENT DISORDER

Reactive attachment disorder: Child rarely seeks or responds to comfort when upset.

Reactive attachment disorder is characterized by a markedly disturbed or developmentally-inappropriate **social relatedness** in most settings. This condition typically begins before the age of five. In order to definitively diagnose this disorder, there must be evidence of pathogenic care, which may include neglect or a constant change of caregivers that made it difficult for the child to form normal attachments.

POST-TRAUMATIC STRESS DISORDER

An individual may be diagnosed with **post-traumatic stress disorder (PTSD)** if he or she develops symptoms after exposure to an **extreme trauma**. An extreme trauma entails: Witnessing the death or injury of another person; experiencing injury to self; learning about the unexpected or violent death or injury of a family member or friend; or repeatedly being exposed to trauma (such as first responders). The traumatic event must elicit a reaction of intense fear, helplessness, or horror. The characteristic symptoms of PTSD are:

1. Persistent re-experiencing of the event
2. Persistent avoidance of stimuli associated with the trauma
3. Persistent symptoms of increased arousal (difficulty concentrating, staying awake, or falling asleep)

The preferred treatment for PTSD is a **comprehensive cognitive-behavioral approach** that includes:

1. Exposure
2. Cognitive restructuring
3. Anxiety management
4. SSRIS to relieve symptoms of PTSD and comorbid conditions

Some psychologists criticize single-session psychological debriefings, because they believe one session amplifies the effects of a traumatic event.

ACUTE STRESS DISORDER

Acute stress disorder has symptoms similar to those of post-traumatic stress disorder. Acute stress disorder is distinguished by symptoms that occur for **more than 3 days and but less than one month**. An individual is diagnosed with acute stress disorder when he or she has **9 or more symptoms** from any of the following 5 categories, which begin after the trauma:

1. Intrusion
2. Negative mood
3. Avoidance symptoms
4. Dissociative symptoms
5. Arousal symptoms

An individual with acute stress disorder persistently **relives** the traumatic event, to the point where he or she takes steps to avoid contact with stimuli that bring the event to mind, and experiences severe anxiety when reminiscing about the event.

> **Review Video: Acute Stress Disorder**
> Visit mometrix.com/academy and enter code: 538946

ADJUSTMENT DISORDERS

Adjustment disorders appear as **maladaptive reactions** to one or more identifiable psychosocial stressors.

In order to make the diagnosis, the onset of symptoms must be **within three months of the stressor**, and the condition must cause **impairments in social, occupational, or academic performance**. The symptoms do not align with normal grief or bereavement. Symptoms remit within six months after the termination of the stressor or its consequences.

Specify if the adjustment disorder is with:

1. Depressed mood
2. Anxiety
3. Mixed anxiety and depressed mood
4. Disturbance of conduct
5. Mixed disturbance of emotions and conduct

DISSOCIATIVE DISORDERS

Dissociative disorders are a disruption in consciousness, identity, memory, or perception of the environment that is not due to the effects of a substance or a general medical condition. These are all characterized by a disturbance in the normally integrative functions of identity, memory, consciousness, or environmental perception.

- **Dissociative identity disorder (previously multiple personality disorder)**: Two or more personalities exist within one person. Each personality is dominant at a particular time.
- **Dissociative amnesia**: Inability to recall important personal data, more than forgetfulness. Is not due to organic causes and comes on suddenly.
- **Depersonalization/derealization disorder**: Feeling detached from one's mental processes or body, as if one is an observer.

Cultural influences can cause or amplify some of the symptoms of dissociative disorders, so take these into account when making a diagnosis. For instance, many religious ceremonies try to foster a dissociative psychological experience; individuals participating in such a ceremony may display symptoms of dissociative disorder without requiring treatment.

DISSOCIATIVE AMNESIA

Individuals may be diagnosed with **dissociative amnesia** if they have more than one episode in which they are unable to remember important personal information, and this memory loss cannot be attributed to ordinary forgetfulness. The gaps in the individual's memory are likely to be related to a traumatic event.

The three most common patterns of dissociative amnesia are:

1. **Localized**, in which the patient is unable to remember all events around a defined period
2. **Selective**, in which the patient cannot recall some events pertaining to a circumscribed period
3. **Generalized**, in which memory loss spans the patient's entire life

It should be specified if this is with **dissociative fugue**, a subtype of dissociative amnesia, which is a purposeful travel that is associated with amnesia.

DISSOCIATIVE FUGUE

A **dissociative fugue** is a subtype of dissociative amnesia, and is an abrupt, unexpected, purposeful flight from home, or another stressful location, coupled with an inability to remember the past. The patient is unable to remember his or her identity and assumes a new identity. Fugues are psychological protection against extreme stressors like bankruptcy, divorce, separation, suicidal or homicidal ideation, and rejection. Fugues happen in wars, natural disasters, and severe accidents. Fugues affect 2 in every 1,000 Americans. There will be no recollection of events that occur during the fugue. Individuals in a fugue state may seem normal to strangers. Dissociative fugue is a specifier that can be used with dissociative amnesia.

DEPERSONALIZATION DISORDER

Depersonalization/derealization disorder is diagnosed when an individual has recurrent episodes in which he or she feels detached from his or her own mental processes or body or to the surroundings. In order to be diagnosed, this condition must be intense enough to cause significant distress or functional impairment.

SOMATIZATION SYMPTOM DISORDER

Somatic symptom disorder is a **somatoform disorder**, meaning that it suggests a medical condition but is not fully explainable by the medical condition, substance abuse, or other medical disorder.

Individuals with somatic symptom disorder often describe their problems in dramatic, overstated, and ambiguous terms. They excessively worry or thought about the symptoms and spend much time and energy worrying about health issues. Somatic symptom disorders cause clinically significant distress or impairment, and are not produced intentionally. A somatic symptom disorder involves recurrent multiple somatic complaints and though no one symptom has to be continuous, some symptoms is present for at least six months. Medical attention has been sought, but no physical explanation has been found.

CONVERSION DISORDER

Conversion disorder is a **somatoform disorder** characterized by either loss of bodily functions or symptoms of a serious physical disease. The patient becomes blind, mute, or paralyzed in response to an acute stressor. Occasionally, patients develop hyperesthesia, analgesia, tics, belching, vomiting, or coughing spells. These symptoms do not conform to physiological mechanisms, and testing reveals no underlying physical disease. The sensory loss, movement loss, or repetitive physical symptoms are not intentional. The patient is not malingering to avoid work, or factitiously trying for financial gain. The symptoms of a conversion disorder can often be removed with hypnosis or Amytal interview. Some researchers believe that suggesting to the patient that his or her symptoms will go away is the best way to relieve them. The patient can develop complications from disuse of body parts.

The etiology of conversion disorder is explained in terms of two **psychological mechanisms**: A conversion disorder may be used for **primary gain** when the symptoms keep an internal conflict or need out of the consciousness. A conversion disorder is used for **secondary gain** when the symptoms help the individual avoid an unpleasant activity or obtain support from the environment. In order to diagnose a conversion disorder, there must be evidence of **involuntary psychological factors**. Conversion disorder is occasionally confused with factitious disorder and malingering, both of which are voluntary.

FACTITIOUS DISORDER AND MALINGERING

An individual diagnosed with **factitious disorder (FD)** intentionally manifests physical or psychological symptoms to satisfy an intrapsychic need to **fill the role of a sick person**. The patient with factitious disorder presents the illness in an exaggerated manner and avoids interrogation that might expose the falsity. FD patients may undergo surgeries and invasive medical procedures. FD patients often hide insurance claims and hospital discharge forms. A disturbing variation of FD is **factitious disorder imposed on another** (sometimes referred to as Munchausen's syndrome by proxy), in which a caregiver intentionally produces symptoms in another individual. Usually, a mother makes her child ill.

Malingering is not considered a mental illness, but a V coded disorder that may be a focus of clinical attention. Malingering is feigning physical symptoms to **avoid** something specific, like going to work, or to gain a specific reward. Consider malingering as a possibility when: A person obtains a medical evaluation for legal reasons or to apply for insurance compensation; There is marked inconsistency between the patient's complaint and the objective findings, or if the patient does not cooperate with a diagnostic evaluation or prescribed treatment; The patient has an antisocial personality disorder. Malingering contrasts with factitious disorder because in FD, the patient does not feign physical symptoms for personal gain or to avoid an adverse event, but does it with no obvious external rewards.

ILLNESS ANXIETY DISORDER

Illness anxiety disorder (formerly hypochondriasis) is the preoccupation with and fear of **serious illness** that lasts for 6 months despite medical reassurance that no physical pathology is present. Symptomatology may be related to an organ system, bodily function, or to a body part. Indications on the part of the patient include:

- Obsessed with personal health despite medical reassurance.
- May be able to admit that the fears are unrealistic.
- May recognize himself as a "hypochondriac" or may not recognize that concerns are exaggerated.
- May deal with fears by seeking information about diseases on the Internet, in books, or through other sources or may avoid the subject altogether.
- Tends to visit multiple clinicians.

Differential diagnoses include schizophrenia and the following disorders: generalized anxiety, body dysmorphic panic, delusional, conversion, and somatization.

ANOREXIA NERVOSA

The characteristics of **anorexia nervosa** are:

- **Criteria A**: Extreme restriction of food, lower than requirements, leading to low body weight.
- **Criteria B**: An irrational fear of gaining weight or behaviors that prevent weight gain, though at low weight.
- **Criteria C**: Distorted body image or a lack of acknowledgement of gravity of current weight.

Anorexia nervosa may be restrictive without binging and purging or may include binging and purging. Anorexia nervosa is usually **chronic** and requires a lifetime of monitoring. Patients with anorexia nervosa exhibit many mental health symptoms and commonly have comorbidity with depression and dysthymia. They may be irritable, have sleep disturbances, experience lack of interest in sex, and withdraw from social interactions. They will be obsessed with the thought of food and may also have other obsessive-compulsive tendencies that may or may not involve food. They are at high risk for suicide. Characteristic physical findings (emaciation, amenorrhea, osteoporosis, hair loss, cardiac dysfunction) result from malnutrition and starvation.

LABORATORY FINDINGS

Many of the abnormal lab findings with **anorexia nervosa** are associated with **malnutrition and starvation**. Some of the common lab findings include:

- **Blood tests** show decreased hemoglobin (anemia), leucopenia (depressed immune system), elevated blood urea nitrogen (BUN) (dehydration), high cholesterol, hypoglycemia (inadequate nutrition), elevated liver function studies, thrombocytopenia (decreased clotting ability), electrolyte imbalances particularly hypokalemia (low potassium), metabolic alkalosis or acidosis.
- **Hormone levels** show hypothyroidism and/or decreased estrogen, luteinizing hormone (LH), and follicle-stimulating hormone (FSH) levels.
- **Electrocardiogram** (ECG) may indicate dysrhythmias.
- **Bone density tests** show demineralization of bones and early-onset osteoporosis.

In the more severe cases, the patient can develop metabolic encephalopathy or increased ventricular/brain ratio, resulting from the complications of starvation. Anorexia nervosa can result in death.

BULIMIA NERVOSA

Characteristics of **bulimia nervosa** include:

- **Criteria A**: Cyclical periods of binge eating:
  - Discretely consuming an amount of food that is larger than most individuals would eat in the same time period and situation.
  - The client feels a lack of control over the eating.
- **Criteria B**: Characterized by binge eating followed by purging via self-induced vomiting/laxatives/fasting/vigorous exercise in order to prevent weight gain.
- **Criteria C**: At least one binge eating episodes per week for three months.
- **Criteria D**: It is marked by a persistent over-concern with body shape and weight.
- **Criteria E**: The eating and compensatory behaviors do not only occur during periods of anorexia nervosa.

Treatment often involves cognitive-behavioral techniques like self-monitoring, stimulus control, cognitive restructuring, problem-solving, and self-distraction. Some antidepressants, like imipramine, have been effective at reducing instances of binging and purging. Many patients seeking treatment have co-morbid psychiatric disorders, including major depression, dysthymia, anxiety disorders, substance abuse problems, obsessive-compulsive disorder, post-traumatic stress disorder, personality disorders, and mood disorders.

PHYSICAL, EMOTIONAL, AND LABORATORY FINDINGS

Many of the physical and laboratory findings associated with **bulimia nervosa** are due to poor nutrition and self-induced vomiting habits. **Physical symptoms** can include loss of dental enamel or increased dental caries, chipped teeth, mouth sores, scars on dorsum of hand, cardiac and skeletal muscle myopathies, esophageal tears with associated bleeding, amenorrhea or irregular menstrual cycles, and decreased normal gastrointestinal functioning due to overuse of laxatives, often resulting in cycles of constipation and fecal impaction. Patients may engage in constant dieting and exercise, exhibit signs of depression, hoard food, and have a distorted self-body image. Some of the associated **laboratory findings** result from repeated self-induced vomiting and laxative use and include fluid and electrolyte imbalances with increased blood urea nitrogen (BUN) and hypokalemia, metabolic alkalosis or acidosis, and elevated amylase levels.

PICA AND RUMINATION DISORDER

Pica: Persistent eating of non-food substances such as paint, hair, sand, cloth, pebbles, etc. Those with pica do not show an aversion to food. In order to be diagnosed, the symptoms must persist for at least a month without the child losing an interest in regular food. Also, the behavior must be independent and not a part of any culturally acceptable process. Pica is most often manifested between the ages of 12-24 months. Pica has been observed in developmentally disabled children, pregnant women, and anemics.

Rumination disorder: Regurgitation and re-chewing of food.

AVOIDANT/RESTRICTIVE FOOD INTAKE DISORDER

The criteria for avoidant/restrictive food intake disorder are listed below:

- **Criteria A**: A disruption in eating evidence by not meeting nutritional needs and failure to gain expected weight or weight loss, nutritional deficiency, requires nutritional supplementation, or interpersonal interference.
- **Criteria B**: This disruption is not due to lack of food or culture.
- **Criteria C**: There does not appear to be a problem with the client's body perception.
- **Criteria D**: The disturbance can't be explained by another medical condition.

ENURESIS

Enuresis is repeated involuntary **urinary incontinence** in children old enough to have bladder control, usually about 5-6 years old. Diabetes and other disorders should be ruled out, although 95% are not associated with structural or neurological disorders. There are 3 types:

- **Primary**: The child has never been dry at night, and incontinence is associated with delay in maturation and small functional bladder rather than stress or psychiatric disorders.
- **Intermittent**: The child stays dry part of the time with episodes of incontinence at night.
- **Secondary**: The child has had long periods (6-12 months) staying dry and then is incontinent because of infection, stress, or sleep disorder.

Incontinence may occur only at night (most commonly in the first third of the night during rapid eye movement [REM] sleep), only during the day (uncommon after age 9), or during both day and night. Some children postpone urination for various reasons until they are incontinent. Criteria include involuntary urination ≥2 times weekly for ≥3 months or severe social/academic impairment.

ENCOPRESIS

Encopresis is the voluntary or involuntary passage of **stool** in places or manners that are inappropriate for a child, 80% of whom are male, 4 years or older. There are 2 types:

- **Retentive:** Accounts for about 80% of those affected and is characterized by a history of long-term, painful constipation and the development of overflow diarrhea. The chronic constipation causes distention of the rectum and stretching of both the internal and external anal sphincters; as a result, the child may no longer feel the urge to defecate, so stool eventually leaks from the rectum, causing chronic fecal incontinence.
- **Non-retentive:** Accounts for the other 20%. Non-retentive encopresis, usually involving passage of normally formed stools on a daily basis, does not involve constipation or bowel abnormalities, except in a small subset that may have irritable bowel syndrome, but is generally a behavioral/psychological problem. When encopresis is deliberate, the child may have conduct disorder or oppositional defiant disorder.

SLEEP-WAKE DISORDERS

Insomnia disorders: Difficulty falling asleep, staying asleep, or early rising without being able to go back to sleep.

Hypersomnolence disorder: Sleepiness despite getting at least 7 hours with difficulty feeling awake when suddenly awoke, lapses of sleep in the day, feeling unrested after long periods of sleep.

Narcolepsy: Uncontrollable lapses into sleep, occurring at least three times each week for at least 3 months.

Obstructive sleep apnea hypopnea: Breathing related sleep disorder with obstructive apneas or hypopneas.

Central sleep apnea: Breathing related sleep disorder w/central apnea.

Sleep-related hypoventilation: Breathing related sleep disorder with evidence of decreased respiratory rate and increased CO_2 level.

Circadian rhythm sleep-wake disorder: Sleep wake disorder w/primary cause a mismatch between circadian rhythm and sleep required.

Non-rapid eye movement sleep arousal disorder: Awakening during the first third of the night associated with sleep walking/sleep terrors.

Nightmare disorder: Recurring dreams that are well remembered and cause distress.

Rapid eye movement sleep behavior disorder: Arousal during REM sleep associated with motor movements and vocalizing.

Restless legs syndrome: The need to move the legs due to uncomfortable sensations, usually relieved by activity.

> **Review Video: Chronic Insomnia**
> Visit mometrix.com/academy and enter code: 293232

SEXUAL DYSFUNCTIONS

A sexual dysfunction is any condition in which the sexual response cycle is disturbed or there is pain during sexual intercourse, and this causes distress or interpersonal difficulty. Types of sexual dysfunctions:

- Delayed ejaculation
- Erectile disorder
- Female orgasmic disorder
- Female sexual interest/arousal disorder
- Genito-pelvic pain/penetration disorder
- Male hypoactive sexual desire disorder
- Premature ejaculation
- Substance-induced sexual dysfunction

Male erectile disorder is the inability to attain or maintain an erection. This condition is linked to diabetes, liver and kidney disease, multiple sclerosis, and the use of antipsychotic, antidepressant, and hypertensive drugs.

Orgasmic disorders are any delay or absence of orgasm after the normal sexual excitement phase. Premature ejaculation is orgasm that occurs with a minimum of stimulation and before the person desires it. Premature ejaculation may be in part due to deficiencies in serotonin.

GENITO-PELVIC PAIN/PENETRATION DISORDER AND SEXUAL DYSFUNCTIONS

Genito-pelvic pain/penetration disorder is persistent difficulty with genital pain associated with sexual intercourse or involuntary spasms in the pubococcygeus muscle in the vagina, which make it difficult to have sexual intercourse, or fear or anxiety related to anticipation of pain during intercourse.

Sexual dysfunctions are categorized as lifelong or acquired, and generalized or situational, depending on their cause. **Generalized dysfunctions** occur with every sexual partner in all circumstances. **Situational dysfunctions** only occur under certain circumstances. The cause may be psychological, physical, or both.

Any patient with sexual dysfunction should be given a **medical evaluation** for diabetes, pelvic scars, kidney disease, hypertension, and drug interactions. Use sleep studies to determine if an impotent male gets an erection at night, and determine whether the cause of impotence is *physical* or *psychological*. **Psychological impotence** can be treated with **cognitive-behavioral therapy**. Sex therapy is most helpful in treating premature ejaculation. *Sensate focus* is used to reduce performance anxiety and increase sexual excitement.

Kegel exercises, which strengthen the pubococcygeus muscle, can improve sexual pleasure. As for pharmacotherapy, Viagra is helpful in attaining and maintaining erections, and Rogaine is helpful for female orgasm.

GENDER DYSPHORIA

DSM-5 defines **gender dysphoria** (formerly gender identity disorder) as a marked incongruence between one's expressed gender and assigned gender that causes significant distress or impairment over a period of at least 6 months. Informally, gender dysphoria is used to describe a person's persistent discomfort and disagreement with their assigned gender. DSM-5 criteria for diagnosis in **children** include:

- Strong desire to be of the other gender or insistence that one is the other gender
- Strong preference for clothing typically associated with the other gender
- Strong preference for playing cross-gender roles
- Strong preference for activities stereotypical of the other gender and rejection of those activities stereotypical of one's assigned gender
- Strong preference for playmates of the other gender
- Strong dislike of one's own sexual anatomy
- Strong desire for the sex characteristics that match one's expressed gender

DSM-5 criteria for diagnosis in **adolescents and adults** include:

- Marked incongruence between expressed gender and one's existing primary and secondary sex characteristics
- Strong desire to rid oneself of these sex characteristics for this reason
- Strong desire for the sex characteristics of the other gender
- Strong desire to be of the other gender and to be treated as such
- Strong conviction that one's feelings and reactions typical of the other gender

CONDUCT DISORDER

Conduct disorder is characterized by a blatant disregard for other people's feelings and property, societal norms, and etiquette. Onset may be during childhood or adolescence. Conduct disorder is more prevalent in males than females. Criteria includes:

Criteria A: Persistent pattern of behavior in which significant age-appropriate rules or societal norms are ignored, and others' rights and property are violated (theft, deceitfulness); aggression to people and animals and destruction of property are common. To meet diagnosis criteria individuals will display three of the fifteen possible symptoms over the course of a year. All the symptoms can be categorized as belonging to one of the four categories below:

1. Aggression to people or animals
2. Destruction of property
3. Deceitfulness or theft
4. Serious violations of rules

Criteria B: The patterns of behavior cause academic, social or other impairments. **Criteria C**: The behaviors couldn't better be classified as antisocial personality disorder.

Individuals with conduct disorder persistently violate either the rights of others or age-appropriate rules. They have little remorse about their behavior, and in ambiguous situations, they are likely to interpret the behavior of other people as hostile or threatening.

OPPOSITIONAL DEFIANT DISORDER

Oppositional defiant disorder (ODD) means the patient has an abnormally intense disregard for **authority figures**, primarily parents or guardians. Behavior with ODD is less severe than with conduct disorder and usually does not involve aggressive behavior toward people, property, or animals. The ODD patient challenges authority figures because of learned behaviors, such as negative reinforcement. A pattern of **mutual negative reinforcement** occurs between patient and authority figure in such a manner that the patient confronts all requests with extreme defiance. The diagnostic criteria for ODD include a negative, hostile pattern of behavior persisting ≥6 months. The behavior is so aberrant as to cause problems at work, school, or play. The person with ODD exhibits **social and academic impairment** that are not the result of a psychotic or mood disorder.

ODD criteria include:

1. Patterns of negative or hostile behavior towards authority figures
2. Frequent outbreaks of temper and rages
3. Deliberately annoying people
4. Blaming others
5. Spite and vindictiveness

SUBSTANCE USE DISORDER

Substance intoxication or **withdrawal** describes the behavioral, psychological, and physiological symptoms due to effects of the substance. It will vary depending on type of substance. Substance related disorders includes the following classes: caffeine; hallucinogens; alcohol; cannabis; stimulants; tobacco; inhalants; opioids; other; and sedatives, hypnotics and anxiolytics. The severity of the particular **substance use disorder** can be determined by the presence of the number of symptoms. Also present may be substance induced delirium, dementia, psychosis, mood disorders, anxiety disorder, sexual dysfunction, or sleep dysfunction. Substance-related and addictive disorders now include gambling disorder, as evidence shows that the behaviors of gambling trigger similar reward systems as drugs.

REMISSION

While many individuals are able to **temporarily abstain** from a substance on which they were formerly dependent, few of them will be able to avoid **relapse**. When an individual relapses into substance abuse behavior, he or she develops an **abstinence violation effect** that is manifested as self-blame, shame, and an increased susceptibility to relapse.

The type of **remission** is based on whether any of the criteria for abuse/dependence have been met and over what time frame:

Early Remission: After the criteria for a substance use disorder have been met, none of those criteria are fulfilled (except for the criteria for craving) for at least three months but not more than 1 year.

Sustained Remission: After the criteria for a substance use disorder have been met, none of those criteria are fulfilled (except for the criteria for craving) for 1 year or longer.

Maintenance Therapy: a replacement medication that can be taken to avoid withdrawal symptoms. The client could still be considered in remission from a substance use disorder if while using maintenance therapy, they do not meet any criteria for that substance use disorder except for craving. For tobacco use disorder this would include using nicotine replacement systems. For opioid use disorder this could include medications such as methadone. If the client is in remission in a controlled environment, this should be specified.

DELIRIUM

Delirium is characterized by a clinically significant **deficit in cognition or memory** as compared to previous functioning. In order for delirium to be diagnosed, the individual must have disturbances in consciousness and either a change in personality or the development of perceptual abnormalities. These changes in cognition may appear as losses of memory, disorientation in space and time, and impaired language. The perceptual abnormalities associated with delirium include hallucinations and illusions. Delirium usually develops over a few hours or days, and may vary in intensity over the course of the days and weeks. If the cause of the delirium is alleviated, it may disappear for an extended period of time.

Delirium criteria for diagnosis:

- **Criteria A**: A disturbance in consciousness or attention.
- **Criteria B**: Develops over a short period of time, and fluctuates throughout the day
- **Criteria C**: There are also changes in cognition.
- **Criteria D**: Not better explained by another condition.
- **Criteria E**: Is caused by a medical condition, toxins, or is substance related (or multiple etiologies).

PERSONALITY DISORDERS

Paranoid personality disorder: Characterized by extreme distrust and suspiciousness of others, assuming others have sinister motives.

Schizoid personality disorder: Characterized as seeming indifferent to the praise or criticism of others, neither desiring nor enjoying close relationships.

Schizotypal personality disorder: Exhibit very odd or strange behavior, associated with suspiciousness or paranoid ideation.

Histrionic personality disorder: Excessive attention seeking and emotionalism associated with dramatic and seductive behavior and an unwarranted need for approval. It may be associated with concurrent somatization disorder in an effort to attract attention.

NEUROCOGNITIVE DISORDERS

Neurocognitive disorders are a decline in cognitive functioning. These may be **major** or **minor** and may be due to:

- Alzheimer's disease
- Frontotemporal lobar degeneration
- Lewy body disease
- vascular disease
- traumatic brain injury
- substance/medication use
- HIV Infection
- prion disease
- Parkinson's disease
- Huntington's disease
- another medical condition
- multiple etiologies

Criteria A: A change in cognitive ability from baseline. This information can be determined by the client, a well-informed significant other, family member, or caretaker, or it can be determined by neuropsychology testing.

Criteria B: For a major neurocognitive disorder, the cognitive change interferes with ADLs and independence. For a minor neurocognitive disorder, the cognitive change doesn't interfere with normal ADLS and independence, if accommodations are used.

Criteria C: The cognitive change cannot be defined as delirium only.

Criteria D: The cognitive change is not better described as another mental disorder.

PERSONALITY DISORDERS

Dependent personality disorder: Characterized by an over-reliance on others, submissive and clinging behavior, subordination of personal needs to those of others, and fear of separation. Patients often arrange for others to assume responsibility for the main areas of their lives. Patients lack self-confidence and may experience intense discomfort when alone for more than brief periods, feeling unable to cope without the help of others. This diagnosis should not be used when dependent behavior may be developmentally appropriate, such as in children and young teenagers.

Antisocial personality disorder: Characterized by a general lack of concern for the rights or feelings of others. Onset is before age 15 and characteristics include: deceitfulness, impulsivity, irresponsibility, disregard for safety of self and others, failure to conform to social norms, lack of remorse, and irritability/aggressiveness.

Narcissistic personality disorder: Characterized by heightened feeling of self-importance, persistent patterns of grandiosity, a need for admiration, disregard for other people's rights, restraint in expression of feelings, and a lack of empathy.

Obsessive-compulsive personality disorder: Characterized by a chronic preoccupation with rules, orderliness, control, emotional constriction, perseverance, stubbornness, and indecisiveness. Affection is usually expressed in a highly controlled fashion. This patient may be very uncomfortable in the presence of others who are emotionally expressive.

Avoidant personality disorder: Characterized by extreme sensitivity to rejection that leads to feelings of inadequacy, mistrust of others, social withdrawal, and social inhibition. Patients often consider themselves socially clumsy, have exaggerated negative beliefs about themselves, and avoid social situations for fear of being ridiculed. This behavior is due to extreme shyness rather than a desire to be antisocial and should not be confused with shyness that is appropriate (such as from being a new immigrant).

BORDERLINE PERSONALITY DISORDER

Borderline personality disorder (BPD) is a pervasive pattern of instability in social relationships, self-image, and affect, coupled with marked impulsivity. A diagnosis of borderline personality disorder requires five of the following symptoms: Frantic efforts to avoid being abandoned; A pattern of unstable and intense personal relationships, in which there is alternation between idealization and devaluation; Instability of self-image; Potentially self-destructive impulsivity in at least two areas; Recurrent suicide threats or gestures; Affective instability; Chronic feelings of emptiness; Inappropriate anger; Paranoid ideation/dissociative symptoms BPD is most common in people between the ages of 19 and 34.

Complementary and Alternative Medicine

Complementary therapies are used as well as conventional medical treatment and should be included if this is what the patient/family wants, empowering the family to take some control. Complementary therapies vary widely and most can easily be incorporated into the plan of care. The National Center for Complementary and Alternative Medicine recognizes the following:

- **Whole medical systems**, including medical systems such as homeopathic, naturopathic medicine, acupuncture, and Chinese herbal medications.
- **Mind-body medicine**, including support groups, medication, music, art, or dance therapy.
- **Biologically-based practices**, including the use of food, vitamins, or nutrition for healing.
- **Manipulative/body-based programs**, including massage or other types of manipulation, such as chiropractic treatment.
- **Energy therapies**, including biofield therapies intended to affect the aura (energy field) that some believe surrounds all living things. These therapies include therapeutic touch and Reiki.
- **Bioelectromagnetic-based therapies**, which use a variety of magnetic fields.

VISUALIZATION TO REDUCE ANXIETY AND PROMOTE HEALING

There are a number of methods used for **visualization** to reduce anxiety and promote healing. Some include audiotapes with guided imagery, such as self-hypnosis tapes, but the patient—even a child—can be taught basic **techniques** that include:

- Sit or lie comfortably in a quiet place away from distractions.
- Concentrate on breathing while taking long, slow breaths.
- Close the eyes to shut out distractions and create an image in the mind of the place or situation desired.
- Concentrate on that image, such as of a favorite place or activity, engaging as many senses as possible and imaging details.
- If the mind wanders, breathe deeply and bring consciousness back to the image or concentrate on breathing for a few moments and then return to the imagery.
- End with positive imagery.

Sometimes, patients are resistive at first or have a hard time maintaining focus, so guiding them through visualization for the first few times can be helpful.

AROMATHERAPY

Aromatherapy uses essential oils derived from plant extracts. These oils are applied topically to the skin, heated and inhaled, or sprayed in the environment. Practitioners believe that aromatherapy can be used to treat and prevent disease, but it is usually used as an adjunct and by itself is rarely harmful, although healing claims are dubious.

MUSIC THERAPY

Music therapy involves listening to music (often classical but any music that the person likes is acceptable). Music therapy is most often used to reduce anxiety. It can also be used as part of visualization or meditation to help the person slow breathing and focus attention. Music is sometimes used as part of an exercise program to help the person pace the exercises. In this case, faster music may be used.

AYURVEDA

Ayurveda is a traditional Indian method of healing that focuses on balancing the mind, body, and spirit to prevent or cure illness. Practitioners believe that when the *prana* (life force) and basic metabolism (*dosha*) are out of balance, the person becomes ill. While people may still use Western medicines, they may also want to follow Ayurvedic traditions through the use of herbs, diet, special breathing exercises, and yoga. Because some herbs contain active ingredients found in medications, the NP should ask about herbal supplements or dietary restrictions (often vegan).

TRADITIONAL CHINESE MEDICINE

Traditional Chinese medicine (TCM) has some similarities to Ayurveda. TCM is concerned with balancing of the vital energy (Qi) of the body through diet, meditation, herbs, acupressure, acupuncture, and exercise, such as Tai Chi. Because TCM relies on the use of herbs, the NP should ascertain which herbs are used.

RESTRICTIVE MEASURES

The use of **restrictive measures** is a last resort in most patient settings. Restrictive measures are utilized to promote patient safety. The most common type of restrictive measures includes **physical restraints and seclusion**. Every patient is entitled to being treated with the greatest personal respect and dignity. When a patient's activity is restricted, very careful monitoring is required. Specific documentation on the patient's wellbeing should be performed per the facilities policy and usually includes a description of what occurred that led to restrictive measures and physical monitoring of the patient while in restraints. If restrictive measures have to be utilized, staff members should have attempted and documented any and all other attempts to de-escalate the situation. These restraint techniques should only be utilized during the time that the patient is considered dangerous to him/herself or others.

SECLUSION

Seclusion involves separating the patients from others by placing them in an environment from which they are unable to leave. In some cases, patients may just be taken to another room under supervision, but a typical **seclusion room** has padded walls, no furniture, and a locked door. Often there are no or only very small shatterproof windows. There is nothing in this environment that patients could utilize to injure themselves or someone else. Once patients have been placed in seclusion, they must be observed continuously to ensure that they do not harm themselves. This particular type of restraint is often viewed negatively, is associated with negative patient outcomes, and is rarely utilized as patients are usually medicated to control their behavior instead of secluded.

RESTRAINTS

Restraints are used to restrict movement, activity, and access. There are 2 primary types of restraints used with patients: clinical and behavioral. **Behavioral restraints** are more commonly used in the psychiatric unit or when patients are at risk of hurting themselves or others. More commonly, **clinical restraints** are used to ensure that the patient does not interfere with safe care. The federal government and the Joint Commission have issued strict guidelines for temporary restraints or those not part of standard care (such as post-surgical restraint):

- There must be a written policy.
- An assessment must be completed.
- An alternative method should be tried before applying a restraint.
- An order must be written.
- The least restrictive effective restraint should be used.
- The restraint must be removed, assessed, and findings documented at least every 2 hours.

Physical restraints may involve the use of a person physically restraining a patient or the use of a mechanical device to restrict movement.

CHEMICAL RESTRAINTS

Chemical restraints involve the use of medications, such as lorazepam or haloperidol, to manage a patient's behavior problems. This type of restraint is indicated when patients are extremely agitated or violent in order to prevent injury to themselves or others. Chemical restraints inhibit patients' physical movements and make their behavior more manageable. Medication used on an ongoing basis as part of treatment is not legally considered a chemical restraint, which is used only in emergent situations, even though the medications may be the same. There is little consensus about the use of chemical restraints although benzodiazepines and/or antipsychotics are frequently used to control severe agitation. Oral medications should be tried first before injections, as oral medication is less coercive. The trend in psychiatric medicine is to target medications to treat particular symptoms, such as severe agitation, rather than simply to chemically restrain the patient.

RESTRAINT AND SECLUSION OF PEDIATRIC PATIENTS

Some consistent recommendations for the use of **restraint and seclusion with pediatric patients**, despite some variations in state, accrediting, and federal regulations, include:

- Using restraint and seclusion only as a last resort and only in cases where the patient and/or others are threatened.
- Maintaining time limits for restraint and seclusion:
  - Children ages 9 to 17 should be restrained and/or secluded no longer than 2 hours.
  - Children under the age of 9 should only be restrained and/or secluded for a maximum of 1 hour.
- Patients are released from restraint and/or seclusion as soon as it is healthy and safe to do so.
- Pressure and unsafe holds should not be applied to patients in restraints.
- Patients must be frequently monitored during the duration of the restraint and seclusion to ensure their safety and changes in behavior.

Diagnostic and Laboratory Tests

THREE UNIVERSAL PRINCIPLES OF DIAGNOSTIC TESTING

First, it is important to remember that the positive and negative predictive values of a test are not absolute. For example, if testing a high-risk population for diabetes (say 180 out of 200 have the disease), and then testing a low-risk population (20 out of 200 have the disease), the sensitivity and specificity of the test will stay the same, but the **predictive values** will change. Also, a test that has less than 100% sensitivity and specificity is most useful for the patient with an equivocal or intermediate probability of disease, rather than a high-risk patient or a low-risk patient. One other important point to remember is that **sensitivity and specificity are inversely related**. If a diagnostic test is modified in order to increase its sensitivity, the specificity of the test will decrease, and vice versa.

HEAD CT FOR PATIENT WITH ALTERED MENTAL STATUS

The **CT scan** is a common imaging technique used to diagnose patients who present with altered mental status. The CT scan can identify **traumatic brain injury** and **mass lesions**, such as brain tumors or hematomas, as well as cerebral edema, so it may be invaluable for neurological disorders, but it is primarily used to **rule out differential diagnoses** rather than to diagnose mental health disorders. CT scans may also be used in addition to other tests to help confirm a possible diagnosis. For example, patients with schizophrenia tend to have enlarged ventricles with increased CSF and a concomitant reduction in brain volume with sulci that are more widened than in a non-schizophrenic brain. Despite these findings, the CT alone cannot be used for diagnosis, and no specific pattern of abnormality has been noted with depression or bipolar disorder although there is evidence that the frontal cortex shrinks in size with uncontrolled bipolar disease and depression and increases with treatment, so long-term monitoring may show differences.

IMPLICATIONS OF CT SCANS THAT SHOW CNS MASS LESIONS OR INTRACRANIAL INJURY

If **head injury** is suspected, then the **non-contrast CT** is most commonly used because it is non-invasive and can be done more quickly than MRI. CTs can identify mass lesions, such as brain tumors, and acute intracranial hematomas and can indicate the presence of a midline shift as well as hydrocephalus. Fractures and pneumoencephaly can be detected. Hyperdense biconvex areas next to the skull indicate extradural hematoma, and hypodense regions within that hematoma indicate that active bleeding is occurring. Subacute subdural hematomas appear isodense in relation to brain tissue and are hard to identify although chronic subdural hematomas appear hypodense. Subarachnoid hemorrhage is indicated by a hyperdense area within the subarachnoid space. Intraventricular hemorrhage appears hyperdense. Diffuse axonal injury is usually not evident on CT although multiple small focal hypo- or hyperdense lesions may be noted. With cerebral edema, definition of the subarachnoid and ventricular spaces is lost.

EEG TESTING IN PATIENT WITH ALTERED LEVEL OF CONSCIOUSNESS

The **electroencephalogram** is sometimes used to test patients with altered level of consciousness in order to evaluate the patients' **electrical impulses** (brain waves). EEG is indicated for suspected seizure activity, encephalopathies, infarcts, and altered consciousness. The purpose is to identify abnormal electrical activity, which may be noted as slowing, which occurs where there has been injury or an infarct. Waves include delta (1-4 cycles/sec), alpha (8-13 cycles/sec), theta (4-7 cycles/sec), beta (12-40 cycles/sec), sleep spindles (12-14 cycles/sec), and spikes and waves (variable duration). Spikes and waves indicate that tissue is irritated. Findings indicate:

- **Metabolic encephalopathy**: Intermittent slowing with triphasic waves.
- **Cerebral anoxic damage**: Generalized slowing in delta and theta range.
- **Coma state**: Prognosis poor if EEG showing unchanging alpha waves with stimulation.
- **CNS depressant overdose**: Transient periods of absence of electrical activity.
- **Epilepsy**: Unusual electrical activity within the brain. Partial seizures are evident in only part of the electrodes while generalized seizures are evident from all electrodes.
- **ADHD**: a 20-minute EEG procedure is FDA-approved to diagnose children with ADHD.

TESTING FOR DELIRIUM

Appropriate testing for a patient presenting with delirium, transient confusion and alterations in consciousness depends on the age and circumstances. **Delirium** is most common in older adults in response to illness or surgery but can occur at any age. **Hyperactive delirium** may be associated with alcohol withdrawal or drug toxicity. **Hypoactive delirium** may result from disease processes, such as hepatic encephalopathy. Some have mixed symptoms, becoming more agitated during the evening and night. Testing includes:

- **Confusion Assessment Method (CAM) or CAM-ICU**: This test helps to differentiate confusion from other causes of altered consciousness.
- **CAM-S**: This form of the CAM test is used to determine the severity of delirium.
- **Delirium Symptom Interview** also helps to identify delirium.
- **Laboratory tests**: If the cause of the patient's confusion is not evident, numerous tests may be done to rule out other causes, including CBC, blood glucose, renal and liver function tests, drug and alcohol screening, sed-rate, thyroid function tests, HIV, and thiamine and vitamin B-12 levels.

LABORATORY TESTS FOR PSYCHIATRIC ILLNESSES

At the current time, diagnosis of psychiatric illnesses is based almost completely on symptoms and history, and no laboratory tests have been FDA approved for diagnosis; however, **biochemical markers** have been identified for some psychiatric disorders, including schizophrenia, bipolar disorder, and depression. Some companies have collected data and applied for FDA approval for these tests and are now marketing tests although this testing is not in common use because use is not yet reimbursed by Medicare/Medicaid or insurance companies. Some researchers believe that genetic testing and imaging (PET, MRI) may also have larger roles in diagnosis in the future. Currently, **laboratory tests** are used for primarily two reasons:

- Rule out differential diagnoses and identify concomitant disorders. Many different tests may be used, but in many cases the results of tests don't alter the original diagnosis, so testing is done selectively, based on patient's age, history, and physical exam.
- Monitor serum levels of drugs during therapy, such as lithium levels.

LABORATORY TESTS FOR PATIENTS PRESENTING WITH NEW ONSET PSYCHIATRIC ISSUE

When patients present with a new onset psychiatric issue, a series of **laboratory tests** may be conducted to determine potential causes, rule out differential diagnoses, and identify concomitant disorders:

- **Blood alcohol level and urine drug screening** to determine if the patient is experiencing overdosing, withdrawal symptoms, or toxic reaction.
- **Blood glucose level** to determine if the patient has hypoglycemia or hyperglycemia that may be affecting mental status.
- **Urinalysis and urine culture** to determine if an infection is present (may result in confusion in older adults).
- **Brain imaging** (CT, MRI) to determine if a lesion is present in the brain.
- **Pregnancy testing** to determine if female patients are pregnant before initiating treatment.
- **Liver and kidney function tests** to evaluate for hepatic and renal encephalopathy.
- **CBC** to assess for anemia, infection, or other abnormalities.
- **HIV antibodies** to rule out HIV/AIDS.
- **EEG** to determine if the patient is experiencing seizure activity.
- **Lyme antibodies** to rule out neuropsychological symptoms related to Lyme disease.
- **Lumbar puncture** to examine cerebrospinal fluid for suspected infection.

Diagnostic Impression

DIAGNOSTIC IMPRESSION AND FORMAL DIAGNOSIS

A **diagnostic impression** is an opinion about a possible diagnosis based on observations and data (both current and previous). For example, if a patient presents with hallucinations, delusions, and flat affect, the diagnostic impression may be schizophrenia. However, subsequent testing, including laboratory tests and MRI, may indicate the patient has a lesion in the brain causing the symptoms. Thus, a diagnostic impression may be correct or incorrect. In that way, it is similar to a differential diagnosis in that the symptoms may match but not the diagnosis.

A **formal diagnosis**, on the other hand, is the best identification of a disease/disorder that can be made based on complete data (signs, symptoms, laboratory tests, imaging) and observations. A formal diagnosis can still be made in error, especially if symptoms are obscure, but a formal diagnosis is used as the basis for treatment and for insurance coverage of treatment.

DIAGNOSTIC REASONING PROCESS

There are a number of models for the **diagnostic reasoning process** but all essentially involve developing a hypothesis and testing it to arrive at a diagnosis. When diagnosing, a healthcare provider first looks for recognizable patterns of symptoms or presentation to suggest a diagnosis. If the patient does not fit a pattern, then a list of possible hypotheses is developed along with **consideration of probabilities**:

- Data is gathered and clustered.
- Diagnostic studies and assessment help to narrow the choice of hypotheses. Decisions are made about the type and extent of testing, including the sensitivity and specificity of different tests and the value of invasive vs non-invasive testing.
- Hypotheses are evaluated, using the gathered data and probabilities, to prioritize differential diagnoses.
- Treatment, based on the probable diagnosis, is provided and evaluated for efficacy. If treatment fails to bring improvement, then further hypothesis testing is indicated.

IMPORTANCE OF DATA GATHERING TO DIAGNOSTIC REASONING

The **gathering and recording of data** are of utmost importance to the diagnostic evaluation process. The history and physical section of the **patient chart** contains a wealth of information (ideally), and should always be taken into consideration when developing a care plan for the patient. Because any number of clinicians can add information to the patient chart (and because all of these clinicians will be reading this information), it is important to record all information clearly and in an organized manner. This can be a daunting task when considering all of the different sources of information, including the patient interview, family member interviews, previous charts, and lab results. By keeping this information clear and concise, the PMH NP can minimize error, and can be sure that the **differential diagnosis** is comprehensive.

PROBLEMS ENCOUNTERED DURING DATA EVALUATION

The **data** that are available on the patient chart are an integral part of the patient's overall care plan. However, **errors** may be present in the records, and these errors may negatively influence clinical decision making; thus, it is important to look at the information as a whole. Does it make sense? Make sure that the patient's **verbal history** agrees with what is in his or her records. Also, remember that not every **test result** in the patient's chart is necessarily accurate. If a test result doesn't make sense in the clinical picture as a whole, consider why this might be. It could simply be an error (e.g., the wrong number was recorded, the blood was drawn incorrectly), or the patient may have a result that would be considered "abnormal," though for this particular patient it is not. For example, a marathon runner may have a resting heart rate of 40 bpm; while this is a bradycardic rate, it is not pathological, but rather a result of physical conditioning.

POSITIVE PREDICTIVE VALUE AND NEGATIVE PREDICTIVE VALUE IN RELATION TO DISEASE PROBABILITY

Predictive values are of importance to the clinician because although sensitivity and specificity are used to evaluate the effectiveness of a diagnostic test, they are not particularly clinically relevant. Since a patient's disease state is more or less unknown at admission, these parameters are of no help. This is where the **positive predictive value (PPV)** and **negative predictive value (NPV)** of a test come in. If the patient tests positive for syphilis, what are the chances that the patient actually has syphilis? The chance that this result is correct is the PPV; this is calculated by dividing the number of true positive results by the number of total positive results (true and false positives). NPV, then, is the probability that a patient with a negative result really does not have syphilis. Dividing the number of true negatives by the number of total negatives will result in the NPV.

SENSITIVITY AND SPECIFICITY IN RELATION TO DIAGNOSTIC TESTING

Some degree of error is inherent in almost all diagnostic testing. When ordering a diagnostic test for a patient, how confident should the PMH NP be that the result will be accurate? The terms sensitivity and specificity are used to illustrate the accuracy of diagnostic tests. The **sensitivity** of a test refers to its ability to correctly identify patients who do have the disease. If a test is administered to 100 patients with diabetes, and all 100 patients test positive, the test is considered to have a sensitivity of 100%. If only 85 of those tested have a positive result, however, that means that the test has a false-negative rate of 15%, and a sensitivity of 85%. On the other hand, the **specificity** of a diagnostic test refers to its ability to identify patients who do not have the disease. If 100 nondiabetic patients are tested for diabetes, and 50 of them have a positive result, the test has a specificity of only 50%.

Differential Diagnosis

DIFFERENTIAL DIAGNOSIS PROCESS

The **differential diagnosis** is an important tool that allows the clinician to familiarize him or herself with the patient's condition, understand the condition, create an effective treatment plan, and follow the progress of the patient. To start, thoroughly examine the patient's **chart**, making a list of all of the abnormal test results and laboratory values. Add to this list all of the patient's **complaints**. Once this list is complete, organize the test results, labs, and complaints by anatomic location or organ system. After breaking the list down by organ site, look for any **relationships** between symptoms and/or results. Create another list of those data that seem to be related, and list all of the diseases or conditions that explain the findings, eliminating any that do not fit.

FACTORS THAT MAY INFLUENCE THE CLINICAL DECISION-MAKING PROCESS

Although one would like to think that there isn't much variation in the **clinical decision-making process**, this simply is not true. The process, of course, will differ depending on the patient, the differential diagnosis, and the clinician. First, let's start with the clinician. The way that the **clinician** conducts the clinical decision-making process is influenced by the knowledge base of the clinician, as well as the level of his experience, the ability he possesses to think both critically and creatively, and the confidence that he has in his ability to make educated decisions. The acuity level of the **patient** is also a factor in the clinical decision-making process, as is the length of the differential. A **time stressor** is placed on the clinician when the condition of the patient is critical, and when there are more diseases that must be eliminated from the differential. An element of stress may also exist if the clinician has a high number of patients, especially if he has multiple high-acuity patients.

FORMULATING A PSYCHIATRIC DIAGNOSIS

The purpose of **formulating a psychiatric diagnosis** is to develop a plan of care to meet the needs of the patient. Steps include:

1. **History**: Include the presenting problem and any initiating factors. Explain how the symptoms are affecting the patient's life. Note any prior history of psychological/psychiatric disorders as well as any history of disorders that may be associated with mental disorders, such as lupus erythematosus.
2. **Mental status exam**: Note important or significant findings.
3. **Physical exam**: Note any abnormalities. Diagnostic tests as indicated to rule out non-psychiatric conditions.
4. **Differential diagnosis**: List only those that are plausible and must be ruled out.
5. **Single diagnosis**: Base diagnosis on best evidence. In some cases, two diagnoses may be determined.
6. **Etiology**: Note significant factors related to the diagnosis.
7. **Management plan**: Outline the recommended treatment options to meet somatic needs (medications), psychological needs (therapy), and social needs (family intervention, support, community programs).

DIFFERENTIATING DELIRIUM FROM DEPRESSION, MANIA, AND SCHIZOPHRENIA

Because **delirium** has symptoms in common with depression, mania, and schizophrenia, a careful history and physical examination may yield information to help **differentiate** among the disorders. The symptoms of delirium may have a sudden onset or may develop more slowly over a period of hours or days while the onset of symptoms of depression, mania, and schizophrenia usually have onset over a period of weeks to months. Delirium symptoms tend to be fluctuating while symptoms of the other disorders are more consistent. Additionally, delirium results from an underlying medical disorder, so if testing determines this disorder and the issue is resolved, then the symptoms generally abate. However, depression, mania, and schizophrenia, while they may occur with other disorders are not the result of those disorders. With depression, mania, and schizophrenia, patients' ability to conduct activities of daily living is often impaired, resulting in personal neglect of appearance; but this ability may or may not remain intact with delirium.

Mental Health Disorders Due to Renal and Hepatic Dysfunction

Renal/Uremic encephalopathy: This **organic brain disorder** results from increased toxins in the blood because of acute or chronic renal failure and a GFR of less than 15 mL/min. BUN and creatinine levels are markedly increased. Symptoms vary from fatigue to seizures and coma and may include confusion, impaired memory, emotional lability, somnolence, and asterixis (common) although the cause is unclear. Some medications, such as lithium and digoxin, may accumulate because of reduced renal function, contributing to encephalopathy. Treatment is dialysis, anemia reversal, and regulation of electrolytes.

Hepatic encephalopathy: This **metabolic brain disorder** is most often associated with cirrhosis of the liver and acute liver failure and results from increased levels of ammonia, which impair function of neurotransmitters and cause damage to astrocytes, inducing swelling of the astrocytes and cerebral edema. Symptoms are progressive, usually beginning with confusion and lethargy. Patients become increasingly somnolent and disoriented and then stuporous and finally comatose with decerebrate posturing. Motor activity decreases as the disease progresses, and asterixis is usually present. Treatment focuses on reducing hyperammonemia.

Mental Health Disorders Associated with Metabolic Dysfunction

Severe mental health disorders, such as schizophrenia and mood disorders, are associated with **metabolic dysfunction**, referred to as the **metabolic syndrome**. This disorder is characterized by insulin resistance and glucose intolerance, obesity, high blood pressure, hyperlipidemia, and hyperuricemia. Patients with metabolic syndrome are at increased risk of diabetes mellitus and cardiovascular disease. Patients with severe mental illness often have high levels of cortisol as a reaction to stress, and this has been associated with increased visceral obesity, a contributing factor to diabetes and hypertension. Studies have shown that patients with schizophrenia tend to have **increased rates of obesity**, especially visceral obesity. Other studies indicate that those undergoing psychotic stress have impairment of beta-cell function in the pancreas and increased insulin sensitivity, and those with depression have increased risk of diabetes. Patients with bipolar also have increased rates of diabetes and high rates of obesity.

COMMON FEATURES SUGGESTIVE OF DEMENTIA WITH LEWY BODIES

Lewy body dementia (LBD) is characterized by diffuse deposits of **abnormal protein** throughout the brain stem and other parts of the brain, including the cerebral cortex. Patients vary in symptoms but a primary feature is progressive dementia with decreased attention and impaired executive function. Cognition often fluctuates, and people typically experience visual hallucinations. Patients may experience falls, autonomic dysfunction, and other psychiatric abnormalities. Two features that are common to LBD and support the diagnosis are:

- **REM sleep disorder**: Patients act out their dreams physically, getting out of bed and carrying out activities. In some cases, patients may also talk or shout and may be physically violent, hitting or striking people or things. Treatment includes melatonin and/or clonazepam.
- **Neuroleptic sensitivity**: Up to half of the patients with LBD have severe sensitivity to neuroleptic/antipsychotic drugs and may develop increased cognitive impairment, severe sedation, increased or irreversible tremors/ Parkinsonism, and neuroleptic malignant syndrome, which may result in death. Antipsychotic drugs should be avoided with suspected LBD.

Evidenced-Based Practice

QUALITATIVE AND QUANTITATIVE DATA

Both **qualitative and quantitative data** are used for analysis, but the focus is quite different:

- **Qualitative data**: Data are described verbally or graphically, and the results are subjective, depending upon observers to provide information. Interviews may be used as a tool to gather information, and the researcher's interpretation of data is important. Gathering this type of data can be time-intensive, and it can usually not be generalized to a larger population. This type of information gathering is often useful at the beginning of the design process for data collection.
- **Quantitative data**: Data are described in terms of numbers within a statistical format. This type of information gathering is done after the design of data collection is outlined, usually in later stages. Tools may include surveys, questionnaires, or other methods of obtaining numerical data. The researcher's role is objective.

SELECTION AND INFORMATION BIAS

Selection bias occurs when the method of selecting subjects results in a cohort that is not representative of the target population because of inherent error in design. For example, if all patients who develop urinary infections are evaluated per urine culture and sensitivities for microbial resistance, but only those patients with clinically-evident infections are included, a number of patients with sub-clinical infections may be missed, skewing the results. Selection bias is only a concern when participants in studies are specifically chosen. Many surveillance studies do not involve selection of subjects.

Information bias occurs when there are errors in classification, so an estimate of association is incorrect. Non-differential misclassification occurs when there is similar misclassification of disease or exposure among both those who are diseased/exposed and those who are not. Differential misclassification occurs when there is a differing misclassification of disease or exposure among both those who are diseased/exposed and those who are not.

POPULATION AND SAMPLING

Defining the **population** is critical to data collection and the criteria must be established early in the process. The population may comprise a particular group of individuals, objects, or events. In some cases, data is gathered on an entire population, such as all cases with a particular disease, all deaths, or all physicians in a particular discipline, usually within a specified time frame. In other cases, **sampling,** using a subset of a population, may be done to measure only part of a given population and to generalize the findings to the larger target population while accurately representing the target population. There are a number of considerations with sampling:

- The sampling must have the characteristics of the target population.
- The design of the collection must specify the size of the sample, the location, and time period.
- The sampling technique must ensure that the sampling represents the target population accurately.
- The design of the collection must ensure that the sampling will not be biased.

RISK STRATIFICATION

Risk stratification involves statistical adjustment to account for confounding and differences in risk factors. **Confounding issues** are those that confuse the data outcomes, such as trying to

135

compare different populations, different ages, or different genders. For example, if there are 2 physicians and 1 has primarily high-risk patients, and the other has primarily low-risk patients, the same rate of infection (by raw data) would suggest that the infection risks are equal for both physicians' patients. However, high-risk patients are much more prone to infection, so in this case risk stratification to account for this difference would show that the patients of the physician with low-risk patients had a much higher risk of infection, relatively speaking. Risk stratification is also used to predict outcomes of surgery by accounting for various risk factors (including ASO score, age, and medical conditions). Risk stratification is an important element of **data analysis**.

HYPOTHESIS AND HYPOTHESIS TESTING

A **hypothesis** should be generated about the probable cause of the disease/infection based on the information available in laboratory and medical records, epidemiologic study, literature review, and expert opinion. A hypothesis, for example, should include the infective agent, the likely source, and the mode of transmission: "Wound infections with *Staphylococcus aureus* were caused by reuse and inadequate sterilization of single-use irrigation syringes used during wound care in the ICU." **Hypothesis testing** includes data analysis, laboratory findings, and outcomes of environmental testing. It usually includes **case control studies**, with 2-4 controls picked for each case of infection. They may be matched according to age, sex, or other characteristics, but they are not infected at the time they are picked for the study. **Cohort studies**, whose controls are picked based on having or lacking exposure, may also be instituted. If the hypothesis cannot be supported, then a new hypothesis or different testing methods may be necessary.

INTERNAL AND EXTERNAL VALIDITY, GENERALIZABILITY, AND REPLICATION

Many research studies are most concerned with **internal validity**, adequate unbiased data properly collected and analyzed within the population studied, but studies that determine the efficacy of procedures or treatments, for example, should have **external validity** as well; that is, the results should be **generalizable** (true) for similar populations. **Replication** of the study with different subjects, researchers, and under different circumstances should produce similar results. For various reasons, some people may be excluded from a study so that instead of randomized subjects the subjects may be highly selected, so when data is compared with another population, in which there is less or more selection, results may be different. The selection of subjects, in this case, would interfere with external validity. Part of the design of a study should include considerations of whether or not it should have external validity or whether there is value for the institution based solely on internal validation.

DATA DEFINITION AND COLLECTION OF DATA

Data definitions must be based on a solid understanding of statistical analysis and epidemiological concepts. Specific issues that must be addressed include:

- The 3 Ss:
  - **Sensitivity**: The data should include all positive cases, taking into account variables, decreasing the number of false negatives.
  - **Specificity**: The data should include only those cases specific to the needs of the measurement and exclude those that may be similar but are a different population, decreasing the number of false positives.
  - **Stratification**: Date should be classified according to subsets, taking variables into consideration.

- 2 Rs:
  - **Recordability**: The tool/indicator should collect and measure the necessary data.
  - **Reliability**: Results should be reproducible.
- UV:
  - **Usability**: The tool or indicator should be easy to utilize and understand.
  - **Validity**: Collection should measure the target adequately, so that the results have predictive value.

OUTCOMES DATA

INTERPRETATION

Outcomes data provides an effective guide for performance improvement activities because it gives evidence of how well a process succeeds but not necessarily the reason; therefore, outcomes data must be evaluated accordingly. There are inherent problems with outcome data that must be considered when utilizing outcomes for process improvement. First, it is almost impossible to provide sufficient **risk stratification** to provide complete validity to outcomes data, and, second, it is also difficult to accurately attribute the outcomes data to any 1 **step** in a process without further study. For example, if outcomes data show a decline in deaths in the emergency department, which recently changed trauma procedures, but doesn't account for the fact that a gang task force has successfully decreased drive-by shootings and killings by 70%, it might be assumed that changes in the emergency department altered the outcome data when, in fact, if the data were adjusted for these external factors, the death rate may have increased.

TYPES

When interpreting outcomes data, one should keep in mind that there are a number of different **types of outcomes data** to be considered, and some data may overlap:

- **Clinical**: This includes symptoms, diagnoses, staging of disease, and indicators of patient health.
- **Physiological**: This includes measures of physical abnormalities, loss of function, and activities of daily living.
- **Psychosocial**: This includes feelings, perceptions, beliefs, functional impairment, and role performance.
- **Integrative**: This includes measures of mortality, longevity, and cost-effectiveness.
- **Perception**: This includes customer perceptions, evaluations, and satisfaction.
- **Organization-wide clinical:** This includes readmissions, adverse reactions, and deaths.

When considering outcomes data, the focus may be on the process or just the outcomes data, and the team analyzing the data should clarify the purpose of reviewing the data and should understand how process and outcomes data interrelate.

INFORMATION QUALITY

Quality information is defined by the following factors:

- **Timeliness:** The necessary data is available (and retrievable) as needed.
- **Precision:** System dictionaries shall describe uniform wording and clear definitions.
- **Accuracy:** The data should be as error-free as possible.
- **Measurability:** The information should be quantifiable so that comparisons can be made.
- **Independently verifiable:** The integrity of the information remains constant regardless of the individual reporting it.
- **Availability:** The information should be accessible where it is needed. In the hospital or clinic environment, the information should usually be available at the patient's location.

INTEGRATING RESULTS OF DATA ANALYSIS

Integrating the results of data analysis is necessary because attempting performance improvement and developing practice guidelines without data is essentially operating blind. This data should be used not only as the basis for long-term strategic planning but for identifying opportunities for performance improvement activities on an ongoing basis. Integration of information includes:

- Identifying issues for tracking.
- Reviewing patterns and trends to determine how they impact care.
- Establishing action plans and desired outcomes based on the need for improvement.
- Providing information to process improvement teams to facilitate change.
- Evaluating systems and processes for follow-up.
- Monitoring specific cases, criteria, critical pathways, and outcomes.

The integration of information should assist with case management, decision making about patient care, improvement of critical pathways related to clinical performance, staff performance evaluations, as well as credentialing and privileging.

MODEL OF INTEGRATION

Integrating the results of data analysis and research into performance improvement or best practice guidelines varies from one organization to another, depending on the **model of integration** that the organization uses:

- **Organizational:** Processes for improvement are identified, and teams or individuals are selected to participate in different areas or departments, reporting to one individual, who monitors progress.
- **Functional/coordinated:** While staff specialties, such as risk management and quality management, are not integrated, they draw from the same data resources to determine issues related to quality of care and efficiency.
- **Functional/integrated:** While staff specialties remain, there is cross-training among specialties. A case management approach to individual care is used so that one person follows the progress of a patient through the system and coordinates with the various specialties, such as infection control and quality management.

TRACKING AND TRENDING

Tracking and trending are central to developing research-supported evidence-based practice and is part of continuous quality improvement. Once processes and outcomes measurements are selected, then at least 1 measure should be **tracked** for a number of periods of time, usually in increments of

138

4 weeks or quarterly. This tracking can be used to present graphical representation of results that will show **trends**. While trends will show some normal variation, if the trend becomes erratic and measures are inconsistent, this suggests that the processes of care are not consistent or are inadequate. For example, if infections in peripherally inserted central catheter (PICC) lines are tracked and the trend shows wild fluctuations with high levels of infection in 1 period, low in another, and vacillations in a third, then the first step is to ensure that the process is being followed correctly. If the process is stable but the variations persist, then the next course would be to modify the process by looking at best practices.

PROCESS OF CRITICAL ANALYSIS

The NP must be taught and understand the **process of critical analysis** and know how to conduct a survey of the literature. Basic concepts related to research include:

- **Survey of valid sources:** Information from a juried journal and an anonymous or personal website are very different sources, and evaluating what constitutes a valid source of data is critical.
- **Evaluation of internal and external validity:** Internal validity shows a cause and effect relationship between 2 variables, with the cause occurring before the effect and no intervening variable. External validity occurs when results hold true in different environments and circumstances with different populations.
- **Sample selection and sample size:** Selection and size can have a huge impact on the results, but a sample that is too small may lack both internal and external validity. Selection may be so narrowly focused that the results can't be generalized to other groups.

IDENTIFYING CLINICAL PROBLEMS AMENABLE TO RESEARCH

Identifying **clinical problems amenable to research** is an evolving skill. Inexperienced NPs, especially those just starting out in nursing practice, are often looking to build information and skills because they lack experiential learning. They may research information about a disease or treatment that they are dealing with in order to have better skills and understanding. More experienced NPs, on the other hand, often look for information to improve patient outcomes, such as researching new procedures, treatments, or equipment for broader application. However, there is a need for both.

Clinical inquiry is a program of questioning and evaluating practice through research and experience. It should include seeking a variety of data on a topic, evaluating the data, pooling results, and making determinations as to validity or applicability to the clinical practice. Clinical inquiry is also part of evidence-based practice in which data is used to support clinical decisions on an ongoing basis.

CRITICAL READING OF RESEARCH ARTICLES

There are a number of steps to **critical reading** to evaluate research:

- **Consider the source** of the material. If it is in the popular press, it may have little validity compared to something published in a juried journal.
- **Review the author's credentials** to determine if a person is an expert in the field of study.
- **Determine thesis** or the central claim of the research. It should be clearly stated.
- **Examine the organization** of the article, whether it is based on a particular theory, and the type of methodology used.

- **Review the evidence** to determine how it is used to support the main points. Look for statistical evidence and sample size to determine if the findings have wide applicability.
- **Evaluate** the overall article to determine if the information seems credible and useful and should be communicated to administration and/or staff.

EVIDENCE-BASED PRACTICE

Evidence-based practice is the use of current research and individual values in practice to establish a **plan of care** for each individual. Research may be the result of large studies of best practices or individual research from observations in practice about the effectiveness of treatment. Evidence-based practice requires a commitment to ongoing research and outcomes evaluations. Many resources are available, such as the *Guide to Clinical Preventive Services* by the Agency for Healthcare Research and Quality of the U. S. Department of Health and Human Services (http://www.ahrq.gov/clinic/cps3dix.htm). Evidence-based practice requires a thorough understanding of research methods to evaluate the results and determine if they can be generalized. Results must also be evaluated in terms of cost-effectiveness. Steps to evidence-based practice include:

- Making a diagnosis.
- Researching and analyzing results.
- Applying research findings to a plan of care.
- Evaluating outcomes.

EVIDENCE-BASED RESEARCH

Evidence-based research is the use of current research and patient values in practice to establish a plan of care for each patient. Research may be the result of large studies of best practices or individual research from observations in practice about the effectiveness of treatment. Evidence-based practice requires a commitment to ongoing research and outcomes evaluations. Many resources are available:

- Guide to Clinical Preventive Services by the Agency for Healthcare Research and Quality of the U.S. Department of Health and Human Services (http://www.ahrq.gov/clinic/cps3dix.htm).

Evidence-based practice requires a thorough understanding of research methods in order to evaluate the results and determine if they can be generalized. Results must also be evaluated in terms of cost-effectiveness. Steps to evidence-based practice include:

- Making a diagnosis.
- Researching and analyzing results.
- Applying research findings to plan of care.
- Evaluating outcomes.

INCORPORATION OF RESEARCH FINDINGS

Incorporating research findings should be central to all work of the NP and should be routinely disseminated as part of practice, education, and consultation. Any time the NP gives a presentation or provides written material, references should be made to **research findings** because this provides supporting evidence and lends credence to the information the NP is providing. Often research can provide guidance for surveillance or interventions and give valuable insights. References that are used or referred to should always be properly **cited** so that the work of researchers is credited. If a presentation is given orally, then the NP should prepare a list of references. Newsletters, e-mail, or Internet reports and communications should include research highlights or summaries of current studies of interest, with links to online articles provided when possible to encourage people to read the research for themselves and become more knowledgeable about issues related to patients.

STRATEGIES

Evidence-based practice must be part of the mission and goal of a health care organization, and **strategies** to attain this must be supported at all levels. **Information technology tools**, such as Internet capability or access to information databases, should be available at the point of care so that health care providers are able to access journal articles and other clinical information. Links may be available through the **patient's health risk evaluation** as well. All staff should receive **training** in the use of equipment and methods of researching and retrieving information and have an understanding of how to interpret research findings; the inability of health care providers to understand and interpret findings can be a significant barrier to evidence-based practice. Because evidence-based practice often results in change, institutional support for change must be evident and may involve incentives. Continuing education classes should be available on-site to help health care providers gain the research skills they need.

OUTCOMES EVALUATION

Outcomes evaluation is an important component of evidence-based practice, which involves both internal and external research. All treatments are subjected to review to determine if they produce positive outcomes, and policies and protocols for outcomes evaluation should be in place. Outcomes evaluation includes the following:

- **Monitoring** over the course of treatment involves careful observation and record keeping that notes progress, with supporting laboratory and radiographic evidence as indicated by condition and treatment.
- **Evaluating** results includes reviewing records as well as current research to determine if outcomes are within acceptable parameters.
- **Sustaining** involves continuing treatment, but continuing to monitor and evaluate.
- **Improving** means to continue the treatment but with additions or modifications in order to improve outcomes.
- **Replacing** the treatment with a different treatment must be done if outcomes evaluation indicates that current treatment is ineffective.

EVIDENCE-BASED BEST-PRACTICE GUIDELINES

Evidence-based best-practice guidelines apply the use of best practices for such things as standing medicine orders or antibiotic protocols that are in common use, but decisions are often made based on studies that lack internal and/or external validity or on expert opinion colored by personal bias, so the process of establishing evidence-based best-practice guidelines should be done systematically. Including those who are resistive to the process often helps to facilitate the establishment of guidelines, but it is important that decisions be made on solid evidence as much as possible. Simply dispensing evidence-based best-practice guidelines often does not change practice, so consideration must be given to **implementation**. Decisions must be made as to whether the use of the guidelines is mandatory (standing orders) and to what degree individual practitioners can choose other options. Guidelines that are too rigid may be counter-productive. In some case, establishing guidelines may affect cost-reimbursement from third-party payers.

Steps to developing **evidence-based best-practice guidelines** include:

- **Focus on the topic/methodology:** This includes outlining possible interventions/treatments for review, choosing patient populations and settings, and determining significant outcomes. Search boundaries (such as types of journals, types of studies, dates of studies) should be determined.
- **Evidence review:** This includes review of literature, critical analysis of studies, and summarizing of results, including pooled meta-analysis.
- **Expert judgment:** Recommendations based on personal experience from a number of experts may be utilized, especially if there is inadequate evidence based on review, but this subjective evidence should be explicitly acknowledged.
- **Policy considerations:** This includes cost-effectiveness, access to care, insurance coverage, availability of qualified staff, and legal implications.
- **Policy:** A written policy must be completed with recommendations. Common practice is to utilize letter guidelines, with "A" the most highly recommended, usually based on the quality of supporting evidence.
- **Review:** The completed policy should be submitted to peers for review and comments before instituting the policy.

SYNERGY MODEL OF CLINICAL INQUIRY

According to the Synergy model, **clinical inquiry** is a continual process of questioning and evaluating practice in order to provide innovative and outstanding care through application of the results of research and experience. Clinical inquiry requires a desire to acquire new knowledge, openness to accepting advice from mentors and other health and allied professionals, competency in identifying clinical problems, the ability search the literature for research, critical skills to interpret research findings, and the willingness and ability to design and participate in research. Levels of clinical inquiry include:

- **Level 1**: This nurse recognizes problems and seeks advice, follows industry standards and guidelines, and seeks further knowledge.
- **Level 3**: This nurse questions industry standards and guidelines as well as current practice and utilizes research and education to improve patient care.
- **Level 5**: This nurse is able to deviate from industry standards and guidelines when necessary for the individual patients and utilizes literature review and clinical research to gain knowledge, establish new practices, and improve patient care.

MEDICATION DOSING, OFF-LABEL MEDICATION USE, AND PSYCHOTHERAPY SELECTION

Evidence based practices include:

- **Medication dosing**: Dosage must depend on drug guidelines as well as gender, age, size, and/or weight (depending on the drug), and the route of administration as well as the presence of kidney or liver disease. In some cases, the correct dosage must be determined through laboratory findings.
- **Off-label use:** Off-label use of drugs is especially common for antidepressants, antipsychotics, and anxiolytics, but use is often not supported by evidence-based research. A resource that can provide information about evidence-based support for off-label use of drugs is DRUGDEX® (Micromedex), which includes summaries of evidence-based findings, indicating the efficacy, recommendations, and strength of evidence.
- **Psychotherapy selection**: Treatment selection should be based on not only diagnosis-specific interventions but also patient-specific factors and needs and evidence-based research for different types of interventions. In many cases, different therapies may all be effective although the rate of improvement may vary. Some treatments may be impractical because of time constraints or unavailability of appropriate therapists.

Psychotherapy and Related Theories

Psychotherapy Principles

GRIEF

Grief is a normal response to loss, and older adults may face the loss of spouse, family, income, status, health, mobility, home, and independence. **Mourning** is the public expression of grief, and **bereavement** is the time period of mourning. There are 3 primary types of grief:

- **Acute**: This occurs immediately in response to some type of loss and may be expressed as sadness, anger, fear, and anxiety.
- **Anticipatory**: This occurs when people fear a loss, such as the impending death of a spouse or transfer to a long-term care facility.
- **Chronic grief** occurs when people are not able to come to terms with loss, so grieving and mourning are prolonged, sometimes for years. People may develop anorexia, insomnia, panic attacks, self-destructive behaviors (alcohol and substance abuse), and contemplate or carry out suicide.

Chronic grief poses a serious risk to people and should be treated as depression, with antidepressants, psychological evaluation, and counselling.

BEREAVEMENT

Bereavement occurs after the death of family, friend, or someone to whom a person identifies closely. It is a time of mourning and is part of the natural grieving process, but some people are not able to move past the grieving process and may suffer signs related to **depression**, such as poor appetite, insomnia, and other symptoms, such as chest pain, that may mimic physical illnesses. Some may enter a stage of denial or anger that interferes with their daily activities and work. People suffering bereavement may present with vague and varied complaints. A careful history is important. *Treatment* varies according to the needs of the individual. In some cases, selective serotonin reuptake inhibitors (SSRIs) (such as Prozac® [fluoxetine]) may provide temporary relief, but the patient should be referred for psychological counselling, bereavement services, or psychiatric care, depending upon the severity of symptoms.

KÜBLER-ROSS'S STAGES OF GRIEF

Grief is a normal response to the death or severe illness/abnormality of a patient. How a person deals with grief is very personal, and each will grieve differently. Elisabeth Kübler-Ross identified **5 stages of grief** in *On Death and Dying* (1969), which can apply to both patients and family members. A person may not go through each stage but usually goes through 2 of the 5 stages:

- **Denial**: Patients/families may be resistive to information and unable to accept that a person is dying or impaired. They may act stunned, immobile, or detached and may be unable to respond appropriately or remember what's said, often repeatedly asking the same questions.
- **Anger**: As reality becomes clear, patient/families may react with pronounced anger, directed inward or outward. Women, especially, may blame themselves and self-anger may lead to severe depression and guilt, assuming they are to blame because of some personal action. Outward anger, more common in men, may be expressed as overt hostility.

144

- **Bargaining**: This involves if-then thinking (often directed at a deity): "If I go to church every day, then God will prevent this." The patient or family may change doctors, trying to change the outcome.
- **Depression**: As the patient and family begin to accept the loss, they may become depressed, feeling as if no one understands, and overwhelmed with sadness. They may be tearful or crying and may withdraw or ask to be left alone.
- **Acceptance**: This final stage represents a form of resolution and often occurs outside of the medical environment after months. Patients are able to accept death/dying/incapacity. Families are able to resume their normal activities and lose the constant preoccupation with their loved one. They are able to think of the person without severe pain.

BELIEFS AND TRADITIONS REGARDING DEATH

Individual **beliefs and traditions regarding death** vary widely, and these affect how the patient and family deal with the end of life. The NP should discuss these issues with the patient and/or family in order to ensure their needs are met. Those with strong spiritual beliefs may want spiritual advisors (priests, shamans, ministers, monks) present to provide support or perform rituals. People who have no belief in an afterlife may face death with resolution or may be frightened at the thought of the total end of their existence. Those who believe in reincarnation may find comfort in the thought of their rebirth but may also fear karma for the mistakes they made in this life. Some people believe in a loving God and others a vengeful God, so some may feel that they will be in a loving place after death while others fear they will suffer torment for their sins. The NP should remain **supportive** and allow patients and families to express their feelings, fears, and concerns.

SUPPORTING FAMILIES OF DYING PATIENTS

Families of dying patients often find themselves in desperate need of adequate support from nursing staff that, unfortunately, often are unprepared for dealing with their grief and unsure of how to provide comfort. Some examples of support nursing staff can provide to families **before death** include:

- Stay with the family and sit quietly, allowing them to talk, cry, or interact if they desire.
- Avoid platitudes, "His suffering will be over soon."
- Avoid judgmental reactions to what family members say or do and realize that anger, fear, guilt, and irrational behavior are normal responses to acute grief and stress.
- Show caring by touching the patient and encouraging family to do the same.
  - Note: Touching hands, arms, or shoulders of family members can provide comfort, but follow cues regarding touching provided by the family.
- Provide referrals to support groups if available.

SUPPORTING FAMILIES DURING DEATH OF PATIENT

The family requires much support **when the patient is about to die:**

- Reassure family that all measures have been taken to ensure the patient's comfort.
- Express personal feeling of loss, "She was such a sweet woman, and I'll miss her" and allow family to express feelings and memories.
- Provide information about what is happening during the dying process, explaining death rales, Cheyne-Stokes respirations, etc.
- Alert family members to imminent death if they are not present.
- Assist to contact clergy/spiritual advisors.
- Respect feelings and needs of spouse, children, and other family.

After the patient has died:

- Encourage parents/family members to stay with the patient as long as they wish to say goodbye.
- Use the patient's name when talking to the family.
- Assist family to make arrangements, such as contacting funeral home.
- If an autopsy is required, discuss with the family and explain when it will take place.
- If organ donation is to occur, assist the family to make arrangements.
- Encourage family members to grieve and express emotions.
- Send card or condolence note if appropriate.

GROUP THERAPY

Groups can be classified according to form:

- **Homogeneous**: Members chosen on a selected basis, such as abused women.
- **Heterogeneous**: An assortment of individuals with different diagnoses, ages, genders.
- **Mixed**: A group which shares some key features, such as the same diagnosis but differs in age or gender.
- **Closed**: A group in which new members are excluded.
- **Open**: A group in which the members and leaders change.

Types of groups according to purpose include:

- **Task**: Emphasis on achieving a particular assignment.
- **Teaching**: Developed to inform, such as teaching the rules of the unit.
- **Supportive/Therapeutic**: Assisting those who share the same experience to learn mechanisms to cope with trauma and to overcome the problem, such as a group for battered women.
- **Psychotherapy**: Helping the client reduce psychological stress by modifying behavior or ideas.

TUCKMAN'S GROUP DEVELOPMENT STAGES

Tuckman's (1965) **group developmental stages** include:

- **Forming**: Group director takes more of an active role while members take their cues from the leader for structure and approval. The leader lists the goals and rules and encourages communication among the members.
- **Storming**: This stage involves a divergence of opinions regarding management, power, and authority. Storming may involve increased stress and resistance may occur, as shown by the absence of members, shared silence, and subgroup formation. At this point, the leader should promote and allow healthy expression of anger.
- **Norming**: It is at this stage where members express positive feelings toward each other and feel deeply attached to the group.
- **Performing**: The leader's input and direction decreases and mainly consists of keeping the group on course.
- **Mourning**: This is most deeply felt in closed groups when discontinuation of the group nears and in open groups when the leader or other members leave.

GESTALT THERAPY

The major concepts of **Gestalt therapy,** according to Perls, include:

- Therapy involves the removal of masks and facades.
- A creative interaction between the client and the therapist needs to be developed so the client can gain an ongoing awareness of what is being felt, sensed, and thought.
- Boundary disturbances may be described as a lack of awareness of the immediate environment, including features such as:
  - Projection: The fantasy of what another person is experiencing.
  - Introjection: Accepting the beliefs and opinions of others without question.
  - Retroflection: Turning back on oneself that which is meant for someone else.
  - Confluence: Merging with the environment.
  - Deflection: A method of interfering with contact, used by receivers and senders of messages.
- The goal of therapy is the integration of self and world awareness.

TECHNIQUES

In **Gestalt therapy**, a number of techniques are used as part of the therapeutic process:

- **Playing the projection:** Stating an observation first about another person and then applying the same statement to oneself to learn about projecting feelings about the self onto others.
- **Making the rounds:** Speaking or doing something to other group members to experiment with new behavior.
- **Completing sentence:** "I take responsibility for…"
- **Exaggerating a feeling or action:** Clarifying the purpose or intent.
- **Mirroring**: Group member does role playing and then volunteers from the group do alternative role playing while the original role player observes.
- **Empty chair dialoguing**: Having an interaction with an imaginary provocateur in an empty chair.
- **Taking the hot seat**: Group member sits across from the leader and describes a personal problem with input by other team members on request of the leader.
- **Role playing the dream world**: Describing and playing parts of a dream.

ALBERT ELLIS' RATIONAL EMOTIVE THERAPY

Key concepts of **Albert Ellis' Rational Emotive Therapy** include:

- People control their own destinies and interpret events according to their own **values and beliefs**.
- **A-B-C theory**: Activating event, belief, consequences (emotional and/or behavioral).
- Forms of **irrational beliefs**:
  - Something should be different.
  - Something is awful or terrible.
  - One cannot tolerate something.
  - Something or someone is damned or cursed.
- **"Musturbatory" ideologies** have 3 forms:
  - I must do well and win approval or I am a rotten person.
  - You must act kindly toward me or you are a rotten person.
  - My life must remain comfortable or life hardly seems worth living.

- Therapy consists of **detecting and eradicating irrational beliefs**:
  - *Disputing*: Detecting irrationalities, debating them, discriminating between logical and illogical thinking, and defining what helps create new beliefs.
  - *Debating*: Questioning and disputing the irrational beliefs.
  - *Discriminating*: Distinguishing between wants and needs, desires and demands, and rational and irrational ideas.
  - *Defining*: Defining words and redefining beliefs.

RICHARD BANDLER AND JOHN GRINDER'S NEUROLINGUISTICS PROGRAMMING

The major concepts of **neurolinguistic programming (NLP)** according to Bandler and Grinder include:

Representation Systems	Sensory models by which people access information (audio, visual, kinesthetic).
Cues to Representation Systems	Preferred predicated: "View" that suggests a visual system. Eye-Accessing cues: Looking upward suggests a visual system. Hand movements: Pointing toward the ear suggests an auditory system. Breathing patterns: Suggest a kinesthetic system. Speech patterns/tones: Suggest an auditory system.
Language Structure	Surface structure: Sentences native language speakers speak and write. Deep structure: Linguistic representations from which the surface structures of a language are derived. Ambiguity: A surface language may represent more than 1 deep structure.
Human Modeling (Representing Through Language)	Generalization: Specific experiences representing the entire category of which they are a member. Deletion: Selected portions of the world are excluded from the representation created by an individual. Distortion: Relationship among the parts of the model that differ from the relationships they were supposed to represent.

AARON BECK'S COGNITIVE THERAPY

Aaron Beck discovered that during psychotherapy patients often had a second set of thoughts while undergoing "free association." Beck called these "automatic" thoughts, which were labeled and interpreted according to a personal set of rules. Beck called dysfunctional automatic thoughts "cognitive disorders." The key concepts in **Beck's cognitive therapy** include:

Therapist/Client Relationship	Therapy is a collaborative partnership.
	The goal of therapy is determined together.
	The therapist encourages the client to disagree when appropriate.
Process of Therapy	Therapist explains: The perception of reality is not reality. The interpretation of sensory input depends on cognitive processes.
	Client taught to recognize maladaptive ideation, identifying: The observable behavior. The underlying motivation. His/her thoughts and beliefs.
	The client practices distancing the maladaptive thoughts and explores his/her conclusions and tests them against reality.
Conclusions	The client makes the rules less extreme and absolute, drops false rules, and substitutes adaptive rules.

BEHAVIOR MODIFICATION

Behavior modification is a type of systematic therapy that works toward the goal of replacing maladaptive behaviors with positive behaviors. This type of therapy can be utilized with individuals, groups, or entire communities. There are 3 types of behavioral modification:

- **Operant conditioning** utilizes positive reinforcement directed towards the desired behaviors. By utilizing positive reinforcement, the participant will want to repeat the good behaviors to gain the reward, creating a new pattern of operant conditioning can be effective with eating disorders, smoking cessation, or addictions.
- **Desensitization,** in which patients are increasingly exposed to those things that cause them stress (such as phobias) so that they can overcome their fears.
- **Aversion therapy** applies a negative consequence to an action (such as using medications to induce vomiting after drinking alcohol) to create negative associations with the action in order to modify behavior.

PSYCHOTHERAPEUTIC OPTIONS FOR PHOBIAS

Psychotherapeutic interventions for patients with **phobias** include:

- **Psychodynamic**: awareness therapy to resolve childhood conflicts and to find healthy ways to deal with anxiety.
- **Behavior therapy**: has been found to be the most effective treatment, and includes:
  - Systematic desensitization:
    - ❖ Patient grades anxiety-provoking stimuli from the least to the most terrifying.
    - ❖ Patient taught to enter a relaxed state.
    - ❖ Maintaining relaxed state, patient envisions each anxiety-provoking stimulus, starting with the least fearful.
    - ❖ When desensitized to 1 stimulus, patient then moves up the list until the list is completed.
    - ❖ Patient then puts into practice the relaxation techniques when encountering a phobia stimulus outside the therapist's office.
  - *Flooding*: Intensive exposure to stimulus through imagery until fear can no longer be felt.

PSYCHOTHERAPEUTIC THERAPY FOR DISSOCIATIVE FUGUE

Dissociative Fugue, a specifier of dissociative amnesia, is characterized by sudden memory loss, moving to a new location, and adopting a new identity; it is not associated with head injury, substance abuse, or any other general medical condition. Therapy includes:

- Restoring memories and identity as soon as possible, sometimes under hypnosis.
- Identifying stressful events leading to the fugue.
- Identifying and treating any condition(s) caused by traumatic events. The trauma needs to be evaluated and resolved by allowing proper emotional expression in a safe environment.
- Hospitalizing if behavior becomes bizarre or injurious to self or others.
- Beginning marital therapy if the marital situation is stressful.
- Educating regarding stress management.

The **family** may be a source of stress, and family customs may forbid open and clear expression of anxiety and emotional pain. If family dynamics are a source of stress, family therapy is needed to improve interaction and problem solving. The family may need education to understand the patient's condition.

Psychotherapeutic Interventions for PTSD for Males and Females

Psychotherapeutic interventions and treatment for **post-traumatic stress disorder** (PTSD) differ by gender because the recovery process needs to be tailored to the particular trauma. The purpose of **individual therapy** includes:

- Educating the patient that PTSD is caused by extraordinary stress rather than weakness.
- Ceasing to minimize the trauma.
- Dispelling inaccurate ideas the person may have about the illness.
- Minimizing or eliminating any shame they may feel about having PTSD.
- Constructing a new, caring relationship with oneself.
- Addressing the sleep problems often associated with PTSD.

Men respond to PTSD differently than females:

- They are generally unwilling to seek treatment.
- They tend to minimize the experience.
- Difficulties exist with male intimacy.
- Symptoms may manifest as aggression, substance abuse, or sexual dysfunction.
- Therapy for men should promote the expression of emotions.

PTSD Psychotherapy

Patients with **post-traumatic stress disorder (PTSD)** are usually treated with antidepressants, mood stabilizers, or antipsychotic drugs, depending on their symptoms, but therapy is essential. Some examples of **PTSD therapy** include:

- **Cognitive-behavioral therapy (CBT):** Patients learn to confront trauma through psychoeducation, breathing, imaginary reliving, and writing and are taught to self-monitor and recognize thoughts related to their trauma and method of coping, such as distraction and self-soothing.
- **Eye-movement desensitization and reprocessing (EMDR):** This form of CBT requires the patient to talk about the experience of trauma while keeping the eyes and attention focused on the therapist's rapidly moving finger. (There is no clear evidence this is more effective than standard CBT.)
- **Family therapy:** PTSD impacts the entire family, so counseling and classes in anger management, parenting, and conflict resolution may help reduce family conflict related to the PTSD.
- **Sleep therapy:** Patients may fear sleeping because of severe nightmares. Sleep therapy teaches methods to cope with nightmares through imagery rehearsal therapy and relaxation techniques.

PSYCHOTHERAPEUTIC INTERVENTIONS FOR CHRONIC PAIN DISORDER

Psychotherapeutic goals and interventions for patients with verified **chronic pain disorder** include:

- **Individual:**
  - Rehabilitate the patient so he/she can return to work.
  - Teach the psychological consequences of acute or chronic pain.
  - Educate the patient about relaxation techniques when pain frustration occurs.
  - Educate patient on activities of daily living (ADLs) within parameters of pain limitations.
  - Encourage exercise within the patient's limitations.
- **Family Dynamics/Therapy:**
  - Educate family members about acute and chronic pain.
  - Educate family on how to respond to patient's pain.
  - The roles and responsibilities of each family member may need to be reorganized to accommodate the patient's pain.
- **Group:**
  - Pain support groups.
  - Exercise groups experiencing same type of pain.
  - Pain management groups.
  - Assertiveness and self-confidence support groups.

DIALECTICAL BEHAVIORAL THERAPY FOR BORDERLINE PERSONALITY DISORDER

Dialectical behavioral therapy was developed for treatment of those with **borderline personality disorder (BPD)**. While accepting the patient, the NP/therapist tries to help him/her change behavior by replacing dichotomous thinking that paints the world as black or white with rational (dialectical) thinking. This therapy is based on the premise that patients with BPD lack the ability to self-regulate, have a low tolerance for distress, and encounter social and environmental factors that impact their behavioral skills. Therapy includes:

- **Cognitive behavioral therapy** (weekly), focusing on adaptive behaviors that help the patient to deal with stress/trauma. Therapy focuses on a prioritized list of problems: suicidal behavior, behavior that interferes with therapy, quality of life issues, post-traumatic stress (PTS) response, respect for self, acquisition of behavioral skills, and patient goals.
- **Group therapy** (2.5 hours weekly) to help the patient learn behavioral skills such as self-distracting and soothing.

> **Review Video: Borderline Personality Disorder**
> Visit mometrix.com/academy and enter code: 550801

Change Theories

TRANSTHEORETICAL MODEL

The **Transtheoretical Model** focuses on changes in behavior based on the individual's (not society's or other's) decisions and is used to develop strategies to promote changes in health behavior. This model outlines stages people go through changing problem behavior and having a positive attitude about change. Stages of change:

- **Precontemplation**: The person is either unaware or under-informed about consequences of a problem behavior and has no intention of changing behavior in the next 6 months.
- **Contemplation**: The person is aware of costs and benefits of changing behavior and intends to change in the next 6 months but are procrastinating and not ready for action.
- **Preparation**: The person has a plan and intends to instigate change in the near future (≤1 month) and is ready for action plans.
- **Action**: The person is modifying behavior change occurs only if behavior meets a set criterion (such as complete abstinence from drinking).
- **Maintenance**: The person works to maintain changes and gains confidence that he/she will not relapse.

MOTIVATIONAL INTERVIEWING

Motivational interviewing (Miller, 1983) aims to help people identify and resolve issues regarding ambivalence about change and focuses on the role of motivation to bring about change. MI is a collaborative approach in which the interviewer assesses the individual's readiness to accept change and identifies strategies that may be effective with the individual.

Elements	Principles	Strategies
Collaboration rather than confrontation in resolving issues.	**Expression of empathy**: Showing understanding of individual's perceptions.	**Avoiding Yes/No** questions: Asking informational questions.
Evocation (drawing out) of the individual's ideas about change rather than imposition of the interviewer's ideas.	**Support of self-efficacy**: Helping individuals realize they are capable of change.	**Providing affirmations**: Indicating areas of strength.
Autonomy of the individual in making changes.	**Acceptance of resistance**: Avoiding struggles/conflicts with patient.	**Providing reflective listening**: Responding to statements.
	Examination of discrepancies: Helping individuals see discrepancy between their behavior and goals.	**Providing summaries**: Recapping important points of discussion.
		Encouraging change talk: Including desire, ability, reason, and need.

RESISTANCE TO ORGANIZATIONAL CHANGE

Performance improvement processes cannot occur without organizational change, and **resistance to change** is common for many people, so coordinating collaborative processes requires anticipating resistance and taking steps to achieve cooperation. Resistance often relates to concerns about job loss, increased responsibilities, and general denial or lack of understanding and frustration. Leaders can prepare others involved in the process of change by taking these steps:

- Be honest, informative, and tactful, giving people thorough information about anticipated changes and how the changes will affect them, including positives.
- Be patient in allowing people the time they need to contemplate changes and express anger or disagreement.
- Be empathetic in listening carefully to the concerns of others.
- Encourage participation, allowing staff to propose methods of implementing change, so they feel some sense of ownership.
- Establish a climate in which all staff members are encouraged to identify the need for change on an ongoing basis.
- Present further ideas for change to management.

Developmental Theories

ERIKSON'S THEORY OF PSYCHOLOGICAL DEVELOPMENT

Erikson's Theory of Psychosocial Development covers the life span, focusing on conflicts at each stage and the virtue that is the outcome of finding a balance in the conflict. The first 5 stages relate to infancy and childhood and the last 3 stages to adulthood, but childhood development affects later adult development:

Trust vs. Mistrust	Birth to 1 year	Can result in mistrust or faith and optimism.
Autonomy vs. Shame/Doubt	1-3 years	Can lead to doubt and shame or self-control and willpower.
Initiative vs. Guilt	3-6 years	Can lead to guilt or direction and purpose.
Industry vs. Inferiority	6-12 years	Can lead to inadequacy and inferiority or competence.
Identify vs. Role Confusion	12-18 years	Can lead to role confusion or devotion and fidelity to others.
Intimacy vs. Isolation	Young adulthood	Can lead to lack of close relationships or love/intimacy.
Generativity vs. Stagnation	Middle age	Can lead to stagnation or caring and achievements.
Ego Integrity vs. Despair	Older adulthood	Can lead to despair (failure to accept changes of aging) or wisdom (acceptance).

PECK'S THEORY OF ADULT DEVELOPMENT

Peck expanded on Erikson's stages of adult development, believing that there were 7 important tasks that were required during the last 2 stages of life:

Stage	Tasks	Outcomes
Middle Age	Valuing wisdom vs physical powers. Socializing vs. sexualizing. Cathectic (libidinal energy) flexibility vs. cathectic impoverishment. Mental flexibility vs mental rigidity.	*Negative* outcomes lead to weak relationships, inflexibility, and resistance to change. *Positive* outcomes lead to strong relationships, flexibility in lifestyle, and adaptability to change.
Older Adulthood	Ego differentiation vs work role preoccupation. Body transcendence vs. body preoccupation. Ego transcendence vs ego preoccupation.	*Negative* outcomes lead to feelings of loss of identity after retiring, depression, inability to accept bodily/functional changes and fear of death. *Positive* outcomes lead to meaningful life after retirement, acceptance of bodily/functional changes, acceptance of death, and feeling that life has been good.

CONTINUITY THEORY AND LIFE-COURSE THEORY

CONTINUITY

Havighurst, Neugarten, and Tobin believed that neither activity theory nor disengagement theory was adequate from a sociological perspective to explain successful aging and that personality type correlated with adjustment to aging. People maintain **continuity** in their adaptation to changing roles according to their basic personality type:

- **Integrated**: Individuals adjust well to aging and changing roles and remain active.
- **Armored-defended**: Individuals maintain roles and activities they had during middle age and with which they feel secure.
- **Passive-dependent**: Individuals become increasingly dependent on others and/or are passive in their changing roles.
- **Unintegrated**: Individuals are unable to cope well with aging.

LIFE COURSE

The life course theory contends that **aging** is a lifelong process of social, psychological, and biological changes that begin with infancy and continue through older adulthood, viewed within cultural, economic, social, and historic context.

RESILIENCY THEORY

The **Resiliency Theory** describes the ability of children to function in healthy ways despite adverse circumstances. This theory explains the dynamics of **response to a crisis**, considering the characteristics inherent in the individual as well as the environmental characteristics. When a crisis occurs, the child (along with his or her family) encounters vulnerability, stress, and increased risks in coping. Families respond in different manners, sometimes relying on extended family or coping with abnormal behavior (such as an alcoholic parent). Children and families also have **protective factors** (such as faith, previous experience, supportive family members, etc.) that provide assistance in coping with changes. The family often goes through a **phase of adjustment to changes**, during which they may be disorganized and unable to cope, but this evolves to an **adaptation phase** during which the child and family appraise the situation and use problem solving to arise at a positive or negative response to the change.

MASLOW'S HIERARCHY OF NEEDS AND JUNG'S THEORY OF INDIVIDUALISM

HIERARCHY OF NEEDS

Maslow stated that human behavior is motivated by needs and that there is a hierarchy of needs that begin with basic needs and progress to personal needs. The hierarchy includes: Physiological needs (the base). Safety and security. Belonging. Self-esteem. Self-actualization (the apex). People may not progress in 1 direction from 1 need to another but movement may be in multiple directions in a lifelong process of working toward self-actualization, which requires creativity and some degree of freedom. Failure to develop toward **self-actualization** may result in depression and feelings of failure.

THEORY OF INDIVIDUALISM

Jung theorized that personality developed over the lifespan. **Personality** comprises ego, personal unconsciousness, and collective unconsciousness. Personality can be introverted or extroverted, but a balance is necessary for emotional health. Jung theorized that during middle age, people begin to question their values, beliefs, and attainments. As they continue to age, they turn more inward. Successful aging is when people **value themselves** more than the concern they have for external things, losses, and physical limitations.

PROBLEMS DURING SCHOOL-AGE YEARS

During the years of **6-12,** routine health assessments should be done at ages 6, 8, 10, and 11-12 to determine if there are **developmental delays or problems**, which may include:

- **6 years**: Peer problems, depression, cruelty to animals, poor academic progress, speech problems, lack of fine motor skills, and inability to catch a ball or state age.
- **8 years:** No close friends, depression, cruelty to animals, interest in fires, very poor academic progress with inability to do math, read or write adequately, and poor coordination.
- **10 years:** No team sports and poor choices in peers (gangs), failure to follow rules, cruelty to animals and interest in fires, depression, failure to understand causal relationships, poor academic progress in reading, writing, math, penmanship, and problems throwing or catching.
- **11-12 years:** Continuation of problems at 10 years with increasing risk-taking behaviors (drinking, drugs, sex) and continued poor academic progress in reading, following directions, doing homework, and organization.

ISSUES FOR EARLY ADOLESCENCE

Early adolescence, **11-14,** is a transitional time for children as their hormones and bodies go through changes. Children mature at varying rates, so there are wide differences. Emotions may be labile, and the child may feel isolated and confused at times, trying to find an identity. Peers take on more influence and the child may challenge the values of the family. Children may have much anxiety about their bodies and sexuality as secondary sexual characteristics develops. **Developmental concerns** include:

- Delayed maturation.
- Short stature (females).
- Spinal curvature (females).
- Poor dental status (caries, malocclusion).
- Chronic illnesses, such as diabetes.
- Lack of adequate physical activity.
- Poor nutrition, anorexia.
- Concerns about sexual identity.
- Negative self-image.
- Depression.
- Lack of close friends, fighting, or violent episodes.
- Poor academic progress with truancy and failure to complete assignments.
- Lack of impulse control.

ISSUES FOR MIDDLE ADOLESCENCE

In middle adolescence, ages **15-17,** most body changes have occurred, and there is less concern about this but more concern about the image they are projecting to others. Girls may worry about weight and boys about muscle development. Teenagers are interested in sexuality and many begin sexual experimentation. There is strong identification with peer groups, including codes of dress and behavior, often putting them at odds with family. **Developmental concerns** include:

- Spinal curvature (females) and short stature (males).
- Lack of testicular maturation/persistent gynecomastia.
- Acne.

- Anorexia, obesity.
- Sexual experimentation, multiple partners, and unprotected sex.
- Sexual identification concerns.
- Depression, poor self-image.
- Lack of adequate exercise, poor nutrition, and poor dental health.
- Chronic diseases.
- Experimentation with drugs and alcohol and problems with authority figures.
- Lack of peer group identification, gang association.
- Poor academic progress, failing classes, truancy, attention deficits and disruptive class behavior, poor judgment, and impulse control.

ISSUES FOR LATE ADOLESCENCE

Late adolescence, **18-21,** is the time when adolescents begin to take on more adult roles and responsibilities, entering the world of work or going to college. Most have come to terms with their sexuality and have a more mature understanding of people's motivations. Some young people will continue to engage in high-risk behaviors. Many of the problems associated with middle adolescence may continue if unresolved, interfering with the transition to adulthood. **Developmental concerns** include:

- Failure to take on adult roles, no life goals or future plans.
- Low self-esteem.
- Lack of intimate relationships, sexual identification concerns.
- Gang association.
- Continued identification with peer group or dependence on parents.
- High-risk sexual behavior, multiple partners, and unprotected sex.
- Poor academic progress or ability.
- Psychosomatic complaints, depression.
- Lack of impulse control.
- Poor nutrition, obesity, anorexia.
- Poor dental health.
- Chronic disease.
- Lack of exercise.

COGNITIVE CHANGES ASSOCIATED WITH NORMAL AGING

Cognitive changes related to age vary among individuals but are usually not evident until >70. Studies have shown that by age 81, about 60-70% of people have a small decline in cognitive abilities. **Fluid intelligence** (information processing skills) tends to decline slightly with age while **crystallized intelligence** (acquired knowledge and applied problem solving) is more likely to stay intact and may even improve. Older adults may have more difficulty in completing complex tasks that require processing of new information. They may become more easily distracted and less able to focus attention. Processing information and reacting may be slowed so that those >60 require more time to complete mental tasks even though their intellectual capability remains intact. Working memory declines making it more difficult for older adults to complete mental processes that require keeping facts in memory (such as calculating costs and tips). **Implicit memories** (skills, reactions) usually remain intact while **explicit memories** (facts, information) may decline. Older adults often have difficulty retrieving words (names of people or objects).

Family Theories

FAMILY SYSTEMS THEORY

Bowen's **Family Systems Theory** suggests that one must look at the person in terms of his/her family unit because the members of a family have different roles and behavioral patterns, so a change in 1 person's behavior will affect the others in the family. There are **8 interrelated concepts**:

- **Triangle theory:** Two people comprise a basic unit, but when conflict occurs, a third person is drawn into the unit for stability with the resulting dynamic of 2 supporting 1 or 2 opposing 1. This, in turn, draws in other triangles.
- **Self-differentiation:** People vary in need for external approval.
- **Nuclear family patterns:** marital conflict, 1 spouse dysfunctional, 1 or more children impaired, and emotional distance.
- **Projection within a family:** Problems (emotional) passed from parent to child.
- **Transmission (multigenerational):** Small differences in transmission from parent to child.
- **Emotional isolation:** Reducing or eliminating family contact.
- **Sibling order:** Influence on behavior and development.
- **Emotional process (society):** Results in regressive or progressive social movements.

> **Review Video: Family Systems Theory**
> Visit mometrix.com/academy and enter code: 591496

HOGARTH'S TECHNIQUES FOR FAMILY THERAPY

Hogarth's (1993) **techniques in family therapy** include:

- **Joining**: Finding and matching commonalities among family behaviors, while respecting their values.
- **Gathering data:** Completing a family history about the parents' original relationship and progressing to each family member in chronological order. A completed family "genogram" delineates significant relationships and events extending over 3 generations of the family.
- **Encouraging interactions and relationships:** Beginning with a family member discussing an issue important to the family, the therapist then clarifies and explains the family's communication. Each individual should be allowed to speak and express their feelings instead of allowing others to speak for them. Family members are then asked to share responsibility for resolution of problems instead of placing blame.

PSYCHOTHERAPEUTIC AND FAMILY THERAPY INTERVENTIONS USED WITH OCD

Psychotherapeutic and family therapy interventions used with **obsessive-compulsive disorder (OCD) patients** include therapy oriented to develop expression of thoughts and impulses in a manner that is appropriate:

Behavioral therapies (which appear to have the greatest success):

- Combined exposure with training to delay obsessive responses. Best used in conjunction with pharmacotherapy.
- Steady decrease of rituals by exposure to anxiety-producing situations until patient has learned to control the related obsessive compulsion.

- Reducing obsessive thoughts by the use of reminders or noxious stimuli to stop chain-of-thought patterns, such as snapping a rubber band on the wrist when obsessive thoughts occur.

Family therapy (Primary issues):

- Attempts to avoid situations that trigger OCD responses.
- The tendency of family members to constantly reassure the patient (this is apt to support the obsession).
- Family therapy involves:
  - Remaining neutral and not reinforcing through encouragement.
  - Avoiding reasoning logically with patient.

PSYCHOTHERAPEUTIC AND FAMILY THERAPY INTERVENTIONS FOR PANIC DISORDERS

Psychotherapeutic interventions for panic disorder:

- *Psychodynamic*: Therapy designed to help the family become aware of and to focus upon the origin of anxiety and develop tools to be able to resolve conflicts.
- Behavioral:
  - Education regarding origin of panic attacks.
  - Desensitization: using real or imagined phobic situations(s).
  - Reinforcement of self-control and relaxation techniques.
  - Patient must anticipate and be able to manage break-through symptoms.

Family dynamics and therapy:

- Patients with agoraphobia may require the presence of family members to be constantly in close proximity, resulting in marital stress and over-reliance on the children.
- Altered role performance of the afflicted member results in family and social situations that increase the responsibility of other family members.
- The family must be educated about the source and treatment of the disorder.
- The goal of family therapy is to reorganize responsibilities to support family change.

CODEPENDENCY

Codependency is a condition that afflicts the "significant others" of an addict. Codependency and other maladaptive behaviors are learned so that each individual may survive in a stressful and emotionally painful environment. Codependent responses are typified by a desire to **change the addict's behavior**—the individual puts the other's needs before his or her own. Codependent individuals are often adult children of alcoholics and generally share the following characteristics: self-defeating; poor self-esteem; seeking approval from others; fearing abandonment; and unable to express anger. A codependent individual attempts to meet other's needs at the expense of personal needs.

Strategies used in family therapy to **manage addiction issues** include:

- Evaluating the family system's level of denial, education, and insight.
- Refraining from blaming family members for the way they feel or act regarding codependency.

- Educating family members about chemical dependency and referral to alcoholics anonymous (AL-ANON) and/or alcoholics anonymous for teens (AL-ATEEN) for support.
- Supporting and reinforcing healthy change.

PARENTING STYLES

Parenting has an essential role in the social and behavioral development of the child. The degree of **warmth** the parents exhibit and the type of **control** have a profound effect on the child.

Style	Parental Behavior	Effects on Child
Indifferent	Shows little warmth and rarely imposes limits, may neglect or dislike child.	Child feels unloved and lacks direction or a positive sense of self, resulting in destructive or delinquent behavior.
Permissive	Shows much warmth and affection for the child but imposes few limits and little guidance although communication remains good.	Child may be creative and extroverted but doesn't negotiate or cooperate well with others, making acceptance by peers difficult. The child may become very self-centered and impulsive with impaired social functioning. The child may bully others or become aggressive and rebellious.
Authoritarian	Shows little warmth or affection for the child and communicates little. Is often inflexible and sets very restrictive limits that allow little independent thought or activity.	Child does not learn to negotiate or direct own behavior and has difficulty learning autonomy. Child may be fearful, passive, withdrawn. During adolescence, girls tend to be more passive and needy while boys tend to become aggressive.
Authoritative	Shows much warmth and affection for the child and provides guidance with minimal restraints. Maintains flexibility and communicates freely with the child, encouraging autonomy.	Child often has a positive self-image and is able to act independently and gets along well with others. The child is accepting of restrictions and often does well in school.

COLLABORATION WITH PATIENT AND FAMILIES

One of the most important forms of collaboration is that between the **NP and the patient/family**, but this type of collaboration is often overlooked. NPs and others in the healthcare team must always remember that the point of collaborating is to improve patient care, and this means that the patient and patient's family must remain central to all planning. For example, including family in planning for a patient takes time initially, but sitting down and asking the patient and family, "What do you want?" and using the synergy model to evaluate patient's (and family's) characteristics can provide valuable information that saves time in the long run and facilitates planning and expenditure of resources. Families, and even young children, often want to participate in care and planning and feel validated and more positive toward the medical system when they are included.

SOCIAL SUPPORT SYSTEM

The family is integral to the **social support system** of the patient, but social support can come from a number of other sources:

- **Friends**: Friends often assume the supportive role of family, especially in modern society when family members may not live in close proximity.
- **Governmental agencies:** Medicare and Medicaid may provide support as well as Social Services for welfare assistance.
- **Religious/spiritual advisors:** Religion or spiritual beliefs provide comfort to many, and some patients may receive not only spiritual support but also concrete support, such as housing or other assistance, from religious institutions.
- **Community agencies:** Many different agencies, such as Meals-on-Wheels, senior citizen centers, and outreach programs may provide practical assistance.
- **Self-help programs:** 12-step programs (such as Alcoholics Anonymous (AA), Overeaters Anonymous (OA), and Narcotics Anonymous (NA)) and other self-help programs provide an ongoing support system for those seeking recovery.
- **Internet:** Increasingly, people are turning to message boards and social networking sites for support although there are always some risks involved in anonymous interactions.

Therapeutic Alliance Development

SELF-AWARENESS

The NP must develop a **self-awareness** of personal values, biases, motivating forces, beliefs, strengths, weaknesses, feelings, and attitudes because these all color interactions with patients. If, for example, a patient senses prejudice, the patient may react negatively to this. In some cases, the NP's personal beliefs about others may affect a patient evaluation when the NP makes judgments based on personal feelings rather than clinical observations. A strong self-awareness based on honest exploration can be an asset when working with the patient as it can guide the NP's behavior and responses to better promote a therapeutic relationship. The NP must be able to maintain a personal sense of values while respecting those with different value systems. NPs can increase self-awareness by maintaining a journal of feelings, discussing values with others and seeking to understand those with differing values and beliefs, and working with a mentor.

THERAPEUTIC RELATIONSHIP

A **therapeutic relationship** is a continuum based on a trusting relationship, caring, empathy, and acceptance. The needs of the patient are the focus, not the feelings or needs of the NP:

1. **Orientation:** The patient seeks or is brought in for help, and needs and concerns are elicited. The NP responds to client, listens actively, and responds, explaining roles and trying to relieve the patient's anxiety while helping the patient focus on problems.
2. **Identification:** The patient begins to identify with the NP and increases understanding of problems and testing behavior decreases as the patient has a better understanding of roles and expectations. The NP shows acceptance and continues to assess and provide support and information.
3. **Working:** The patient makes better use of the relationship, shows better problem-solving skills, and improved communication, but may engage in exploitative behavior (with wide behavior shifts in dependence and independence). The NP supports client and explores feelings at client's own pace.
4. **Termination:** The patient establishes independence from the NP and sets new goals. The NP encourages family/community support and preventive care.

BUILDING AND MAINTAINING A TRUSTING RELATIONSHIP

It is essential that the NP **builds and maintains a trusting relationship** with the patient by **respecting** the individual and maintaining **confidentiality**. Patients are often stressed and frightened and may express this through criticizing, withdrawing, or refusing to cooperate; the NP should not react negatively but should remain supportive and encourage communication. The NP should take the time to understand the cultural needs of the patient and to ensure that the NP's own personal preferences don't interfere with provision of care. The patient's healthcare issues should be viewed from the patient's perspective. If the NP must rush out of the patient's room, the practitioner should explain why he/she is rushed and return at a later time. Using the patient's name routinely and taking even a minute or two to talk to the patient can help to reassure the patient and build trust.

NP-PATIENT RELATIONSHIP

The **NP-patient relationship** is a delicate marriage of skill, ethics, and trust. It is a particularly vulnerable relationship in a psychotherapy setting, as the NP and patient discuss a wide range of negative experiences, thoughts, and family history. NP and patient must respect each other, even though they may not like one another. The NP motivates and empowers the patient towards lifestyle change and therapeutic compliance. In a mental health setting, the NP is responsible for the overall health and wellbeing of the patient, so conditions must be established under which rules are enforced and privileges are awarded. The NP is legally responsible for reporting to the police when he/she fears for the patient's life or that of another individual. The practitioner must not allow personal feelings for the patient to affect his/her treatment or professional recommendations and, if unable to deal with personal emotions, should inform a colleague and refer the patient to another competent individual.

THERAPEUTIC ALLIANCE

The **therapeutic alliance** between the patient and the NP is a critical aspect of a therapeutic relationship. This alliance involves:

- **Goals**: Collaboration in treatment goals is essential because it forms a partnership between the NP and the patient.
- **Tasks**: Both the NP and the patient should have an understanding of the tasks required of them.
- **Bond**: Over time, a personal relationship and bond develops as patient and NP work to achieve goals.

The strength of the therapeutic alliance directly relates to the **treatment outcomes**. Factors that affect the alliance include qualities of the NP, qualities of the patient, and aspects of therapy. Patients who have demonstrated difficulty establishing relationships in their personal lives sometimes also have difficulty establishing a therapeutic alliance with a mental healthcare provider. Showing respect for the patient, showing sensitivity to culture, and asking the patient for input can strengthen the alliance.

TERMINATION

The final stage of the patient-provider relationship is the **termination or resolution phase**. The NP should establish the basis for termination of treatment at the onset. Reasons for termination may include non-compliance with treatment, reaching therapeutic goals, or referral and should be explained verbally and in writing. Termination can be very difficult for both the patient and the provider. The patient must now focus on continuing without the guiding assistance of the therapy. The patient will need to utilize newfound approaches and behaviors. This time may be one of varying emotions for the patient who may be reluctant to end the relationship. The patient may experience anxiety, anger, or sadness. The provider may need to guide the patient in utilizing newfound strategies in dealing with feelings about the termination of the relationship. Focus should be placed on the future.

TRAUMA-INFORMED APPROACH

The **trauma-informed approach** to care of patients recognizes that trauma occurs much more commonly than previously thought and has profound effects on patients' wellbeing and mental health. With the trauma-informed approach, all mental health patients are routinely asked about their experience of trauma but are not forced or coerced into sharing information that they are not yet ready to share. When they do disclose trauma, the NP should acknowledge the patients' stress and pain and provide emotional support without undue questioning or judgmental statements. However, patients can be asked if they have told anyone else and if they believe that the trauma is affecting their lives or current conditions. Procedures that might increase trauma, such as isolation, restriction, and restraints, should be eliminated. The goal is to allow patients to feel safe and to disclose trauma so that trauma services can be provided.

TRAUMA-INFORMED INTERVENTIONS

Trauma-informed interventions must be carried out in such a way that they do not inflict more trauma, so interventions must be individualized in collaboration with the patient. The psychiatric and mental health NP must take care to avoid imposing expectations on the patient. Interventions include:

- **Safe haven**: Consistent safe nonviolent environment in which patient is treated with respect and confidentiality assured. Patient should be told who will have access to information shared (such as other NPs and the psychiatrist).
- **Collaboration**: Patient understands rights and works with healthcare providers to determine appropriate treatment.
- **Decision-making**: Patient is encouraged to make choices and to exercise autonomy.
- **Empowerment**: Patient treated as survivor and not a victim. Previous coping mechanisms explored with a focus on skill building.
- **Person-first language and avoidance of jargon**: Nonjudgmental, non-shaming environment.
- **Support systems**: Patient helped to identify support systems and to find resource in the community to assist in recovery.

BOUNDARIES

PROFESSIONAL BOUNDARIES

Professional boundaries that show respect for the individual can be difficult to establish as part of delivery of care, especially with diverse populations because the NP may unknowingly violate personal or spiritual values. **Diverse groups** include those on the fringes of society, such as the homeless or the abused. It's very important that NPs remain cognizant of the potential to abuse a position of power in which the patient and family are in many ways dependent upon the NP and because of language, fears, or cultural constraints may not feel able to state their concerns. A relationship with a patient must be caring but at the same time professional and non-judgmental. The needs of the patient/family must always be considered, and this may mean utilizing a translator to ensure that the patient/family are assuming an active role in the plan of care or making referrals to others in the healthcare or allied professions.

SEXUAL BOUNDARIES

When the **boundary** between the role of the NP and the vulnerability of the patient is breached, a **boundary violation** occurs. Because the NP is in the position of "authority," the responsibility to maintain the boundary rests with the NP; however, the line separating them is a continuum and sometimes not easily defined. It is inappropriate for NPs to engage in **sexual relations with patients**, and if the sexual behavior is coerced or the patient cognitively impaired, it is illegal. However, more common violations with older adults or mentally incompetent adults include exposing a patient unnecessarily, using sexually demeaning gestures or language (including off-color jokes), harassment, or inappropriate touching. Touching should be used with care, such as touching a hand or shoulder. Hugging may be misconstrued.

GIFTS

Over time, patients may develop a bond with NPs they trust and may feel grateful to the NP for the care provided and want to express thanks, but the NP must make sure to maintain **professional boundaries.** Patients often offer gifts to NPs to show their appreciation, but older adults, especially those who are weak and ill or have cognitive impairment, may be taken advantage of easily. Patients may offer valuables and may sometimes be easily manipulated into giving large sums of money. Small tokens of appreciation that can be shared with other staff, such as a box of chocolates, are usually acceptable (depending upon the policy of the institution), but almost any other gifts (jewelry, money, clothes) should be declined: "I'm sorry, that's so kind of you, but NPs are not allowed to accept gifts from patients." Declining may relieve the patient of the feeling of obligation.

ATTENTION

Nursing is a giving profession, but the NP must temper giving with recognition of **professional boundaries.** Patients have many needs; and, as acts of kindness, NPs, especially those involved in home care, often give them extra **attention**, may offer to do favors such as cooking or shopping, and may become overly invested in the patients' lives. While this may benefit a patient in the short term, it can establish a relationship of increasing **dependency and obligation** that does not resolve the long-term needs of the patient. Making referrals to the appropriate agencies or collaborating with family to find ways to provide services is more effective. Becoming overly invested may be evident by the NP showing favoritism or spending too much time with the patient while neglecting other duties. On the other end of the spectrum are NPs who are disinterested and fail to provide adequate attention to the patient's detriment. Lack of adequate attention may lead to outright neglect.

COERCION

Power issues are inherent in matters associated with **professional boundaries.** Physical abuse is both unprofessional and illegal, but behavior can easily border on abusive without the patient being physically injured. NPs can easily **intimidate** patients into having procedures or treatments they don't want. Regardless of age, patients have the right to choose and the right to refuse treatment. Difficulties arise with cognitive impairment, and in that case, another responsible adult (often a child, parent, or spouse) is designated to make decisions, but every effort should be made to gain patient cooperation. Forcing the patient to do something against his/her will borders on abuse and can sometimes degenerate into actual abuse if **physical coercion** is involved.

PERSONAL INFORMATION

When pre-existing personal or business relationships exist, other NPs should be assigned care of the patient whenever possible, but this may be difficult in small communities. However, the practitioner should strive to maintain a professional role separate from the personal role and respect **professional boundaries**. The NP must respect and maintain the confidentiality of the patient and family members, but must also be very careful about disclosing **personal information** about himself/herself because this establishes a social relationship that interferes with the professional role of the NP and the boundary between the patient and the NP. The NP and patient should never share "secrets." When the NP divulges personal information, he/she may become vulnerable to the patient, resulting in a reversal of roles.

Ethical and Legal Principles

Patient's Bill of Rights

PATIENTS' RIGHTS

Patients' (families') rights in relation to what they should expect from a healthcare organization are outlined in both standards of the Joint Commission and National Committee for Quality Assurance. Rights include:

- Respect for patient, including personal dignity and psychosocial, spiritual, and cultural considerations.
- Response to needs related to access and pain control.
- Ability to make decisions about care, including informed consent, advance directives, and end-of-life care.
- Procedure for registering complaints or grievances.
- Protection of confidentiality and privacy.
- Freedom from abuse or neglect.
- Protection during research and information related to ethical issues of research.
- Appraisal of outcomes, including unexpected outcomes.
- Information about organization, services, and practitioners.
- Appeal procedures for decisions regarding benefits and quality of care.
- Organizational code of ethical behavior.
- Procedures for donating and procuring organs/tissue.

PATIENT RIGHTS IN PSYCHIATRIC CARE

A right is a fair claim that is due to an individual, established by policies or laws. Important **patient rights in psychiatric care** include:

- **Right to privacy**: No information will be shared with unauthorized people about the patient. Exceptions include:
  - Presence of suspected child abuse.
  - Credible patient threats of physical harm to another. The potential victim must be alerted (per "Tarasoff" regulations).
  - During guardianship or involuntary commitment hearings.
- **Right to treatment**: Patients cannot be held against their will without an individualized treatment plan.
- Right to treatment in a **least restrictive setting**. Examples include:
  - Patients who pose no danger to themselves or others cannot be involuntarily hospitalized.
  - Patients who can function in an open ward cannot be held in a locked ward.
  - Clients who can live in the community and who have a support system must be treated in an outpatient setting.
  - Seclusion and restraint can only be utilized when it is in the patient's overriding best interest.

ADDITIONAL CRUCIAL PATIENT RIGHTS

Crucial **psychiatric patient rights** include:

- The right to **informed consent:** A patient is to be made aware of any procedure to be performed and must give permission on his or her own accord. Only court-ordered commitment procedures give hospitals the right to involuntarily treat patients.
- The right to **refuse treatment:** Patients may not be forcefully medicated; however, legal guardians can give permission if a court order is obtained. Patients may be forcibly medicated if they could possibly cause harm to self or others.
- The right to **habeas corpus:** Committed patients must be brought before a judge or court and must be released if insufficient reasons for confinement exist.
- The right to **independent psychiatric examination:** Patients may demand an evaluation by a mental health specialist of their choice and must be released if it is determined that they are not mentally ill.

INFORMED CONSENT

Patients or family must provide **informed consent** for all treatment the patient receives. This consent includes a thorough explanation of all procedures and treatment and associated risks. Patients/family should be apprised of all options and allowed input on the type of treatments. Patients/family should be apprised of all reasonable risks and any complications that might be life threatening or increase morbidity. The American Medical Association has established **guidelines** for informed consent:

- Explanation of diagnosis.
- Nature and reason for treatment or procedure.
- Risks and benefits.
- Alternative options (regardless of cost or insurance coverage).
- Risks and benefits of alternative options.
- Risks and benefits of not having a treatment or procedure.
- Providing informed consent is a requirement of all states.

ADVANCE DIRECTIVES, DNR, AND DURABLE POWER OF ATTORNEY

In accordance to Federal and state laws, individuals have the right to self-determination in health care, including decisions about end-of-life care through **advance directives** such as living wills and the right to assign a surrogate person to make decisions through a **durable power of attorney**. Patients should routinely be questioned about an advanced directive as they may present at a healthcare organization without the document. Patients who have indicated they desire a **do-not-resuscitate (DNR) order** should not receive resuscitative treatments for terminal illness or conditions in which meaningful recovery cannot occur. Patients and families of those with terminal illnesses should be questioned as to whether the patients are Hospice patients. For those with DNR requests or those withdrawing life support, staff should provide the patient palliative rather than curative measures, such as pain control and/or oxygen, and emotional support to the patient and family. Religious traditions and beliefs about death should be treated with respect.

NEGLIGENCE

Risk management must attempt to determine the burden of proof for acts of **negligence**, including compliance with duty, breaches in procedures, degree of harm, and cause. Negligence indicates that proper care has not been provided, based on established standards. Reasonable care uses rationale for decision-making in relation to providing care. State regulations regarding negligence may vary but all have some statutes of limitation. There are a number of different types of negligence:

- **Negligent conduct** indicates that an individual failed to provide reasonable care or to protect/assist another, based on standards and expertise.
- **Gross negligence** is willfully providing inadequate care while disregarding the safety and security of another.
- **Contributory negligence** involves the injured party contributing to his/her own harm.
- **Comparative negligence** attempts to determine what percentage amount of negligence is attributed to each individual involved.

INVOLUNTARY COMMITMENT OF PEDIATRIC PSYCHIATRIC PATIENTS

Involuntary commitment of pediatric psychiatric patients occurs in some instances. Assent is a productive and helpful aspect of treating pediatric patients. However, if the child does not assent, parents and guardians may still consent to therapy. **Involuntary mental holds** for 72 hours are sufficient to commence therapy. The legal premise behind these regulations is that parents act in good faith to ensure the wellbeing of their children. The legal guardian and healthcare provider are acting in place of the parents (*in loco parentis*). In most cases, the triage team on inpatient units has the option of deciding whether or not a patient should be admitted for evaluation or as protection for the patient's safety. For example, a teenager who attempts suicide may be placed on a 72-hour hold. Those healthcare professionals responsible for triage and treatment in the first 72 hours must act in the best interest of the patient and not under the influence of financial gain or parental desire.

Confidentiality

HIPAA

In 1996, Congress passed the **Health Insurance Portability and Accountability Act** (HIPAA), which includes a number of provisions that aim to improve the portability of health information records. The Department of Health and Human Services was charged with establishing national **healthcare standards** for storage and transfer of electronic healthcare information to improve the exchange of information from 1 insurance company/physician to another. In the past, a patient's complete record would be stored and others could access these records easily. Strides are being made toward improving the privacy of the patient, however standardization has not yet occurred and different electronic storage systems are often incompatible. HIPAA requires that healthcare providers use a National Provider Identifier (NPI), which is a 10-digit number. HIPAA includes strong provisions to protect the privacy of the individual in order to prevent abuse and misuse of records.

PRIVACY AND PHI

The Health Insurance Portability and Accountability Act (HIPAA) addresses the rights of the individual related to **privacy** of health information. The NP must not release any information or documentation about a patient's condition or treatment without **consent**, as the individual has the right to determine who has access to personal information. Personal information about the patient is considered **protected health information (PHI)**, and consists of any identifying or personal information about the patient, such as health history, condition, or treatments in any form and any documentation, including electronic, verbal, or written. Personal information can be shared with spouse, legal guardians, those with durable power of attorney for the patient, and those involved in care of the patient (i.e., physicians) without a specific release, but the patient should always be consulted if personal information is to be discussed with others present to ensure there is no objection. Failure to comply with HIPAA regulations can make an NP liable for legal action.

CONFIDENTIALITY

Confidentiality is the obligation that is present in a professional-patient relationship. NPs are under an obligation to protect the information they possess concerning the patient and family. Care should be taken to safeguard that information and provide the **privacy** that the patient deserves. This is accomplished through the use of required passwords when the family calls for information about the patient and through the limitation of who is allowed to visit. The NP should not assume that family members can be apprised of an older adult's health information without that person's consent. There may be times when confidentiality must be broken to save the life of a patient, but those circumstances are rare. The NP must make all efforts to safeguard patient records and identification. Computerized record keeping should be done in such a way that the screen is not visible to others, and paper records must be secured.

> **Review Video: Confidentiality**
> Visit mometrix.com/academy and enter code: 250384

NEED-TO-KNOW INFORMATION

Patients have a right to expect that when they divulge personal information to an NP that only those with a **need to know** will be provided this information. When NPs must document care, they must be sensitive to the information that they put into the written record or report because many people have access to these records. If the information is health-related, then the practitioner is obligated to record this and should tell the patient. Need-to-know issues also relate to the patient's need to know about care and prognosis. Patients may be overwhelmed by information or they may be cognitively impaired or confused. Older adults and families should be asked how much information they want. Some patients/families want to know all of the details, including treatment options and expected outcomes. Others want only the basic information or don't want to discuss health issues at all.

COMPUTER SYSTEM STANDARDS

The Joint Commission has described the need for **computer system standards** in the following areas:

- Access to databases that are located outside the organization and used to compare information, need to be supported and secured.
- Patient confidentiality related to personal health information (PHI) and data security must be ensured.
- Knowledge-based systems should be developed and promoted to allow resident organizational expertise to be used throughout the organization.
- A means to link physician information systems while protecting patient privacy and data security.
- Projects that are designed to achieve quality improvements should be supported.
- Data integrity and overall system security must be ensured.
- Procedural controls that are currently in place for documentation should be integrated into the new computerized standards.
- A regular assessment of needs and system capacity for growth should be supported.

IMPORTANT FACTORS FOR INFORMATION SYSTEMS IN THE ACCREDITATION PROCESS

The Joint Commission outlined factors it believes are important for **information standards**:

- Measures must be adopted that are designed to **protect** an individual's personal health information. This may be accomplished by limiting access to information based on a user's need to know, having strict policies regarding the removal of records, and making sure data is physically and electronically safeguarded.
- A national **standard for data entry** should be created and followed. All users should be trained both in system use and information management. Educational courses may include lectures on how information that is entered into a computer system is transformed into data that can later be used to perform statistical analysis and support decision-making.
- All information should be available both on the **computer** and in **print** form.

ELECTRONIC MEDICAL RECORDS AND ELECTRONIC HEALTH RECORDS

Although many in healthcare use the terms electronic medical record (EMR) and electronic health record (EHR) interchangeably, there are major distinctions between the two. The **electronic medical record** is created by a hospital or other health care delivery organization (CDO). The CDO owns the information in the EMR. The EMR consists of clinical documentation, orders, medications, treatments, and other clinical decision support, and is a legal record. The **EHR** includes information from EMRs, likely from multiple health care delivery organizations. The EHR relies on the information from the EMR to complete it. The EHR is owned by the patient and stakeholders, which could include the government, insurance companies, and healthcare providers among others. Important to the EMR is using controlled medical vocabulary so that information will be comparable among providers and other interested stakeholders. Currently in the United States the use of EHRs is limited, mostly due to many healthcare delivery organizations not having an established EMR using decided predetermined standards. There may soon be an increase in the number of organizations using EMRs with standardized language conducive to EHRs, as

170

organizations now receive financial incentives to install EMR and EHR systems from health care reform.

The Healthcare Information and Management Systems Society (HIMSS) define the electronic health record (EHR) as a "secure, real-time, point-of-care, patient-centric information resource for clinicians."

HIMSS has also published a series of guidelines for EHR known as the **HIMSS Electronic Health Record Definitional Model**. According to the model, the EHR should record and manage information for both the short- and long-term. The EHR should be the healthcare professional's main resource when taking care of patients. Evidence-based care can be planned using the EHR on both the individual and community level. Another important job of the EHR is its use in continuous quality improvement, performance management, risk management, utilization review, and resource planning. The EHR aids in the billing process as well. Finally, the EHR is a boon to evidence-based research, clinical research, and public health reporting. Since it is computerized, clinicians are assured that the EHR information is up to date and relevant for patients and research protocols.

DUTY TO WARN

While the law is very clear on issues related to privacy and confidentiality, there are some exceptions related to a **duty to warn** if the patient poses a danger. Under law, the mental healthcare provider must breach confidentiality if the patient poses a serious risk to him/herself or others. This regulation resulted from a court ruling, *Tarasoff v Regents of the University of California* (1976), in which the court ruled that the university therapists were negligent when they did not report that a patient was obsessed with Tatiana Tarasoff. When the patient subsequently attacked and killed Tarasoff, her family filed suit against the university and those involved. This issue is somewhat of a gray area, as vague or general statements may not constitute actual threats. The mental healthcare provider must exercise "reasonable" care and report any direct threats to potential victims and indications of suicidal ideation to family/caregivers/authorities.

ANA Scope and Standards of Practice

LEADERSHIP STYLES

Leadership styles often influence the perception of leadership values and commitment to collaboration. There are a number of different leadership styles:

- **Charismatic:** Depends upon personal charisma to influence people, and may be very persuasive, but this type leader may engage "followers" and relate to one group rather than the organization at large, limiting effectiveness.
- **Bureaucratic:** Follows organization rules exactly and expects everyone else to do so. This is most effective in handling cash flow or managing work in dangerous work environments. This type of leadership may engender respect but may not be conducive to change.
- **Autocratic:** Makes decisions independently and strictly enforces rules, but team members often feel left out of process and may not be supportive. This type of leadership is most effective in crisis situations, but may have difficulty gaining commitment of staff.
- **Consultative:** Presents a decision and welcomes input and questions although decisions rarely change. This type of leadership is most effective when gaining the support of staff is critical to the success of proposed changes.
- **Participatory**: Presents a potential decision and then makes final decision based on input from staff or teams. This type of leadership is time-consuming and may result in compromises that are not wholly satisfactory to management or staff, but this process is motivating to staff who feel their expertise is valued.
- **Democratic**: Presents a problem and asks staff or teams to arrive at a solution although the leader usually makes the final decision. This type of leadership may delay decision-making, but staff and teams are often more committed to the solutions because of their input.
- **Laissez-faire (free rein)**: Exerts little direct control but allows employees/ teams to make decisions with little interference. This may be effective leadership if teams are highly skilled and motivated, but in many cases, this type of leadership is the product of poor management skills and little is accomplished because of this lack of leadership.

NETWORKING

Networking is the act of meeting others in order to make mutually beneficial connections. The NP should attend local, state, and national **conferences**. Conferences offer the opportunity to network, build skills, and refresh an organization's style. An essential aspect of business is networking. Effective networking involves speaking with others and learning about their services and ideas. Sharing contact information is a must when networking. Conferences also offer NPs the opportunity to learn new skills and approaches to various situations, and to comply with national standards. Conferences offer NPs opportunities for personal professional development, so that he/she will be more knowledgeable. Conferences also allow the NP an opportunity to gain recognition for his/her research and/or the institution he/she represents.

COMMUNICATION SKILLS FOR LEADING INTRA- AND INTERDISCIPLINARY TEAMS

A number of **communication skills** are needed to lead and facilitate coordination of **intra-** and **interdisciplinary teams**, such as the following:

- Communicating **openly** is essential with all members encouraged to participate as valued members of a cooperative team.
- Avoiding **interrupting or interpreting** the point another is trying to make allows free flow of ideas.
- Avoiding **jumping to conclusions** as this can effectively shut off communication.

- Active listening requires **paying attention** and **asking questions** for clarification rather than challenging the ideas of others.
- **Respecting** the opinions and ideas of others, even when they are opposed to one's own, is absolutely essential.
- Reacting and responding to **facts** rather than feelings allows one to avoid angry confrontations or diffuse anger.
- **Clarifying** information or opinions stated can help avoid misunderstandings.
- Keeping **unsolicited advice** out of the conversation shows respect for others and allows them to solicit advice without feeling pressured.

PROMOTING COLLABORATION

Promoting collaboration and assisting others to understand and use resources and expertise of others requires a commitment in terms of time and effort. Examples of promoting collaboration include:

- Coaching others on methods of collaboration can include providing information in the form of **handouts** about effective communication strategies and, in turn, **modeling** this type of communication with the staff being coached.
- **Team meetings** are commonly held on nursing units and provide an opportunity to model collaboration and suggest the need for outside expertise to help with planning patient care plans. The mentoring NP can initiate discussions about resources that are available in the facility or the community.
- Selecting a **diverse group** for teams or inviting those with expertise in various areas to join the team when needed can help team members to appreciate and understand how to use the input of other resources.

INTERDISCIPLINARY COLLABORATION

Interdisciplinary collaboration is absolutely critical to practice if the needs and best interests of the patients and families are central. Interdisciplinary practice begins with NPs and physicians but extends to pharmacists, social workers, occupational and physical therapists, nutritionists, and a wide range of allied healthcare providers, all of whom cooperate in diagnosis and treatment; however, state regulations determine to some degree how much autonomy an NP can have in diagnosing and treating. While NPs have increasingly gained more legal rights, they have also become more dependent upon collaboration with others for their expertise and for referrals if the patient's needs extend beyond the NP's ability to provide assistance. Additionally, the prescriptive ability of NPs varies from state to state, with some requiring direct supervision by other disciplines (such as physicians), while others require particular types of supervisory arrangements, depending upon the circumstances.

INTRA- AND INTERDISCIPLINARY TEAMS

The complexity of patient care requires collaboration among **intra- and interdisciplinary teams**. Collaboration may begin between the NP and patient, but often the expertise of others in the healthcare community must be included. Often the NP is in the position to seek collaboration and to recognize when multiple perspectives can be helpful in solving conflicts or making decisions about health care. Collaboration requires open sharing of ideas and respect for the expertise of the individual. Collaboration requires more than just talking, however. In many cases it may be more formalized, with specialized committees formed in order to solve specific problems. Studies have indicated that patients benefit from collaborative efforts between NP and physician, and this benefit extends to others as well. In a collaborative environment, all of the participants benefit from sharing ideas and discussion that can lead to innovative problem solving.

173

Synergy Model of Collaboration

The **Synergy model of collaboration** is a team approach of working with a variety of others (physicians, NPs, dietitians, therapist, families, social workers, community leaders and members, clergy, intra- and interdisciplinary teams) in a cooperative manner, using good therapeutic communication skills, to ensure that each person is contributing optimally toward reaching patient goals and positive outcomes. Collaboration requires mutual respect, professional maturity, common purpose, and a positive sense of self. Levels of collaboration include:

- **Level 1**: This nurse participates in collaborative activities, learns from others (including mentors), and respects the input of others.
- **Level 3**: This nurse not only participates in collaborative activities but also initiates them and actively seeks learning opportunities.
- **Level 5**: This nurse takes a leadership role in collaborative activities by mentoring and teaching others while still seeking learning opportunities and actively seeks additional resources as needed.

Collaboration with External Agencies

The NP must initiate and facilitate **collaboration with external agencies** because many have direct impacts on patient care and needs:

- **Industry** can include other facilities sharing interests in patient care or pharmaceutical companies. It's important for nursing to have a dialog with drug companies about their products and how they are used in specific populations because many medications are prescribed to women, children, or the aged without validating studies for dose or efficacy.
- **Payors** have a vested interest in containing health care costs, so providing information and representing the interests of the patient is important.
- **Community groups** may provide resources for patients and families, both in terms of information and financial or other assistance.
- **Political agencies** are increasingly important as new laws are considered about NP-patient ratios and infection control in many states.
- **Public health agencies** are partners in health care with other facilities and must be included, especially in issues related to communicable disease.

Conflict Resolution

Conflict is an almost inevitable product of collaboration with the patient, and the NP must assume responsibility for **conflict resolution.** While conflicts can be disruptive, they can produce positive outcomes by forcing people to listen to different perspectives and opening dialogue. The NP should make a plan for dealing with conflict resolution. The best time for conflict resolution is when differences emerge but before open conflict and hardening of positions occur. The NP must pay close attention to the people and problems involved, listen carefully, and reassure those involved that their points of view are understood. Steps to conflict resolution include:

- Allow both sides to present their side of conflict without bias, maintaining a focus on opinions rather than individuals.
- Encourage cooperation through negotiation and compromise.
- Maintain the focus, providing guidance to keep the discussions on track, and avoid arguments.
- Evaluate the need for renegotiation, formal resolution process, or third party.

- Utilize humor and empathy to diffuse escalating tensions.
- Summarize the issues, outlining key arguments.
- Avoid forcing resolution if possible.

STANDARDS OF ADVANCE PRACTICE

The nurse practitioner (NP) must practice within the **standards of advance practice** and the individual's scope of practice, which is directly related to the individual's educational preparation and certification. An NP must have 2 types of licenses/certificates: a registered nurse (RN) license and an advanced practice certificate. Advance practice nurses are those who have completed additional education in an **accredited nursing program** (usually at a Master's level) and have received certification with a **national certifying organization**, such as the American Nurse's Credentialing Center. The NP must function legally under the Nurse Practice Act of the state in which the person resides. In some cases, an NP license/certification in 1 state is automatically recognized in other states through the Compact agreement, but advance practice nurses are often excluded from these agreements. Educational experience and scope of practice must relate to patient population in terms of age, disease, diagnosis, and treatment.

ADVANCED PRACTICE REGISTERED NURSING

Advanced practice registered nursing (APRN) – According to the NCSBN, it is acting as a nurse with a foundation on information and proficiency that was obtained in basic nursing school. This nurse has a license to be an RN and has completed and received a diploma from graduate school in an APRN program that has been accredited from a nationwide accrediting body. This nurse has up-to-date certification from a nationwide certification board to work in the proper APRN area. Being an APRN defines the nurse as someone that has more **responsibility**, which may or may not come with more pay or gain for the nurse.

Some responsibilities include:

- Give professional education and leadership.
- Handle patient and medical center leadership.
- Support the patient and local area by keeping the ideal concerns for the patient or community.
- Assess reactions of involvement and how well medical routines are working.
- Be in touch with and act together with patients, patient relatives, and colleagues.
- Employ research; get and use new information and equipment.
- Educate others regarding APRN.

CARE PROCESS, ESTABLISHING PRIORITIES, AND COLLABORATION

The nurse practitioner (NP) is guided by the **standards of advance practice**, which provide the framework for practice and describes the NP's responsibilities, related to the values and priorities of the profession:

- **Care process:** In assessing, diagnosing, developing, and implementing a plan of care, as well as evaluating the patient's response, the NP must use scientific method and national standards as the basis for care.
- **Establishing priorities:** Providing education and encouraging the patient/family to take an active role in self-care is of primary concern. The NP must ensure that the patient can make informed decisions. The NP must assist the patient through all aspects of health care to ensure patient safety and optimal care.

- **Collaboration**: The NP is a member of the interdisciplinary health team and consults with others when appropriate and refers the patient to specialists as needed. When collaboration is mandated by law, the NP complies with all requirements.

DOCUMENTATION, PATIENT ADVOCACY, CONTINUOUS QUALITY IMPROVEMENT, RESEARCH, AND EDUCATION

The specific responsibilities involved in **standards of advance practice** include:

- **Documentation**: The nurse practitioner (NP) keeps accurate, legal, and legible records and also maintains patient confidentiality. The NP ensures that the patient signs a release before providing medical records to other parties.
- **Patient advocacy:** The NP advocates for the individual patient in the process of care but also advocates for patients at the state and national level in order to facilitate patient access to care and improve the quality of care.
- **Continuous quality improvement:** The NP recognizes the need for constant learning, evaluation, and reevaluation and participates in quality review, continuing education while maintaining certification, and utilizing clinical guidelines and standards of care.
- **Research and education:** The NP initiates, participates in, and utilizes the results of research in clinical practice.

SCOPE OF PRACTICE FOR APRN AND NURSING PRACTICE ACTS

Scope for the APRN – It is dependent on each state and what the APRN in this position can do beneath the Nurse Practice Act for that state. The scope gives guidelines instead of particular directives. There is a big range, depending on the state. Many times, the scope is founded on what is allowed legally both in the state and in the nation. The initial **Scope of Practice for PNPs** occurred in 1983 by the National Association of Pediatric Nurse Practitioners. This has been updated in 1990 and in 2000. Scope is always changing and improving.

Nursing practice acts – See the NCSBN Web site to find the complete list of **state practice acts** (not for every state, but 31 states are included): http://www.ncsbn.org. An authorizing board of nursing is available in every state to lead statutes with regard to licenses for an RN. They have responsibility for how titles are used, scope of work, and how to handle discipline cases. Nurse practice acts come out of statutory law.

NP PRIVILEGES

Depending upon the state's nurse practice act, **nurse practitioner (NP) privileges** vary:

- NPs may be able to practice **independently** or in **collaboration/agreement** with a physician, podiatrist, or chiropractor. The type of physician oversight and collaboration required varies considerably. Only 12 states have no collaboration requirement.
- NPs can be **reimbursed** by Medicare, Medicaid, The Civilian Health and Medical Program of the Uniformed Services (CHAMPUS), and private insurance. Currently, governmental reimbursement for NPs is at the rate of 85% of the customary physician reimbursement. However, a billing rate of 100% is allowed with "incident to" billing that allows the physician to charge for services that are incident to practice as though he/she performed the service.
- **Prescriptive authority** varies from state to state. Many states require physician oversight for all or some prescriptions. There are often limits to the types of treatments/drugs that can be prescribed. Only 11 states and Washington, D.C. allow NPs to be completely independent in prescribing medication.

PRESCRIPTION MEDICATION AND DIAGNOSTIC TESTS

Both **prescribing** medications and treatment and ordering **diagnostic** tests are within the scope of practice of NPs but, as with other aspects of practice, each state establishes how that will be carried out. Additionally, insurance reimbursement varies from 1 area to another and must be considered.

- **Prescription**: Terminology varies from state to state with NPs allowed to "furnish" or "prescribe" some types of medications. In some states they may do so independently; in others, they must be "supervised" by a physician under whose auspices they provide care to patients. The NP should maintain a list of medications and consider cost-effectiveness when ordering medications.
- **Diagnostics**: NPs can order laboratory, electrocardiogram, and radiographic tests for routine screening and health assessment as well as make a diagnosis based on assessment. There are limitations, depending upon the individual state nursing practice act.

CONSULTATION, REFERRAL, AND COORDINATION

As part of the **scope of practice**, the NP is able to provide and augment primary care to patients/families through a number of different services:

- **Consultation services** may include a variety of services, such as assessment of growth, development, and risk factors; providing interventions, (i.e., diet and exercise programs); and educating patients/families.
- **Referral services** include referring patients to physicians, such as specialists, and to organizations or agencies, such as drug rehabilitation programs.
- **Coordination services**, with the NP maintaining contact and receiving reports from referrals in order to provide an integrated plan of care, serves as a valuable service to patients/families, who often must deal with many different healthcare providers who have little or no contact with each other. This type of service can prevent unnecessary duplications of service but also ensure that findings are not overlooked.

DELEGATION OF TASKS TO UNLICENSED ASSISTIVE PERSONNEL

The scope of nursing practice includes **delegation of tasks** to unlicensed assistive personnel, providing those personnel have adequate training and knowledge to carry out the tasks. Delegation should be used to manage the workload and to provide adequate and safe care. The NP who delegates remains accountable for patient outcomes and for supervision of the person to whom the task was delegated, so the NP must consider the following:

- Whether knowledge, skills, and training of the unlicensed assistive personnel provides the ability to perform the delegated task.
- Whether the patient's condition and needs have been properly evaluated and assessed.
- Whether the NP is able to provide ongoing supervision.

Delegation should be done in a manner that **reduces liability** by providing adequate communication. This includes specific directions about the task, including what needs to be done, when, and for how long. Expectations related to consultation, reporting, and completion of tasks should be clearly defined. The NP should be available to assist if necessary.

ROLE OF THE PMHNP

The **role** of the psychiatric and mental health NP (PMHNP) can be quite varied depending on the setting and job description but can include providing direct care and treatment; consulting; educating patients, families, and staff members; supervising; administering, carrying out independent practice, and conducting research. The PHMNP may also be actively engaged in needs identification and planning, implementing, and evaluating change. The PMHNP is often the primary advocate for the patient and, as such, must often work to ensure that all patients have access to needed treatment. The PHMNP works collaboratively with other members of the healthcare team. As an advocate for the role of the PMHNP, the NP serves as a role model for the profession by upholding the highest standards and sharing expertise with other healthcare providers. The PHMNP should be actively engaged in political efforts to expand the scope of practice of the PHMNP and should address the organization and community groups about the role of the PHMNP.

APRN CREDENTIALS

Credentials for APRN:

- Make sure there is answerability and conscientiousness for proficient work.
- Authenticates that the practitioner has received the correct instruction, has a license, and is certified.
- Compulsory to make sure that the local and national laws are followed. Recognizes the furthered scope for the APRN.
- Allows for needed ways for patients to make a grievance.
- Allows for responsibility for the community by making sure standards of practice are met.
- Debates between the State boards of Nursing and different education accrediting organizations were more heated in the 1990s due to more NP programs coming available.
- National task force with regard to the excellence of NP schools met in 1995. Many organizations were present.
- The government does not have a hand in credentialing.
- Credentials may be obtained through an AACN-acknowledged certifying body.

CONTRACT FOR SERVICES

A NP working as an independent contractor may sign a **contract for services**, a legal financial agreement that outlines the conditions of service. Typically, a contract includes:

- The name of the NP and the client, outlining the qualifications, appropriate licensure, and/or certification.
- Purpose of the service agreement.
- Contract period, including beginning date and ending date of the contract.
- Compensation, including daily, weekly, or hourly rate of payment.
- Expenses, such as travel pay or money for office support, equipment, or training and methods of submitting invoices.
- Performance description outlining the type of services that the independent contractor will perform, including any limitations and legal responsibilities.
- Disclaimers.

CONSULTANT

The mental health professional often serves as a **consultant** to others, especially during discharge planning, to ensure that patients receive the continued care and services that they need. The NP may serve as an **educational consultant**, providing general information about the needs of those with psychiatric or mental health issues, or may specifically deal with the needs of a particular patient, in which case the NP must be sure that proper release forms have been signed and issues of privacy are respected. Areas of consultation include:

- **Schools**: The school nurse or educators may require information on dealing with behavioral or treatment issues.
- **Housing**: If a patient is placed in housing such as board-and-care homes or supervised apartments, authorities need to understand the patient's condition and needs.
- **Social Services**: The NP may provide consultation services to social workers. If a child is placed in foster care, the foster parents should be provided information necessary to provide care and support to the child.

QUALITY IMPROVEMENT

Quality improvement (QI) – Accomplished through peer review or another form of assessment. In **peer review**, the approach is to acknowledge and prize the work NPs do. This shows the way toward better standards of work and puts off work that is not within what the practitioner can legally do. It heightens the quality of medical attention and gives a means for attaining answerability and conscientiousness. Another form of **assessment** may include an audit, question/answer or appraisal, or patient contentment question/answer or appraisal.

Risk management – Organizations and actions meant to acknowledge and intercede resulting in less chance of harm to a patient and ensuing claims in opposition to the medical attention workers. This is founded on the supposition that a lot of harm done to patients could be stopped from happening in the first place. Risk management is an assessment of places when legal responsibility is an issue, like patients, methods, or how accounts are maintained. Risk management also involves instruction used to lessen the chance of a problem in a recognized part.

CONTINUOUS QUALITY IMPROVEMENT

Continuous Quality Improvement (CQI) emphasizes the organization and systems and processes within that organization rather than individuals. It recognizes **internal customers** (staff) and **external customers** (patients) and utilizes data to improve processes. CQI represents the concept that most processes can be improved. CQI uses the scientific method of experimentation to meet needs and improve services and utilizes various tools, such as brainstorming, multivoting, various charts and diagrams, storyboarding, and meetings. **Core concepts** include:

- Quality and success, defined as meeting or exceeding internal and external customer's needs and expectations.
- Problems relate to processes, and variations in process lead to variations in results.
- Change can be in small steps.

Steps to CQI include:

- Forming a knowledgeable team.
- Identifying and defining measures used to determine success.
- Brainstorming strategies for change.
- Plan, collect, and utilize data as part of making decisions.
- Test changes and revise or refine as needed.

INTEGRATION OF KEY QUALITY CONCEPTS WITHIN THE ORGANIZATION

There are a number of **key concepts** related to quality that must be communicated to all members of an organization through inservice, workshops, newsletters, fact sheets, and team meetings. Quality care/performance should be:

- **Appropriate** to needs and in keeping with best practices.
- **Accessible** to the individual despite financial, cultural, or other barriers.
- **Competent**, with practitioners well-trained and adhering to standards.
- **Coordinated** among all healthcare providers.
- **Effective** in achieving outcomes based on the current state of knowledge.
- **Efficient** in methods of achieving the desired outcomes.
- **Preventive**, allowing for early detection and prevention of problems.
- **Respectful and caring** with consideration of the individual needs given primary importance.
- **Safe** so that the organization is free of hazards or dangers that may put patients or others at risk.

JOINT COMMISSION AND LINES OF AUTHORITY AND ACCOUNTABILITY

The **Joint Commission** has established **leadership standards** that apply to healthcare organizations and help to establish management's lines of authority and accountability. Under these standards, leadership comprises the governing body, the CEO and senior managers, department leaders, leaders (both elected and appointed) of staff or departments, and the nurse executive and other nurse leaders. The governing body is ultimately responsible for all patient care rendered by all types of practitioners (physicians, NPs, laboratory staff, support staff, etc.) within and under the jurisdiction of the organization, so this governing body must clearly outline the line of authority and accountability for others in management positions. At each level of management, performance standards and performance measurements should be established so that accountability becomes transparent based on data that can be used to drive changes when needed and to bring about improved outcomes.

ACCREDITATION

Accreditation is a primary requirement for organization because it establishes that the organization is committed to standards based on evaluation. General accreditation is usually done by the following:

- The **Joint Commission** accredits more than 20,000 healthcare programs, both nationally and internationally, and is the primary accrediting agency in the United States, so accreditation by the Joint Commission indicates a commitment to improving care and provides information about compliance with core measures.
- The **Healthcare Facilities Accreditation Program of the American Osteopathic Association** also accredits many healthcare programs, including acute care, ambulatory care, rehabilitation and substance abuse centers, behavioral care centers, and critical access hospitals, and also provides guidelines for patient safety initiatives as well as reports of common deficiencies.

A healthcare organization may also seek to become accredited by agencies with a narrower focus to demonstrate excellence in that area, such as the Intersocietal Commission for the Accreditation of Echocardiography Laboratories (ICAEL). Leadership and staff must determine what type of accreditation is most appropriate based on the programs offered and the commitment to improving standards.

CONSUMER-FOCUSED HEALTH CARE

Consumer-focused health care recognizes that the needs of the patient are central to delivery of care and that provision of care should try to match the expectations of the patient. With the Internet, patients have easy access to much more medical information than previously, and as patients become better informed, they expect a greater role in their own healthcare decisions and better-quality care at lower prices. A primary component of consumer-focused health care is evaluating customer satisfaction and utilizing continuous quality improvement methods to improve service. The needs of the patient are viewed holistically, so that all healthcare needs are met, ranging from housing to medical treatment. The NP must be an advocate for the patient, assessing patients' expectations and implementing changes to assure that the needs are met. Because patients often fail to express their dissatisfaction directly to healthcare providers, the NP should ask patients directly if they have concerns.

POLITICAL ISSUES FACING PSYCHIATRIC AND MENTAL HEALTH NPS

Psychiatric and mental health NPs face a number of **political issues**:

- **Scope of practice**: This is the primary concern because of differences from state to state with some states allowing independent practice while others allow delegated practice (under supervision of a physician) and some others do not differentiate between RNs and APNs. Resistance from physicians to increasing the role and responsibilities of psychiatric NPs is a major roadblock.
- **Licensure portability**: The Nurse Licensure Compact allows licensure portability across 25 states for RNs, but APNs have not been covered. However, in 2015, the National Council of State Boards of Nursing approved an APRN Compact model, but it has not yet been widely adopted.
- **Healthy, safe work environment**: Safety issues, such as NP-patient ratios, work schedules, and security provisions continue to be a concern with only the state of California having established prescribed NP-patient ratios and with little consistency in safety provisions.

ANA SOCIAL POLICY STATEMENT

The **American Nurses Association (ANA) Social Policy Statement** was originally written in 1980, revised in 1995, and again in 2003. The ANA Social Policy Statement provides a description and definition of nursing practice and outlines the knowledge base required for nursing and requirements and scope of practice for advance practice nurses, such as the NP. The ANA Social Policy Statement recognizes the **social contract** that exists between nursing and society and the responsibilities that entails. Nursing requires a **holistic approach** rather than a problem-focused approach to care, integrating objective data and knowledge and utilizing the scientific method. The ANA Social Policy Statement also describes regulation of nursing, including self-regulation, professional, and legal, centering on the code of ethics, and meeting of certification requirements. NPs are accountable for their actions under the law but also must assume personal responsibility for maintaining their knowledge base.

APNA AND ISPN

National and international organizations are available for psychiatric and mental health NPs. Many of these organizations have annual meetings where the newest information on the forefront of mental health nursing is presented. There are membership fees to join these associations:

- The **American Psychiatric Nurses Association (APNA)** is the largest psychiatric nursing organization. The APNA focuses upon the advancement of nursing practice along with continued improvements in cultural diversity, families, groups, and communities.

- **The International Society of Psychiatric-Mental Health Nurses (ISPN)** comprises 3 specialty divisions, which include the Association of Child and Adolescent Psychiatric Nurses, the International Society of Psychiatric Consultation Liaison Nurses, and the Society for Education and Research in Psychiatric-Mental Health Nursing. The main goal of the ISPN is to bring together all psychiatric-mental health nurses and to advance quality care available for both the individual and the family unit.

HEALTH CARE REFORM

Health care reform initiatives are spurring the switch from paper to electronic health records and sharing of health care information among health care providers, increasing the demand for health information technology and people with expertise in informatics. New programs have been developed to focus on wellness with an increased emphasis on cost-effective measures because of increases in health costs. Internal data analysis and research are becoming important means by which to identify waste, institute best practices, and reduce costs. Increasing numbers of people are covered by health plans, even those with preexisting conditions, placing more demand on health care providers for services. There is an increased need for health literacy so that people are better informed about the services available, especially those newly insured. Medicaid costs have increased, resulting in some cutbacks in care. Early transfer from acute care facilities to extended care or home health care is also increasing.

HEALTH POLICY AND MEDICAL ATTENTION

Health policy – Movement in the direction of primary medical attention and getting prevention earlier; encourages utilization of APRNs. The main elements that control healthcare delivery are payors, insurance companies, providers, and suppliers. Legislation regarding ways to do things and politics is included in this topic.

Medical attention – May be primary health care or managed care. Managed care includes Health Maintenance Organizations (HMO), Preferred Provider Organizations (PPO) and Point of Service (POS) plans.

NURSING'S AGENDA FOR HEALTH CARE REFORM FROM ANA (1991)

The **Nursing's Agenda for Health Care Reform** encourages development of health care which gives patients the ability to get to good medical attention and help without it costing too much, and it encourages continual primary care. It fundamentally asks for **vital medical attention** to be found for everyone and for there to be a **reorganized health care system** that centers on patients, well-being and conditions so that they may get medical help in familiar, easy to get to places. It advocates providing for ongoing medical needs and insurance changes so that patients can use their coverage more easily. It asks for organizational assessment on public and private sectors regarding the use of resources, lowering expenses, and getting balanced and even reimbursement for each provider.

IMPACT OF SOCIAL, POLITICAL, REGULATORY, AND ECONOMIC FORCES ON DELIVERY OF CARE

The **delivery of care** is impacted by numerous forces:

- **Social forces** are increasing demand for access to treatment and medical services, both traditional and complementary. As society views equitable medical care as a right, then delivery of care must be available to all.
- **Political forces** affect medical care as the Federal and state governments increasingly become purchasers of medical care, imposing their guidelines and limitations on the medical system.

- **Regulatory forces** may be local, state, or Federal and can have a profound effect of delivery of care and services, differing from one state or region to another.
- **Economic forces**, such as managed care or cost-containment committees, try to contain costs to insurers and facilities by controlling access to and duration of treatment, and limiting products. Economic pressure is working to prevent duplication of services in a geographical area, and providers are creating networks to purchase supplies and equipment directly.

MEDICARE

Medicare provides payment to private healthcare providers, such as physicians and hospitals, but limits reimbursement. Physicians receive 80% of usual, customary, and reasonable (UCR) fees if they accept Medicare assignment. If they do not, they can charge up to 115% of what Medicare allows. Patients are responsible for the remaining 20% or up to 115% if the physicians do not accept Medicare. Parts include:

- **Medicare A:** Hospital insurance covers acute hospital, limited nursing home care, and/or home health care, as well as hospice care for the terminally ill. There is no premium for this part.
- **Medicare B:** Medical insurance covers physicians, NPs, laboratory, physical, and occupational therapy. Patients must pay an annual deductible as well as a monthly payment.
- **Medicare D:** Prescription drug plan covers part of the costs of prescription drugs at participating pharmacies. It is administered by private insurance companies, so monthly costs and benefits vary somewhat.

MEDICAID

Medicaid is a combined federal and state welfare program authorized by Title XIX of the Social Security Act and regulated by the Centers for Medicare and Medicaid Services (CMS) to assist **low-income individuals** with payment for medical care. This program provides assistance for all ages, including children. Older adults receiving supplemental security income (SSI) are eligible, as are others who meet state eligibility requirements. The Medicaid programs are administered by the individual states, which establish eligibility and reimbursement guidelines, so benefits vary considerably from 1 state to another. Older adults with Medicare are eligible for Medicaid as a secondary insurance. Expenses that may be covered for adults include inpatient and outpatient hospital services, physician payments, nursing home care, home health care, and laboratory and radiation services. Adults who are legal resident aliens are ineligible for Medicaid for 5 years after attaining legal resident status. Some states pay for preventive services, such as home and community-based programs aimed at reducing the need for hospitalization.

EPO, HMO, PPO, AND POS

There are a number of different **models** for managed care to provide healthcare services:

- **Exclusive provider organization (EPO):** Healthcare providers provide services at discounted rates to those enrolled in a service. Some providers may be prohibited from caring for those not enrolled and enrollees are only reimbursed for care within the network.
- **Health maintenance organization (HMO):** With an HMO, there is a prepaid contract between healthcare providers, payors, and enrollees for specified services in a specified time period, provided by a list of providers, usually representing a variety of specialties.

- **Preferred provider organizations (PPO):** This involves healthcare providers who have agreed to be part of a network providing services to an enrolled group at reduced rates of reimbursement. Care received outside of the network is usually only partially covered.
- **Point-of-service plans (POS):** This is a combination HMO and PPO structure so that people can receive service in the network but can opt to seek treatment outside the network in some situations.

TRICARE

Tricare is the healthcare program serving active military, retired military, and their spouses and dependents. Tricare provides a number of different plans, depending upon location and eligibility. For those with Medicare, Tricare becomes the **secondary insurer**. If patients choose to opt out of Medicare (such as those with no insurance or private insurance), Tricare pays the amount equivalent to a secondary insurer (20% of allowable), and the patient is responsible for the rest. By law, all other insurances must pay before Tricare. Patients may access care at military treatment facilities (MTF) on a space-available basis, but must enroll in Tricare Plus to receive primary care at MTFs. Those eligible for both Tricare and Veterans Affairs (VA) programs may receive care at VA medical facilities, if the service is covered under Tricare and the facility is part of the Tricare network; however, the VA cannot bill Medicare so costs not covered by Tricare must be paid by the patient even if the patient has Medicare coverage.

BILLING CODES

In order to be reimbursed by insurance companies and Medicare or Medicaid, the NP must provide appropriate **billing codes.** Reimbursement may require use of different codes. Most healthcare providers use standard forms with checklists of diagnosis and appropriate coding. In many cases, denial of services relates to incorrect coding. Coding systems include:

- **International Classification of Disease (ICD):** Developed by the World Health Organization (WHO) and used to code for diagnosis.
- **Diagnostic-related group (DRG):** Used to classify a disorder according to diagnosis and treatment.
- **Current procedural terminology (CPT):** Developed by the American Medical Society and used to define those licensed to provide services and to describe medical treatments and procedures.
- **Universal billing (UB):** Used to describe hospital services, including demographic information, diagnostic and treatment codes, and charges for services. UB-04 is the current version.

Cultural and Spiritual Competence

MEXICAN PATIENTS

Many areas of the country have large populations of **Mexican** and **Mexican-Americans**. As always, it is important to recognize that cultural generalizations do not always apply to individuals. Recent immigrants, especially, have cultural needs that the NP must understand:

- Most Mexicans identify themselves as **Catholic** and may like the NP to make arrangements for a priest to visit.
- Large **extended families** may come to visit to support the patient and family, so patients should receive clear explanations about how many visitors are allowed, but some flexibility may be required.
- **Language barriers** may exist as some may have limited or no English skills, so translation services should be available around the clock.
- Mexican culture encourages outward expressions of **emotions** so family may react strongly to news about a patient's condition. Also, people who are ill may expect some degree of pampering so extra attention to the patient/family members may alleviate some of their anxiety.
- Some immigrant Mexicans have very little formal education, so **medical information** may seem very complex and confusing, and they may not understand the implications or need for follow-up care.
- Mexican culture perceives **time** with more flexibility than American culture, so if patients or their family need to be present at a particular time, the NP should specify the exact time (1:30 PM) and explain the reason rather than saying something more vague, such as "after lunch."
- People may appear to be unassertive or unable to make decisions when they are simply showing **respect** to the NP by being deferent.
- In traditional families, the **males** make decisions, so women may wait for the husband or other males in the family to make decisions about treatment or care.
- Families may choose to use **folk medicine** instead of Western medical care or may combine the 2.
- **Children and young women** are often sheltered and are taught to be respectful to adults, so they may not express their needs openly.

MIDDLE EASTERN PATIENTS

There are considerable cultural differences among **Middle Easterners,** but religious beliefs about the **segregation** of males and females are common. It is important to remember that segregating the female is meant to protect her virtue. Female nurses and NPs have low status in many countries because they violate this segregation by touching male bodies, so families may not trust or show respect for the female who is caring for their family member. Additionally, male patients may not want to be cared for by female nurses, NPs, or doctors, and families may be very upset at a female being cared for by a male nurse or physician. When possible, these cultural traditions should be accommodated:

- In Middle Eastern countries, **males** make decisions, so issues for discussion or decision should be directed to males, such as the spouse or son, and males may be direct in stating what they want, sometimes appearing demanding.
- If a male nurse must care for a female patient, then the family should be advised that **personal care** (such as bathing) will be done by a female while the medical treatments will be done by the male nurse.

Caring for **Middle Eastern patients** requires understanding of cultural differences:

- Families may practice strict **dietary restrictions**, such as avoiding pork and requiring that animals be killed in a ritual manner, so vegetarian or kosher meals may be required.
- People may have **language difficulties** often requiring a translator, and same-sex translators should be used if at all possible.
- Patients may be accompanied by large **extended families** that want to be kept informed and with whom patients consult before decisions are made.
- Most medical care is provided by **female relatives**, so educating the family about patient care should be directed at females (with female translators if necessary).
- Outward expressions of **grief** are considered as showing respect for the dead.
- Middle Eastern families often offer **gifts** to caregivers. Small gifts (candy) should be accepted graciously, but for other gifts, the families should be advised graciously that accepting gifts is against hospital policy.
- Middle Easterners often require less **personal space** and may stand very close.

ASIAN PATIENTS

There are considerable differences among different **Asian** populations, so cultural generalizations may not apply to all, but practitioners caring for Asian patients should be aware of common cultural attitudes and behaviors:

- Nurses, NPs, and doctors are usually viewed with **respect**, so traditional Asian families may expect the NP to remain authoritative and to give directions. Traditional Asian families also may not ask questions, so the NP should ensure that they understand by having them review material or give demonstrations and should provide explanations clearly, anticipating questions that the family might have but may not articulate.
- **Disagreeing** is considered impolite. "Yes" may only mean that the person is heard, not that they agree with the person. When asked if they understand, they may indicate that they do even when they clearly do not, so as not to offend the practitioner.
- Asians may **avoid eye contact** as an indication of respect.

Caring for **Asian** patients requires understanding of cultural differences:

- Patients/families may not show outward expressions of **feelings/grief**, sometimes appearing passive. They also avoid public displays of affection. This does not mean that they don't feel, just that they don't show their feelings.
- Families often **hide** illness and disabilities from others and may feel ashamed about illness.
- Terminal illness is often **hidden** from the patient, so family may not want patients to know they are dying or seriously ill.
- Families may use cupping, pinching, or applying pressure to injured areas, and this can leave **bruises** that may appear as abuse, so when bruises are found, the family should be questioned about alternative therapy before assumptions are made.
- Patients may be treated with **traditional herbs**.
- Families may need **translators** because of poor or no English skills.
- In traditional Asian families, **males** are authoritative and make the decisions.

GAY, LESBIAN, BISEXUAL, AND TRANSGENDERED PATIENTS

Gay, lesbian, bisexual, and transgendered patients often experience **hostility and discrimination** because of their sexual identification. Some experience anxiety and stress when coming to terms with their sexuality and/or when coming out to family or friends. Increasingly, adolescents are self-identifying as homosexual, some as early as age 12, and they may face intense pressure from family and peers. Hate crimes against homosexual/transgendered people continue. Children of gay/lesbian parents may face discrimination as well. While some religious groups and therapists recommend "reparation" therapy to convert homosexuals to heterosexuals, the American Psychiatric Association (APA) opposes such therapy, and evidence suggests it is virtually never successful and can be damaging psychologically. The NP must respect the individual's sexual identification, remain supportive, and should be knowledgeable about issues important to gay, lesbian, bisexual, and transgendered patients. The rights and needs of partners should also be respected.

BARRIERS PREVENTING ACCESS TO CARE

There are many **barriers that prevent access to care** for those with psychiatric and mental health issues:

- Lack of insurance or limited mental health coverage.
- Low income and unemployment.
- Lack of transportation to treatment facilities.
- Language barriers that prevent people from receiving care.
- Inadequate provision of care for children with programs fragmented and often not available, inadequate testing.
- Ethnic minorities with cultural concerns about mental health care or belief systems that preclude their seeking care. Areas with large immigrant populations often lack mental health care tailored to the cultural and language needs of the immigrants.
- Homelessness.
- Lack of mental health care in rural areas.
- Social stigma to mental illness preventing some from seeking care.
- Older adults often overlooked and not assessed for mental health problems.

LIMITS OF BEING LOW INCOME

Low income often limits **access to care**. Some people may be eligible for Medicaid, but many of those with psychiatric and mental health problems are ineligible and often lack insurance or the financial resources to pay for care. Free clinics and mental health programs are sometimes available, especially in urban areas, but many people lack access to care or transportation to available care and cannot afford medications. Additionally, rates of depression are higher among those with low income, and depression often prevents people from seeking help. Research indicates that over 40% of those with low income have mental health problems (including depression, panic attacks, and anxiety) or have been diagnosed with a mental disease. Single parents and the unemployed are especially at risk.

POVERTY'S IMPACT ON ACCESS TO CARE

There are a number of issues that impact access to care, but **poverty** is one of the most significant and can affect care in many ways:

- People may not have health insurance and may not qualify for state medical assistance or may not be aware that they are eligible, so they do not take themselves or children for **routine medical visits**.
- Practitioners may not accept state medical assistance payments because of **low reimbursement rates**, leaving people with few options.
- Employers may not allow people to take **time off from work** during the times that most practices are open to provide care, or people cannot afford to lose income, so most medical care is provided by emergency departments when a crisis arises.
- People may lack **automobiles** or have insufficient **funds** for, or access to, public transportation to go to medical visits, especially in more rural areas.

CORRECTIONAL INSTITUTIONS AND MENTAL ILLNESS

The Bureau of Justice Statistics estimates that about 16% of **inmates** in adult prisons and jails suffer from **mental illness**. Correctional institutions are often severely overcrowded and lack resources to adequately care for patients. The increasing rate of mentally ill inmates may relate to **deinstitutionalization** that resulted in large numbers of mentally ill people becoming homeless with some becoming involved in substance use disorder and criminal activity. In most correctional facilities, the mentally ill are housed with the general population, leaving them vulnerable to abuse. Mentally ill inmates, such as those with schizophrenia, may find it difficult or impossible to follow rules, so they may be punished for misconduct with loss of privileges, solitary confinement, or extended sentence, all increasing anxiety and stress. Treatment, if available, is often geared toward controlling behavior rather than treating the disorder.

HOMELESS POPULATION

The **homeless population** has disproportionate rates of **mental illness**, estimated at about 40 to 45%, many with serious illnesses, such as schizophrenia and bipolar disorder, complicated by **substance use disorder**.

The need for **adequate housing** is an ongoing problem with homeless patients. Once released from inpatient care services, the homeless do not have anywhere to live. A safe and affordable option is vital to the success of their treatment. Many of these patients have a relapse of their mental illnesses, suffer medical illnesses, incarceration, or abuse by others. The homeless often resist treatment (sometimes not believing they are ill), fail to keep appointments, and lack transportation or money for transportation. They may have no money for medications, may not qualify for assistance, or may be reluctant to deal with government agencies in order to gain assistance.

MENTAL ILLNESS AMONG MIGRANT WORKERS

Migrant workers are at risk for mental illness because of long hours, stress about providing for families, and using substance abuse as a coping mechanism. Many are non-English speakers, undocumented, far from family support systems, experiencing racism, and lacking access to medical care. Mental health issues of primary concern for migrant workers are depression, stress, substance use disorder, and domestic violence. Most migrant workers are ethnic minorities, and some feel a stigma is attached to mental health problems and may resist treatment even if outreach programs are available or may fear loss of employment if they get treatment. Additionally, they may lack transportation to get to treatment or a flexible schedule to allow them to keep appointments. Programs for migrant workers must be affordable and should address both language and cultural concerns and allow for flexible hours to accommodate work schedules.

Ethics

NURSING CODE OF ETHICS

The American Nurses Association (ANA) developed the **Nursing Code of Ethics**. There are 9 **provisions**:

1. The nurse treats all patients with respect and consideration, regardless of social circumstances or health condition.
2. The nurse's primary commitment is to the patient regardless of conflicts that may arise.
3. The nurse promotes and advocates for the patient's health, safety, and rights, maintaining privacy, confidentiality, and protecting them from questionable practices or care.
4. The nurse is responsible for his/her own care practices and determines appropriate delegation of care.
5. The nurse must retain respect for self and his/her own integrity and competence.
6. The nurse participates in ensuring that the healthcare environment is conducive to providing good health care and consistent with professional and ethical values.
7. The nurse participates in education and knowledge development to advance the profession.
8. The nurse collaborates with others to promote efforts to meet health needs.
9. The nursing profession articulates values and promotes and maintains the integrity of the profession.

AUTONOMY AND JUSTICE

Autonomy is the ethical principle that the individual has the right to make decisions about his/her own care. In the case of children or mental incompetence, the person cannot make autonomous decisions, so the parents/guardians serve as the legal decision maker. The NP must keep patients/parents/guardians fully informed so that they can exercise their autonomy in informed decision making.

Justice is the ethical principle that relates to the distribution of the limited resources of healthcare benefits to the members of society. These resources must be distributed fairly. This issue may arise if there is only 1 bed left and 2 sick patients. Justice comes into play in deciding which patient should stay and which should be transported or otherwise cared for. The decision should be made according to what is best or most just for the patients and not colored by personal bias.

BENEFICENCE AND NON-MALEFICENCE

Beneficence is an ethical principle that involves performing actions that are for the purpose of benefitting another person. In the care of a patient, any procedure or treatment should be done with the ultimate goal of benefitting the patient, and any actions that are not beneficial should be reconsidered. As a patient's condition changes, procedures need to be continually reevaluated to determine if they are still of benefit.

Non-maleficence is an ethical principle that means healthcare workers should provide care in a manner that does not cause direct intentional harm to the patient:

- The actual act must be good or morally neutral.
- The intent must be only for a good effect.
- A bad effect cannot serve as the means to get to a good effect.
- A good effect must have more benefit than a bad effect has harm.

SAFETY FACTORS THAT MAY INFLUENCE DECISION-MAKING ABILITIES

In 2005, Ebright et al published a study of factors related to **safety** and the **decision-making ability** of the NP. Every clinical decision made by the NP has an effect on the safety of the patient, and therefore any factor that influences the NP's decision-making ability may adversely affect the patient. Ebright at al identified the following factors that influence decision-making and patient safety: knowledge base, attention, barriers to care, number of tasks, missing essential information, and behaviors that are not encouraging of productive thought. The presence of, or a change in, any of these factors can result in unnecessary harm for the patient.

ETHICAL ISSUES OF COMPETENCY AND DECISION-MAKING IN PSYCHIATRIC CARE

Competence and incompetence are legal issues, not diagnostic. In order to give informed consent, a patient is supposed to be **competent** enough to understand the issues to which the person is consenting. However, some psychiatric patients are not competent enough to make decisions about treatment; but, unless a person is a minor, is unable to respond, or has been declared legally incompetent, the ethical principle of **autonomy** applies, meaning that the person has the right to make decisions about treatment and care—even if those decisions are not in the person's best interests. In most states, **involuntary commitment**, which occurs without patient consent, is only allowed in emergency situations in which the person poses a threat to self or others, for observation and treatment (as decreed by the courts), and when a patient is so gravely disabled that the person cannot take care of personal needs. Emergency commitments are usually only for 72 hours, at which time the patient must have a competency hearing.

CHALLY AND LORIZ MODEL FOR ETHICAL DECISION MAKING

It is important for NPs to avoid making decisions solely based on their beliefs that they know what is best for patients. In 1998, Chally and Loriz developed a **model for ethical decision making** for NPs to use when faced with ethical dilemmas or choices. Steps to ethical decision making include:

1. Clarifying the extent/type of dilemma and who is ultimately responsible for making the decision.
2. Obtaining more data, including information about legal issues, such as the obligation to report.
3. Considering alternative solutions.
4. Arriving at a decision after considering risk/benefits and discussing it with the patient.
5. Acting on the decision and utilizing collaboration as needed.
6. Assessing the outcomes of the decision to determine if the chosen action was effective.

PROMOTING AN ENVIRONMENT FOR ETHICAL DECISION-MAKING AND PATIENT ADVOCACY

An environment for ethical decision-making and patient advocacy does not appear when it is needed; it requires planning and preparation. The expectation for the institution should clearly communicate that NPs are legally and morally responsible for assuring competent care and respecting the rights of patients and other stakeholders. Decisions regarding ethical issues often must be made quickly with little time for contemplation; therefore, ethical issues that may arise should be **identified and discussed**. Clearly defined **procedures and policies** for dealing with conflicts, including an active ethics committee, in-service training, and staff meetings, must be established. Patients and families need to be part of the ethical environment, which means empowering them by providing patient/family information (e.g., print form, video, audio) that outlines patient's rights and procedures for expressing their wishes and dealing with ethical conflicts. Respect for privacy and confidentiality and a nonpunitive atmosphere are essential.

VARIABLES IN RESOLVING ETHICAL CONFLICTS

In the health care setting, it is important that ethical conflicts be **resolved** without harming the patient or compromising care. There are several factors that will affect the course and outcome of an ethical conflict. First, the **level of commitment** the clinician has to the patient will determine the amount of effort put forth in resolving an ethical conflict. Second, the **degree of moral certainty** the clinician has will determine the approach to resolution; if the clinician feels that he or she is correct, he or she will most likely not waver in the decision. Third, the **amount of time available for resolution** is important; if the clinician is pressed for time, he or she will most likely come to a decision faster than if there is not a time constraint, in which case avoidance may occur. Fourth is the **cost-benefit ratio**; if the patient refuses to negotiate a certain point, for example, it is not worth the time to the clinician to try to influence the patient's decision.

ETHICAL DILEMMAS

While the terms *ethics* and *morals* are sometimes used interchangeably, ethics is a study of morals and encompasses concepts of right and wrong. When dealing with **ethical dilemmas,** one must consider not only what people should do but also what they actually do, as these 2 things are sometimes at odds. Ethical issues can be difficult to assess because of personal bias, and that is 1 of the reasons that sharing concerns with other internal sources and reaching consensus is so valuable. **Issues of concern** might include options for care, refusal of care, rights to privacy, adequate relief of suffering, and the right to self-determination. **Internal sources** might include the ethics committee, whose charge is to make decisions regarding ethical issues. Risk management can provide guidance related to personal and institutional liability. **External agencies** might include government agencies, such as the public health department.

ETHICAL ISSUE OF UNAVAILABLE RESOURCES

The issue of **unavailable resources** as it applies to psychiatric care relates to the ethical principal of **justice**, which deals with the distribution of limited healthcare resources. According to this principle, distribution should be based on decisions that are the most **just** and should not reflect personal bias, attempting to make objective decisions when decision-making is inherently subjective. All individuals in need of psychiatric care should have equal access, and if resources are limited, those in **greatest need** should be provided healthcare services first. However, the reality is that there is little equal access. People with insurance or the means to pay privately are often treated first and usually have access to the best care. People without the means to pay often have little access to care, a long wait for care, or substandard care. Psychiatric care for the uninsured often takes place in over-crowded and understaffed facilities.

HUMAN SUBJECT PROTECTION

The Food and Drug Administration, Code of Federal Regulations, Title 21, Volume 1, regulates **protection of human subjects** and states that any researcher involving patients in research must obtain informed consent, in language understandable to the patient or the patient's agent. The elements of this informed consent must include an explanation of the research, the purpose, and the expected duration, as well as a description off any potential risks. Potential benefits must be described and possible alternative treatments. Any compensation to be provided must be outlined. The extent of confidentiality should be clarified. Contact information should be provided in the event the patient/family has questions. The patient must be informed that participation is voluntary and that he/she can discontinue participation at any time without penalty. Informed consent must be documented by a signed, written agreement.

OLMSTEAD DECISION

The **Olmstead Decision** (1999) by the Supreme Court ensures that disabled patients, including mental health patients, be kept in the **least restrictive environment**—an integrated environment that allows the patient to interact with those who are not disabled as much as possible and that is appropriate to the needs of the patient. This decision applies to all those protected from discriminatory acts by Title II of the Americans with Disabilities Act (ADA). Under this decision, states must provide community-based services when healthcare professionals deem it appropriate, when the patient agrees, and when placement can be accommodated, considering the resources available. States may be in compliance if they have an effective plan in place for placing patients in the least restrictive environment, but states are allowed a waiting list if the wait is not excessive. Because the decision did not allocate additional funding, resources in some areas are limited.

MALPRACTICE

Nurse practitioners (NPs), as all advance practice nurses, are usually insured for **malpractice** at a higher rate than for registered nurses because their scope of practice is much wider. An NP may be sued individually or as part of a medical group to which the NP is associated. Because a suit is a civil matter, loss of judgment may not be reported to the state board of nursing. If a charge of **negligence** is brought to the attention of the board, the board may initiate an investigation and disciplinary action. Negligence may involve a number of failures, such as not referring a patient when needed, incorrect diagnosis, incorrect treatment, and not providing the patient/family with adequate or essential information. Once an NP has established a duty to a patient—by direct examination or even casual or telephone conversation that involves professional advice—the NP may be liable for malpractice if he/she does not follow-up with adequate care.

Patient Advocacy

PATIENT ADVOCACY AND ANA's DEFINITION OF NURSING

Patient advocacy is defined as the process of speaking on behalf of a patient to ensure that his or her rights are protected, and that he or she is provided with necessary information and services. The NP frequently serves as patient advocate, although physicians, social workers, and other individuals in the health care industry may act on behalf of the patient as well.

The ANA defines **nursing** as "the protection, promotion, and optimization of health and abilities, prevention of illness and injury, alleviation of suffering through the diagnosis and treatment of human response, and advocacy in the care of individuals, families, communities, and populations."

SYNERGY MODEL IN REGARDS TO ADVOCACY

Nurse competencies under the Synergy Model include **advocacy/moral agency**:

- **Advocacy** is working for the best interests of the patient despite personal values in conflict and assisting patients to have access to appropriate resources.
- **Agency** is openness and recognition of issues and a willingness to act.
- **Moral agency** is the ability to recognize needs and take action to influence the outcome of a conflict or decision.

The levels of advocacy/moral agency include:

- **Level 1**: This nurse works on behalf of the patient, assesses personal values, has awareness of patient's rights and ethical conflicts, and advocates for the patient when consistent with the nurse's personal values.
- **Level 3**: This nurse advocates for the patient/family, incorporates their values into the care plan even when they differ from the nurse's, and can utilize internal resources to assist patient/family with complex decisions.
- **Level 5**: This nurse advocates for patient/family despite differences in values and is able to utilize both internal and external resources to help to empower patient/family to make decisions.

BARRIERS TO PATIENT ADVOCACY

Patient advocacy is often seen as a moral obligation that the NP must fulfill, and is a rewarding part of the NP's job; however, patient advocacy can be difficult in certain situations. One **barrier to advocacy** is a **feeling of powerlessness** on the part of the NP; sometimes it may feel as if it is the NP against the world, especially if the NP has no support; lack of support in general is another barrier. A **lack of knowledge of the law** is another barrier; certain laws may exist, though the NP may not be aware of them. If the NP and his or her peers are **lacking in time, communication, or motivation**, advocacy will also prove difficult. Another problem that NPs frequently encounter is the **risk** associated with advocacy; included are disagreeing with other NPs and physicians, and lack of legal support for the advocate.

FACILITATORS OF PATIENT ADVOCACY

Perhaps the greatest facilitator of patient advocacy is the **NP-patient relationship**; if a strong relationship exists between the NP and the patient, the NP will be motivated to perform the duties of advocate. If the patient and NP have a strained or limited relationship, advocacy can be difficult. **Recognizing the patient's needs** is another facilitator, one that goes hand in hand with a good NP-patient relationship. If the NP feels a sense of responsibility and accountability on behalf of the patient, he or she is more likely to serve as a good patient advocate; conscience is a strong motivator. Another facilitator is if the **physician acts as a colleague**, instead of a superior; this strengthens the NP-physician relationship, and the NP feels that he or she can question the physician's judgment instead of constantly deferring. That being said, the greater the knowledge base and skill level of the NP, the greater he or she will be as an advocate.

DECREASING THE STIGMA ASSOCIATED WITH MENTAL ILLNESS

Studies have shown that up to a third of Americans relate mental illness to defects of character. Negative beliefs about mental illness persist with people often fearing those who are mentally ill. Effective methods to decrease the **stigma** associated with mental illness include:

- **Educating people about mental illness**: People need to know factual information, including about levels of violence associated with those who are mentally ill since this is a pervasive concern. People should be advised of the incidence of mental illness and available treatments.
- **Using words carefully**: Healthcare providers and others should choose words carefully, avoiding words such as "nuts" and "crazy," and remembering to put the person first: "person with schizophrenia" rather than "schizophrenic."
- **Providing support services**: Helping the mentally ill finds places to live and providing other necessary services may help to reduce substance abuse and homelessness, which increase stigma.
- **Increasing contact**: Integrating those with mental illness into the community through job placement and housing helps others to become more familiar with those who are mentally ill.

OLDER AMERICANS ACT/OMBUDSMAN

The **Older Americans Act (OAA)** (Title III) of 1965 (amended in 2006) provides improved access to services for older adults and Native Americans, including community services (meals, transportation, home health care, adult day care, legal assistance, and home repair). The OAA provides funding to local **area agencies on aging (AAA)** or state or tribal agencies, which administer funding. These local agencies can assess community needs and contract for services. One of the programs commonly supported with funds from the OAA is meals-on-wheels. Low cost adult day care is also offered in some communities. The OAA includes the **National Family Caregivers Support Act**, which provides services for caregivers of older adults. The OAA also provides grants for programs that combat violence against older adults and others to provide computer training for older adults. Additionally, the OAA mandates that each state have an ombudsman program. Ombudsmen provide services to residents of nursing homes and other facilities to ensure that care meets state standards.

OBRA

The **Omnibus Budget Reconciliation Act** (OBRA) of 1987 contains the 1990 **Nursing Home Reform Amendments (NHRA)**. These amendments establish guidelines for nursing facilities (such as long-term care facilities). Provisions include:

- Complete physical and mental assessment of each patient on admission, annually, and with change of condition.
- Requirement for 24-hour nursing care with registered nurses (RNs) on duty for at least 1 shift.
- Nurse aide training is mandated as well as regular inservice and state registry of trained/qualified aides.

- Rehabilitative services must be available.
- Physicians/physician's assistant/NP must visit every 30 days for the first 3 months and then every 90 days.
- Outlawing/discouraging Medicaid discrimination.
- Requirement for independent monitoring of psychopharmacologic drugs.
- Recognition of patients' rights.
- Survey protocols to assess patient care and patient outcomes.
- State sanctions to enforce nursing home regulations.

EMTALA

The Emergency Medical Treatment and Active Labor Act (EMTALA) is designed to prevent patient "dumping" from emergency departments (EDs) and is an issue of concern for risk management, requiring staff training for compliance: EMTALA guidelines concerning the transfer of an ED patient include:

- Transfers from the ED may be intrahospital or to another facility.
- Stabilization of the patient with emergency conditions or active labor must be done in the ED prior to transfer, and initial screening must be given prior to inquiring about insurance or ability to pay.
- Stabilization requires treatment for emergency conditions and reasonable belief that, although the emergency condition may not be completely resolved, the patient's condition will not deteriorate during transfer.
- Women in the ED in active labor should deliver both the child and placenta before transfer.
- The receiving department or facility should be capable of treating the patient and dealing with complications that might occur.
- Transfer to another facility is indicated if the patient requires specialized services not available intrahospital, such as to burn centers.

MENTAL HEALTH PARITY ACT

The **Mental Health Parity Act** (1996) is a law that applies to large group health plans. This act is designed as a protection for individuals with mental disabilities and disorders. The Mental Health Parity Act mandates equal annual and lifetime dollar benefits for mental health treatment compared to that available for medical and surgical treatments. This act only applies to the financial responsibility of the plan and does allow for other restrictions within the plan, such as a limit on the number of visits to a mental health professional and access to network providers only. substance use disorders are not covered by the law. The exact specifications vary by plan and the provisions of the Mental Health Parity Act do not apply to small group health plans.

AMERICANS WITH DISABILITIES ACT

The 1992 **Americans with Disabilities Act (ADA)** is civil rights legislation that provides the disabled, including those with mental impairment, access to employment and the community. While employers must make reasonable accommodations for the **disabled**, the provisions related to the community apply more directly to **older Americans**. The ADA covers not only obvious disabilities but also disorders such as arthritis, seizure disorders, psychiatric disorders, cardiovascular, and respiratory disorders. Communities must provide transportation services for the disabled, including accommodation for wheelchairs. Public facilities (schools, museums, physician's offices, post offices, restaurants) must be accessible with ramps and elevators as needed. Telecommunications must also be accessible through devices or accommodations for the deaf and blind. **Compliance** is not yet complete because older buildings are required to provide access that is possible without "undue hardship," but newer construction of public facilities must meet ADA regulations.

PATIENT SELF-DETERMINATION ACT

The **Patient Self-Determination Act** (1990), an amendment to the Omnibus Budget Reconciliation Act, allows a mental health patient to develop an **advance psychiatric directive (APD)** during a period when a professional mental healthcare provider certifies the person is of sound mind. The APD allows the patient to determine in advance the types of treatment that are acceptable and those that are not. The patient can also designate another person, such as a family member, to make decisions if the patient is unable to do so. State regulations regarding APDs may vary somewhat. The APD is particularly valuable to those who have severe chronic psychiatric illnesses, such as schizophrenia, and may face involuntary commitment. A patient may outline preferences regarding specific treatments and interventions, such as medications, seclusion, restraint, and electroshock therapy.

FMLA

The *Family and Medical Leave Act* (FMLA) (1993) is a federal law that requires employers (such as hospitals and rehabilitation centers) with 50 or more employees to provide unpaid leave and job-protected time off up to 12 weeks during any 12-month period for medical and family reasons to fulltime and part-time employees who have worked more than 1250 hours within the previous year. During leave time, the employer must continue the same benefits and insurance coverage and must maintain the position or provide another that is approximately equal in salary, benefits, and area of responsibility. Leave may be used to care for a newborn, adopted, or fostered child; sick spouse; child; or parent; and for adverse health conditions that prevent the employee from carrying out work functions. FMLA allows extended leave up of up to 26 workweeks in a 12-month period to care for a service member's spouse, parent, or children.

SCHOOL RESOURCES

School resources vary widely. Most colleges and universities provide **mental health services** to students. Some have mental health clinics or other counselling services available, and these services can provide valuable support for students with psychiatric or mental health concerns. K-12 schools are more limited in the mental health services that they provide. In some cases, the school nurse or academic counselors may provide some mental health counselling or referrals, but mental health professionals are usually not available on site. Children who are receiving mental health care and/or medications may need support in the school environment, so the NP and family may need to discuss the needs with the school administration to determine what services the school is able to provide. **SchoolMentalHealth.org**, a feature of the Baltimore School Mental Health Technical Assistance and Training Initiative, provides resources for students, healthcare providers, educators, and educators with protocols for management of different types of behavioral problems, such as anger management.

RESOURCE UTILIZATION

Resource utilization refers to the consideration of all factors related to the planning and delivery of quality patient care. Resources may be allotted to the physical environment for building or remodeling, staffing, equipment, literature, training, and outreach programs. **Utilization review** requires consideration of patient safety, treatment effectiveness, and cost of care. The patient should receive mental health care that meets all of the factors. The care should be safe, effective, and affordable for each individual patient. Treatment decisions should take into consideration rising healthcare costs and how to maximize the use of resources while continuing to provide quality patient care. The goal of resource utilization is to provide quality, cost-effective care, while utilizing the best-qualified staff and appropriate resources.

SAMHSA AND NMHIC

The **Substance Abuse and Mental Health Services Administration's** (SAMHSA's) **National Mental Health Information Center** (NMHIC) provides information about opportunities for grants and application forms as well as a number of resources for mental health professionals. SAMSHA (http://www.samhsa.gov/index.aspx) provides grants in a wide range of areas, including supportive housing, suicide prevention, family intervention, jail diversion, traumatic stress, and substance abuse prevention. The NMHIC provides fact sheets and brochures, which can be ordered for distribution, on all aspects of mental illness. Training guides are also available free of charge. NMHIC also provides state resource guides for each state. Many fact sheet and reports are available for download directly from the website. SAMHSA provides a newsroom that lists all press announcements, including information about available grants and recent awards.

NAMI

The National Alliance on Mental Illness (NAMI) is an invaluable community resource for those with mental illness and their families. Programs include:

- **Family-to-Family:** Free 12-week course intended to help family members or caregivers of those with severe psychiatric disorders (such as schizophrenia or bipolar disorder).
- **In Our Own Voice:** People living with mental illness speak about their experiences and recovery.
- **NAMI Connection:** Weekly support groups for those with mental illness.
- **Parents and Teachers as Allies:** Two-hour inservice program for teachers about early signs of mental illness, interventions, and dealing with families.
- **Peer-to-Peer:** Nine 2-hour courses taught by trained mentors with a history of mental illness, teaching participants to better manage their mental illness and avoid relapses.
- **NAMI Provider Education:** Ten-week course taught by a panel of 5 (2 family members, 2 mental health patients, and a mental health professional) for staff working directly with people with mental illness.

HOME MEAL DELIVERY PROGRAMS

Home meal delivery programs (such as Meals-on-Wheels) provide nutritious meals for homebound older adults or others who are physically or mentally disabled. The programs usually serve meals 5-7 days a week with home delivery, often by volunteers. Meals are usually low cost ($2-5 per meal) but this varies with program. Most programs deliver 1 hot meal a day and may provide food for 1 or 2 other meals (such as a sandwich for dinner and cold cereal for breakfast the next day). Requirements and age restrictions vary with some primarily serving those ≥60 and others ≥65. People with temporary disabilities may be restricted in length of service. Some programs are intended for those with low incomes but others do not have income restrictions. Most programs provide little choice in menu but may offer low-fat, low-salt, or low-carbohydrate diets. Many home meal delivery programs have waiting lists because the need outpaces the number of programs.

RISK MANAGEMENT

Risk management is an organized and formal method of decreasing liability, financial loss, and risk or harm to patients, staff, or others by doing an assessment of risk and introducing risk-management strategies. Much of risk management has been driven by the insurance industry in order to minimize costs, but quality management utilizes risk management as a method to ensure quality health care and process improvement. An organization's risk management program usually comprises a manager and staff with a number of **responsibilities**:

- **Risk identification** begins with an assessment of processes to identify and prioritize those that require further study to determine risk exposure.
- **Risk analysis** requires a careful documenting of process and utilizing flow charts, with each step in the process assessed for potential risks. This may utilize root cause analysis methods.
- **Risk prevention** involves instituting corrective or preventive processes. Responsible individual or teams are identified and trained.
- **Assessment/evaluation** of corrective/preventive processes is ongoing to determine if they are effective or require modification.

NP Practice Test

1. If the psychiatric and mental health nurse practitioner (PMHNP) notes that therapists are using a variety of treatment modalities for patients with depression and he or she believes that cognitive behavioral therapy (CBT) is the most effective and takes less time than many other therapies, the best course of action is to:

    a. ask the administration to mandate the use of CBT.
    b. tell the therapists that CBT is the best approach to treatment.
    c. carry out evidence-based research and present his or her findings.
    d. recognize that a PMHNP cannot influence therapists.

2. Mike Brown has completed gender reassignment surgery (male-to-female) and is now legally Mikaela Brown. Mikaela states that she is still attracted to females and not males. The PMHNP should classify Mikaela's sexual orientation as:

    a. lesbian.
    b. heterosexual.
    c. homosexual.
    d. bisexual.

3. A 14-year-old states that she has occasional episodes of sleep paralysis at the onset of sleep, especially after staying up late to study. She is taking no medications and has no other symptoms. The most appropriate initial intervention is:

    a. sleep medications.
    b. reassurance.
    c. testing for narcolepsy.
    d. testing for epilepsy.

4. When serving as an agent of change in quality improvement, the PMHNP recognizes that innovation adopters who won't bring forth an innovation but are willing to readily adopt it when proposed by others are classified as:

    a. early adopters.
    b. early majority.
    c. late majority.
    d. laggards.

5. A patient scheduled for electroshock therapy tells the PMHNP, "I'm so afraid of how much this will hurt." The most appropriate response is:

    a. "Don't worry, you won't feel a thing."
    b. "I'm sure your doctor explained this treatment."
    c. "Tell me what you think is going to happen."
    d. "Electroshock therapy is a common treatment."

6. The PMHNP is aware that environmental, social, physiological, and psychological stressors may all impact the quality of care. An example of a social stressor is:

    a. negative thoughts.
    b. noise.
    c. inadequate sleep.
    d. deadlines.

7. As unit supervisor, the PMHNP uses disciplinary action to control the behavior of a staff member. The type of power the PMHNP is using is:
   a. expert.
   b. coercive.
   c. legitimate.
   d. referent.

8. If a PMHNP tells a patient, "If you don't stop yelling, we're going to hold you down, put you in restraints, and give you an injection," this could be considered as:
   a. an assault.
   b. a battery.
   c. negligence.
   d. malpractice.

9. When assessing the relationship between a patient and her 10-month-old infant, the PMHNP notes that the infant showed no distress when the mother briefly left the room and did not acknowledge the mother on her return. The PMHNP classifies this attachment style as:
   a. secure.
   b. ambivalent.
   c. disorganized.
   d. avoidant.

10. In managing a conflict among staff on the psychiatric unit, the PMHNP helped those in disagreement to reach a compromise with each side giving up something and each side gaining something. One disadvantage of compromise is:
   a. one side is a winner and one side a loser.
   b. it may lead staff members to believe that conflict is not tolerated.
   c. the conflict may arise again because of the losses.
   d. the parties to the conflict may feel taken advantage of.

11. A 45-year-old patient is undergoing alcohol withdrawal. A medication that the PMHNP can prescribe to relieve symptoms is:
   a. amitriptyline (Elavil).
   b. chlordiazepoxide (Librium).
   c. lorazepam (Ativan).
   d. bupropion (Wellbutrin).

12. The PMHNP is assessing a patient with the Controlled Oral Word Association Test (COWAT) and has asked the patient to name as many items as possible starting with the letter "D," but the patient is only able to name two items. This suggests brain damage to the:
   a. frontal lobe.
   b. parietal lobe.
   c. temporal lobe.
   d. occipital lobe.

13. The area of psychology that involves the study of the mental process involved in attention, memory, and perception and how these processes affect behavior is:

    a. social psychology.
    b. psychoanalysis.
    c. cognitive psychology.
    d. Gestalt psychology.

14. If the PMHNP is applying the STAR approach to patient safety, the letter T represents:

    a. teach the patient.
    b. think about the task.
    c. test understanding.
    d. track patient needs.

15. When the PMHNP is communicating with colleagues about a problem in an email, the most appropriate message is:

    a. "ATTENTION!! MEETING AT 3 PM TO DISCUSS PROBLEMS WITH STAFFING."
    b. "Critical meeting at 3 p.m. to discuss requests for time off."
    c. "Meeting for all staff members scheduled for 3 p.m. this afternoon."
    d. "Please attend a 15-minute meeting at 3 p.m. to discuss coordinating time-off requests."

16. According to the National Center for Complementary and Integrative Health (NCCIH—previously called the National Center for Complementary and Alternative Medicine [NCCAM]), which of the following is an example of a whole medical system?

    a. Acupuncture.
    b. Meditation.
    c. Vitamin therapy.
    d. Massage.

17. During an interview with a 76-year-old patient with moderate cognitive impairment, the patient gets up abruptly and states that she is going for a walk. The best intervention of the PMHNP is to:

    a. direct the patient to stay seated until the interview is over.
    b. ask to accompany the patient on the walk.
    c. reschedule the interview.
    d. conclude the interview with the patient's spouse.

18. When conducting observational research of patients in a group therapy setting, the PMHNP notes that patients seem to behave as they believe they should in the group setting but that this behavior does not carry over into interactions in the unit. The patients are likely responding to:

    a. groupthink.
    b. fear of authority.
    c. learned behaviors.
    d. demand characteristics.

19. An outpatient with generalized anxiety disorder (GAD) has as an emotional support animal (a cat) and wants to take the cat to work with her when she returns to her job. The PMHNP should advise the patient that, according to Title II and Title III of the Americans with Disabilities Act (ADA), an emotional comfort animal:

    a. does not qualify as a service animal.
    b. must be accommodated by employers as a service animal.
    c. can be certified as a service animal only if it is a dog.
    d. is certified as a service animal only on special request.

20. Cocaine and amphetamine may produce symptoms similar to schizophrenia primarily because they:

    a. inhibit dopamine receptors.
    b. stimulate dopamine receptors.
    c. inhibit serotonin receptors.
    d. stimulate serotonin receptors.

21. According to Piaget, during which stage would a child be expected to first understand conservation of physical properties?

    a. Sensorimotor.
    b. Preoperational.
    c. Concrete operational.
    d. Formal operational.

22. As the supervisor, the PMHNP carried out a time study that showed that the nursing staff members spent only 25% of their time in direct patient care, 30% of their time documenting, and 45% of their time on other activities. The next step is to:

    a. tell staff members they must increase time spent in direct patient care.
    b. review documentation procedures.
    c. closely review the "other activities" that require 45% of their time.
    d. hire more staff to assist with direct patient care.

23. A 24-year-old patient with autism spectrum disorder, level 1, cannot judge the intention behind commands and often becomes distraught over simple directions, such as "eat your lunch now," and ignores important directions, such as "leave by the fire exit." The PMHNP would classify this type of deficit as:

    a. impaired social interaction.
    b. mind blindness.
    c. meltdown.
    d. stereotypy.

24. Based on research of best practices, the PMHNP has recommended a number of best practice guidelines to improve patient safety and patient outcomes. The type of best practice that the PMHNP should generally attempt to institute first is a practice that:

    a. requires new equipment.
    b. involves the entire staff.
    c. requires organizational change.
    d. requires simple changes in procedure.

25. A 12-year-old child dying of leukemia tells the PMHNP that she is worried about how her parents will cope after she dies. The most appropriate response is:

    a. "Just think about getting better, and don't worry about your parents."
    b. "I'll let your parents know that you are worried about them."
    c. "Perhaps you can tell your parents what your hopes are for them."
    d. "It's not your job to worry about taking care of your parents."

26. The psychiatric unit is changing from a primary care nursing model with all registered nurses or advance practice nurses to a team nursing model that includes LPNs and psychiatric technicians. To help combat resistance, the PMHNP should focus on the:

    a. benefits of working in a team.
    b. cost savings that will result.
    c. challenges to be faced.
    d. need to cooperate.

27. A 35-year-old recently widowed patient was a happily married stay-at-home mom but has experienced severe anxiety and panic attacks since her husband's death left her with few employable skills, little money, and three children to raise. Considering Maslow's hierarchy of needs, the patient's primary need at this time is likely to be:

    a. physiological.
    b. love/belonging.
    c. esteem.
    d. safety/security.

28. When conducting psychoeducation for a patient and family members, the initial action of the PMHNP is to:

    a. evaluate current knowledge.
    b. develop written materials.
    c. identify and mitigate barriers to learning.
    d. plan lessons from simple to complex.

29. A patient is admitted for an extended stay in a rehabilitation facility for drug and alcohol addiction. The patient's 8-year-old child asks the PMHNP if his mother will be able to come home soon. The most appropriate response is:

    a. "You should talk about that with your father."
    b. "Not soon because your mom needs to get well first."
    c. "Why do you want to know that?"
    d. "Just take one day at a time and try not to worry."

30. The evidence-based therapy that the PMHNP recommends for adolescents with anorexia nervosa is:

    a. family-based therapy.
    b. cognitive behavioral therapy (CBT).
    c. reality-based therapy.
    d. psychoanalysis.

31. The three steps in the process of valuing are (1) choosing, (2) prizing, and (3) _____

a. confirming.
b. collaborating.
c. sharing.
d. acting.

32. An example of secondary prevention used by the PMHNP for an at-risk adolescent is:

a. refer to Alateen if the parents are alcoholics.
b. refer to a support group for children of divorce.
c. work with the patient to modify negative behaviors.
d. provide sex education courses.

33. If a patient states, "I don't understand! My daughter said that she had to leave town," an appropriate clarifying question for the PMHNP to ask would be:

a. "Your daughter said that she had to leave town?"
b. "Are you confused because you don't know why she had to leave town?"
c. "Did she say anything else about it?"
d. "Why don't you call her and ask for more information?"

34. A 9-year-old girl has vaginal tearing, bruising, and scarring, which the mother claims occurred as a result of horseback riding. The child seems emotionally stable and repeats that she hurt herself riding, but the PMHNP suspects sexual abuse. The most appropriate action is to:

a. assume that the mother is correct about the injuries.
b. ask for further assessment and a second opinion.
c. ask to do follow-up visits with the child.
d. report the suspected abuse to the appropriate authorities.

35. When working with a 28-year-old female patient with bulimia nervosa, the PMHNP finds a container of laxatives hidden in the patient's bed linens. The best response is to:

a. tell the patient about finding the laxatives.
b. reprimand the patient for having the laxatives.
c. ignore the finding and say nothing about it.
d. ask the psychiatrist what action to take.

36. Memory (immediate, remote, and recent) can be assessed in a young child beginning at about:

a. 2 years of age.
b. 3 years of age.
c. 4 years of age.
d. 5 years of age.

37. A patient who has received long-term treatment with haloperidol as an antipsychotic agent has developed repetitive behaviors, including tongue thrusting, lip smacking, and hair pulling. The most likely cause is:

a. pseudoparkinsonism.
b. serotonin syndrome.
c. neuroleptic malignant syndrome.
d. tardive dyskinesia.

38. The PMHNP overhears a nurse telling a disruptive patient, "Shut up, stop acting stupid, and go to your room." The best response to the nurse is:
    a. "You were very rude to that patient."
    b. "I heard you tell the patient to shut up, stop acting stupid, and go to her room."
    c. "Your behavior was completely inappropriate."
    d. "It's understandable that the patient would upset you."

39. If the PMHNP is gathering data about a patient, a tertiary source of information is:
    a. medical records.
    b. patient statements.
    c. family statements.
    d. personal observation.

40. As the supervisor of the psychiatric unit of a large hospital, the PMHNP carries out assessment of patient satisfaction and then devises a strategy to reduce patient complaints regarding the time required for staff members to respond to patient needs. The competency skill that he or she is exhibiting is:
    a. technical.
    b. conceptual.
    c. interpersonal.
    d. functional.

41. The PMHNP has prescribed chlorpromazine hydrochloride (Thorazine) for a patient with psychosis, and the patient is to continue on the oral medication after discharge from the psychiatric unit. As part of educating the patient about the medication, the PMHNP should advise him or her to avoid:
    a. exercise.
    b. milk products.
    c. tobacco products.
    d. sun exposure.

42. The parents of a 15-year-old boy are concerned that their son no longer wants to be involved in family activities. The PMHNP points out that, according to Erikson's stages of human development, the key event during the stage of adolescence (12 to 18 years) is:
    a. school.
    b. love relationships.
    c. peer relationships.
    d. independence.

43. With rational emotive behavior therapy (REBT), the ABCDE model suggests that adversity (A—the activating event) and consequences (C) are strongly influenced by _____ (B)
    a. beliefs about the event.
    b. behavior associated with the event.
    c. background leading to the event.
    d. behavior of others.

44. As part of evidence-based research, the PMHNP finds that one instrument produces the same results whenever it is used to measure a similar behavior, suggesting that the instrument has:

   a. reliability.
   b. validity.
   c. sensitivity.
   d. variability.

45. A patient experiencing auditory hallucinations tells the PMHNP that he hears voices warning him of danger, "Don't you hear them?" The most therapeutic response is:

   a. "There are no voices. You are hallucinating."
   b. "I know the voices seem real to you, but I don't hear them."
   c. "I can't make them out. What are they saying?"
   d. "Try to stay focused on what's real. There are no voices."

46. The PMHNP is concerned that the state's nurse practice act needs revision to more accurately reflect the competencies of PMHNPs. The best means of promoting revision of the act is to:

   a. encourage the administration to lobby the state.
   b. survey other PMHNPs in the area.
   c. write to the state legislature.
   d. become active in a state nursing organization.

47. Which of the following statements by a patient is most likely to indicate suicidal ideation and risk for suicide?

   a. "My children would be better off without me."
   b. "I can't stop crying when I think about my mother's death."
   c. "My brother thinks he is so much better than I am."
   d. "Sometimes I think this therapy is totally pointless."

48. A patient believes that messages are being sent to her in newspapers, magazines, radio, and television and that she must decipher them. This type of delusion is a:

   a. delusion of persecution.
   b. delusion of control.
   c. delusion of reference.
   d. delusion of grandeur.

49. When conducting evidence-based research, the PMHNP observes that a natural correlation appears to exist between two variables. Based on this, the PMHNP considers that:

   a. one variable is the cause, and the other is the effect.
   b. there may be a third-variable correlation.
   c. the correlation is valid, and either may be the cause.
   d. the research procedures were likely inadequate.

50. When using clinical pathways, patient progress is measured in relation to:
   a. length of stay.
   b. cost of care.
   c. actual outcomes.
   d. expected outcome.

51. In establishing a therapeutic relationship with a patient, the PMHNP's goal for the patient at the end of the orientation phase is for the patient to:
   a. exhibit alternating periods of effort and resistance.
   b. be able to sustain change.
   c. develop trust in the PMHNP.
   d. express feelings of sadness or anger.

52. A patient whose partner has left him for someone else and who spends an hour discussing all of the positive aspects of being single is probably using the ego defense mechanism of:
   a. displacement.
   b. intellectualism.
   c. denial.
   d. rationalization.

53. The four essential elements of informed consent before a patient can make a decision about care are:
   a. competence, disclosure, options, and voluntarism.
   b. competence, comprehension, noncoercion, and disclosure.
   c. voluntarism, competence, noncoercion, and disclosure.
   d. voluntarism, competence, disclosure, and comprehension.

54. The PMHNP is interviewing a 20-year-old patient who has a four-year history of cyclothymia but is currently asymptomatic. Based on this diagnosis, the maximum period of time during which the PMHNP expects the patient to remain asymptomatic is:
   a. one month.
   b. two months.
   c. three months.
   d. four months.

55. According to Maslow's hierarchy of needs, which of the following nursing diagnoses would have priority?
   a. Risk for injury.
   b. Ineffective coping.
   c. Sleep deprivation.
   d. Social isolation.

56. A patient with obsessive-compulsive disorder (OCD) will begin medication to control symptoms. An FDA-approved drug for OCD that the PMHNP may prescribe is:
   a. nefazodone.
   b. imipramine (Tofranil).
   c. amitriptyline (Elavil).
   d. fluoxetine (Prozac).

57. According to Peplau's interpersonal relations theory, a patient who is miserly, suspicious, and envious of others has likely failed to complete developmental tasks associated with the stage of:

    a. infancy (learning to count on others).
    b. toddlerhood (learning to delay satisfaction).
    c. early childhood (identifying oneself).
    d. late childhood (developing participatory skills).

58. As leader of an interdisciplinary team, the PMHNP notes that one team member who has worked on the unit for more than 20 years frequently criticizes younger and less experienced nurses. The best initial approach to resolving this is to:

    a. ask the experienced nurse to serve as a mentor.
    b. ask the experienced nurse to be more patient and supportive.
    c. tell the experienced nurse that the behavior is detrimental to the team.
    d. suggest that the experienced nurse transfer to a different team.

59. The structure in the brain that plays a role in emotional memories is the:

    a. hippocampus.
    b. thalamus.
    c. amygdala.
    d. basal ganglia.

60. The PMHNP is conducting a smoking cessation class for a group of patients, and two patients are adamant in stating that they plan to resume smoking after discharge from the psychiatric facility. The best solution is to:

    a. exclude the two patients from the group.
    b. warn patient that smoking could endanger their lives.
    c. arrange for the two patients to meet a person with lung cancer from smoking.
    d. provide information about symptoms of concern, such as increased cough.

61. The PMHNP is observing a patient whose behavior is aggressive. The behavior that would differentiate aggression from anger is:

    a. passive-aggressive behavior.
    b. holding clenched fists.
    c. yelling and shouting.
    d. verbal threats.

62. Under provisions of the Americans with Disabilities Act (ADA) related to people with psychiatric disabilities, employers are required to:

    a. provide reasonable accommodations.
    b. hire a person with psychiatric disabilities.
    c. provide any work accommodations that the person requests.
    d. hold the person's position indefinitely until the person can return to work.

63. During a severe storm, four psychiatric unit staff members are unable to report for duty, leaving the unit understaffed. The PMHNP should proceed by:
    a. working from one room to another in order.
    b. prioritizing patient care needs.
    c. demanding more staff from the administration.
    d. asking responsible patients to assist with routine tasks.

64. A 28-year-old female patient who experienced sexual abuse as a child expresses distorted feelings of guilt and shame, blaming herself for the abuse and exhibiting low self-esteem. The most effective therapeutic approach is likely:
    a. therapeutic milieu.
    b. psychoanalysis.
    c. cognitive behavioral therapy (CBT).
    d. eye movement desensitization and reprocessing (EMDR).

65. A patient with a right-sided above-elbow (AE) amputation has become increasingly depressed because of persistent severe phantom limb pain. The PMHNP suggests the use of a mirror box to create the illusion that the limb has been restored. This therapeutic treatment is based on:
    a. biofeedback.
    b. self-hypnosis.
    c. cognitive behavioral therapy (CBT).
    d. neuroplasticity.

66. If a patient who has been using heroin is admitted to the psychiatric unit, the PMHNP will advise the staff that after the last dose of heroin the patient is likely to exhibit withdrawal symptoms within:
    a. 6 to 12 hours.
    b. 12 to 24 hours.
    c. 24 to 48 hours.
    d. 48 to 74 hours.

67. A patient with antisocial personality disorder tells the PMHNP (who is sensitive about her weight) that other staff members are making fun of her appearance and state that she is "fat and lazy." The PMHNP should:
    a. confront the other staff members.
    b. report this to the department head.
    c. advise the patient that he is lying.
    d. advise the patient that his comments are inappropriate.

68. The most appropriate documentation regarding an incident with a disturbed patient is:
    a. "Patient threw a plate at his father, grabbed him by the shirt, and threw him onto the floor."
    b. "Patient became very upset with his father during their visit."
    c. "Patient exhibited violent behavior during his father's visit."
    d. "Patient required intervention to control aggressive behavior."

69. A patient in CBT for major depressive disorder is experiencing negative thoughts. The statement by the patient that indicates that she is applying principles learned in therapy is:

    a. "I know I need to change because I feel so worthless all the time."
    b. "I can't fix this situation, so I'm going to think about being on a vacation."
    c. "I should have known better than to think I could fix this situation."
    d. "I want to feel better about this situation."

70. The PMHNP notes during a patient interview that the patient consistently expresses surprise at information of which the PMHNP knows that he is already aware. The display rule that this behavior exemplifies is:

    a. intensification.
    b. deintensification.
    c. masking.
    d. neutralizing.

71. For a patient taking lithium to control bipolar disorder, the serum level for maintenance should be:

    a. 0.5 to 1.5 mEq/L
    b. 1.5 to 2.0 mEq/L.
    c. 2 to 3 mEq/L.
    d. 3 to 4 mEq/L.

72. If a patient has an intellectual disability and an IQ of 45, a realistic maximal expectation is that he or she may:

    a. develop minimal self-help skills.
    b. be able to acquire vocational skills.
    c. be capable of working in a sheltered workshop.
    d. benefit from systematic habit training.

73. A Southeast Asian patient is admitted to the psychiatric unit with major depressive episode. On physical examination, the PMHNP notes a symmetrical pattern of bruising and petechiae up and down her back, chest, and shoulders, and across the forehead. The PMHNP recognizes this as:

    a. coining.
    b. cupping.
    c. sadistic/masochistic ritual.
    d. physical abuse.

74. When prescribing lithium for a patient with bipolar disorder, the PMHNP reviews the patient's list of medications and identifies a drug that may increase the risk of lithium toxicity. The medication that the PMHNP recognizes should not be taken concurrently with lithium is:

    a. oral contraceptive (Ortho-Novum).
    b. hydrochlorothiazide.
    c. levothyroxine.
    d. amoxicillin.

75. An example of feedback that is directed at an action/state that the patient cannot modify is:

    a. "Your comment is inappropriate."
    b. "You seem angry at your therapist."
    c. "You have memory problems because of your alcohol abuse."
    d. "I noticed that you didn't make eye contact with your son."

76. According to CBT, the type of automatic thought exemplified when a patient states, "My mother thinks I'm a failure" is:

    a. personalizing.
    b. all-or-nothing thinking.
    c. discounting positives.
    d. mind reading.

77. In a group process, the three major types of roles that group members assume within the group are (1) completing group tasks, (2) supporting the group process, and (3) _____

    a. fulfilling personal needs.
    b. controlling the group.
    c. challenging the group.
    d. providing moral guidance.

78. The daughter of a 68-year-old patient with Alzheimer's disease states that the patient, who had exhibited only mild symptoms on rivastigmine (Exelon), has suddenly had a marked increase in confusion. In reviewing the patient's medications, the PMHNP recognizes that one of the patient's drugs that may increase confusion when taken with rivastigmine is:

    a. clopidogrel (Plavix).
    b. atorvastatin (Lipitor).
    c. budesonide/formoterol (Symbicort) per nebulizer.
    d. oxybutynin.

79. A patient with dementia related to Alzheimer's disease has severe confusion and agitation. The PMHNP recognizes that the most appropriate intervention is:

    a. a selective serotonin reuptake inhibitor (SSRI).
    b. an antipsychotic.
    c. an anticonvulsant
    d. nonpharmacological measures.

80. A new member of a team on the psychiatric unit failed to follow unit safety protocols when a patient became aggressive and, as a result, sustained injuries when attacked by the patient. In a just culture model, the appropriate response would be:

    a. consolation/support.
    b. punitive action.
    c. coaching/additional training.
    d. no action because of the injuries.

81. The PMHNP is caring for a patient who has been experiencing blackouts associated with drinking alcohol, which he often sneaks and denies drinking. According to the four phases of alcoholic drinking behavior (Jellinek), the blackouts and other behaviors are a characteristic of:

   a. Phase I, prealcoholic.
   b. Phase II, early alcoholic.
   c. Phase III, crucial alcoholic.
   d. Phase IV, chronic alcoholic.

82. When conducting an outreach program to screen homeless people for mental health and/or substance abuse disorders, the best method for the PMHNP to use to encourage participation is to:

   a. offer free food, water, and hygiene products.
   b. advertise on TV and radio and in local newspapers.
   c. ask the police department to refer homeless people.
   d. advertise through community volunteers.

83. A patient is undergoing opioid withdrawal. The medication that the PMHNP prescribes to relieve symptoms is:

   a. phenobarbital.
   b. clonidine (Catapres).
   c. naloxone (Narcan).
   d. diazepam (Valium).

84. If a patient who was voluntarily committed to a psychiatric facility wants to leave and is restrained from doing so by the PMHNP, this may constitute:

   a. assault and battery.
   b. intentional tort.
   c. negligence.
   d. false imprisonment.

85. The PMHNP is caring for a patient admitted to the hospital with schizophrenia and polydipsia, drinking water excessively and becoming increasing confused and psychotic. The electrolyte imbalance of most concern to the PMHNP is:

   a. hyponatremia.
   b. hypernatremia.
   c. hypocalcemia.
   d. hypercalcemia.

86. A 55-year-old patient complains of increasing memory loss. When reviewing the patient's list of medications, the PMHNP notes one drug that may induce memory impairment. The drug of concern is:

   a. levothyroxine.
   b. calcitonin.
   c. atorvastatin (Lipitor).
   d. docusate (DSS).

87. During a patient interview, the PMHNP notes that the patient is rubbing her hands together, sitting tensely, answering abruptly, and avoiding eye contact. The PMHNP tells the patient, "I can see that you are upset." This therapeutic technique is:
   a. clarifying.
   b. observing.
   c. restating.
   d. empathizing.

88. After an automobile accident resulted in the death of his wife months earlier, a Mexican immigrant has become very depressed and relates multiple health complaints, including headache, stomachache, insomnia, nausea, and diarrhea. The patient agrees to take an antidepressant but insists that he needs to also receive treatment by a *curandero* for *susto* (loss of soul). The best response is to:
   a. tell the patient that a *curandero* cannot help.
   b. caution the patient that the *curandero* ritual may interfere with treatment.
   c. tell the patient that he must choose between the *curandero* or Western medicine.
   d. be supportive and facilitate *curandero* treatment.

89. A patient with bulimia nervosa is very angry at the PMHNP because of the restrictions that the PMHNP has prescribed after meals to prevent the patient from purging. However, the patient denies she is angry and accuses the PMHNP of being angry with her. This is an example of:
   a. suppression.
   b. denial.
   c. projection.
   d. repression.

90. During assessment and problem identification for a newly admitted patient with multiple physicians, if inconsistencies in medical data are found, the PMHNP should first:
   a. consult with the client.
   b. accept the latest information as being the most accurate.
   c. consult with the source(s) of inconsistent data.
   d. ask for a medical review of the patient's care.

91. Which of the following tests used to assess cognitive abilities for a patient with dementia includes remembering and later repeating the names of three common objects and drawing the face of a clock with all 12 numbers and with the hands indicating a specified time?
   a. Mini-Mental State Exam (MMSE).
   b. Mini-Cog test.
   c. Instrumental Activities of Daily Living (IADLs).
   d. Confusion Assessment Method.

92. The PMHNP is the manager of the unit and has hired two new graduate nurses to work on the unit. The PMHNP expects that the nurses will likely need the most guidance related to:
   a. acting professionally.
   b. documenting correctly.
   c. maintaining ethical standards.
   d. delegating tasks.

93. The PMHNP has discovered that Medicare and Medicaid are routinely being charged for services that patients have not received and records are being falsified. The most appropriate action is for the PMHNP to:
    a. confront the administration.
    b. contact the local district attorney.
    c. file a *qui tam* lawsuit.
    d. notify a local newspaper.

94. A patient is diagnosed with psychogenic nonepileptic seizure (pseudoseizure). The most appropriate treatment approach includes:
    a. antianxiety medication and psychological counseling.
    b. an anticonvulsant drug.
    c. no treatment is necessary.
    d. anticonvulsant and antianxiety drugs.

95. A 17-year-old girl with a history of anorexia and depression is taking topiramate (Topamax) to control generalized tonic-clonic seizures. The adverse effect associated with topiramate that is of most concern is:
    a. initial sedation.
    b. anorexia/weight loss.
    c. increased appetite/weight gain.
    d. dulling of cognition.

96. According to the theory of cognitive dissonance (Festinger), which of the following is most likely to change if dissonance occurs?
    a. beliefs.
    b. behaviors.
    c. actions.
    d. emotions.

97. The PMHNP should monitor adolescents taking atypical antipsychotics, such as olanzapine and risperidone, for:
    a. drug-induced anemia.
    b. hypertension.
    c. weight gain.
    d. acne.

98. The PMHNP prescribes antipsychotic medications for patients even though the PMHNP is aware that the medications have numerous adverse effects that may impair overall health, basing treatment on the ethical principle of:
    a. nonmaleficence.
    b. beneficence.
    c. fidelity.
    d. justice.

99. A 45-year-old female patient visits the PMHNP with complaints of increasing depression. The patient reports increasing lethargy, weight gain, hair loss, dry skin, and sensitivity to cold. Her BP is 110/68 and her pulse is 58. The initial diagnostic test(s) indicated to determine potential causes for the depression include(s) which one of the following:

    a.   kidney function tests.
    b.   liver function tests.
    c.   magnetic resonance imaging (MRI) of the brain.
    d.   thyroid function tests.

100. If the PMHNP is basing her leadership style on expectancy theory (Vroom), then she is expected to focus on:

    a.   positive reinforcement.
    b.   working conditions and salary.
    c.   safety and security.
    d.   feedback from staff.

101. If a PMHNP is interested in becoming a leader in health-care reform and the role of the PMHNP, his first step is to:

    a.   join a number of organizations promoting health-care reform.
    b.   begin to write to politicians expressing opinions about health care.
    c.   become knowledgeable about the current health-care system.
    d.   ask other leaders what topics to focus on for activism.

102. The ethnic group with the highest rates of suicide in the United States is:

    a.   Caucasian.
    b.   African American.
    c.   Native American.
    d.   Asian.

103. As a nurse manager, the PMHNP has informational, decisional, and interpersonal responsibilities. An example of a decisional responsibility is:

    a.   disseminating policies.
    b.   conflict negotiations.
    c.   serving as a spokesperson.
    d.   allocation of resources.

104. The PMHNP is the project manager for a quality improvement project that requires multiple activities and stages of development over a 12-month period. The best method of illustrating the sequence of tasks is by developing a:

    a.   Q & A report.
    b.   program evaluation and review technique (PERT) flowchart.
    c.   narrative explanation.
    d.   decision-making grid.

105. A patient being treated for antisocial personality disorder became very agitated and refused to participate in activities. The PMHNP best engages in reflective thinking by:

    a. telling the patient several positive reasons for participating.

    b. asking the patient why he doesn't want to participate.

    c. reviewing interactions to determine how to better deal with the patient.

    d. describing the event to other nursing staff and asking for input.

106. The type of organizational structure in which the PMHNP would likely need to report to more than one manager is:

    a. matrix.

    b. flat.

    c. tall.

    d. product line.

107. The PMHNP is considering how to use technology in therapy. The PMHNP recognizes that virtual reality programs may best be used as part of:

    a. CBT.

    b. therapeutic milieu.

    c. family therapy.

    d. exposure therapy.

108. The PMHNP discovers that a coworker has posted information on a social media site about a patient who is well known in the community, giving the person's name and diagnosis and describing the patient's condition. The PMHNP should:

    a. tell the coworker to remove the information.

    b. tell the patient what the coworker has done.

    c. notify the administration of a breach in confidentiality.

    d. advise the coworker that this is a Health Insurance Portability and Accountability Act of 1996 (HIPAA) violation.

109. If the PMHNP has been offered a leadership position but feels unprepared, the best solution is to:

    a. study books on leadership.

    b. ask subordinates for guidance.

    c. find a mentor.

    d. turn down the position.

110. A 16-year-old patient with diabetes mellitus, type 1, since age 4 has been hospitalized twice recently for elevated serum glucose and once for diabetic ketoacidosis. In all three cases, the patient was with friends and failed to follow dietary and medication protocols because of peer pressure to conform. The PMHNP recommends:

    a. assertiveness training.

    b. diabetes education.

    c. separation from peers.

    d. parental disciplinary actions.

111. The PMHNP can withhold bad news about a patient's diagnosis from the patient if:
   a. the family of an adult patient requests that the nurse withhold the information.
   b. the patient is depressed, and bad news may worsen the patient's condition.
   c. if the PMHNP believes doing so is in the best interest of the patient.
   d. the patient requests that the nurse not tell the truth about negative results.

112. Under the legal doctrine of *respondeat superior*, if the PMHNP is in private practice and directs a nurse employed by the practice to give a patient a half dose of medication but the nurse gives a double dose and the patient has a severe reaction, then the PMHNP is:
   a. exempt from liability because the nurse made the error.
   b. liable only if aware of the dose the nurse was administering.
   c. liable for the employee's negligence.
   d. exempt from liability because the order was correct.

113. A patient complains to the PMHNP that she is exhausted because the unit is so noisy in the daytime and she is awakened repeatedly during the night. The response that shows the best collaborative response to the patient's needs is:
   a. "I'll talk about this with staff members."
   b. "Let's talk about ways to allow you to get more rest."
   c. "We can provide you with a sedative at night to help you sleep better."
   d. "I understand your concerns, but there is little that can be done."

114. Which element of malpractice is violated if the PMHNP gives a patient a sedative and fails to monitor the patient's response?
   a. Foreseeability.
   b. Causation.
   c. Breach of duty owed.
   d. Duty owed to the patient.

115. In communicating with an interdisciplinary group, the PMHNP is aware that the most critical skill is:
   a. listening.
   b. making eye contract.
   c. verbal tracking.
   d. using body language.

116. The organization has flattened the chain of command and widened the span of control. As a supervisor, the PMHNP expects that this will mean:
   a. decreased authority to make decisions.
   b. increased numbers of managers to report to.
   c. increased numbers of staff to manage.
   d. decreased numbers of staff to manage.

117. An 8-year-old boy has been sleeping poorly, complaining of stomachaches, crying frequently, and refusing to go to school. A complete physical examination ruled out a physical ailment. As part of an assessment for anxiety, the simplest assessment tool to use with a child is the:

    a. Hamilton Anxiety Scale (HAS).
    b. Beck Anxiety Inventory (BAI).
    c. Beck Depression Inventory (BDI).
    d. Revised Children's Manifest Anxiety Scale (RCMAS).

118. The PMHNP is using SWOT analysis as part of a quality improvement process. The S represents *strength*, the W *weaknesses*, and the O *opportunities*. What does the T represent?

    a. Time.
    b. Threats.
    c. Targets.
    d. Testing.

119. According to Rogers' Innovation–Decision Process, individuals can bring about personal change and accept innovations in five stages that begin with:

    a. confirmation.
    b. decision.
    c. knowledge.
    d. persuasion.

120. An observant Muslim patient is hospitalized during the month of Ramadan. When advising staff members about the patient's needs, the PMHNP points out that they should expect the patient to:

    a. refuse treatment during the month.
    b. refuse to eat or drink from sunup to sundown.
    c. insist on staying separate from non-Muslims.
    d. pray 10 times a day.

121. In a recovery-oriented system of care, a patient who is discharged after treatment for drug or alcohol addiction should expect:

    a. referral to community resources.
    b. to need no further treatment.
    c. to be provided a sheltered living situation.
    d. to receive disability payments.

122. When helping individuals to resolve conflicts, the PMHNP realizes that the most difficult conflicts to resolve are:

    a. goal based.
    b. fact based.
    c. approach based.
    d. value based.

123. The administration has asked the PMHNP for guidance in eliminating lateral violence (bullying among coworkers) from the workplace. The initial recommendation should be to:

a. conduct an anonymous survey.
b. publish a zero-tolerance policy.
c. interview key personnel.
d. discuss the issue at staff meetings.

124. The PMHNP using the STAMP acronym as a guide to identify behaviors that pose the risk of violence knows that the "S" stands for:

a. scowling.
b. sarcasm.
c. staring.
d. speech change.

125. A patient who looks at a picture of red roses and perceives a monster dripping blood from its mouth is experiencing:

a. an illusion.
b. a delusion
c. a hallucination.
d. magical thinking.

126. Which of the following is NOT true about the epidemiology and risk factors of violent behavior?

a. More than 50% of people who commit criminal homicides and who engage in assaultive behavior have imbibed significant amounts of alcohol immediately beforehand.
b. For aggression classified as homicide, battery, assault with a weapon, or rape, the frequency among males clearly exceeds that among females.
c. Most adults with and without mental disorders who commit aggressive acts do so against people they do not know, that is, strangers.
d. For domestic violence, in which one partner hurts another, the frequency among men and women is about equal.

127. A client is a 14-year-old girl brought in by her parents for evaluation because of episodes of defiance over curfews and of staying out late with friends. The initial approach to her situation is which of the following?

a. Meet with the family and tell the parents that such separation-individuation behavior is healthy and normal.
b. Meet with the girl alone and explain that her behavior is exposing her to many high-risk behaviors, including substance abuse, delinquency, unprotected sex, pregnancy, and sexually transmitted diseases.
c. Arrange for a separate therapist for the girl, a separate therapist for the parents, and yourself as the family counselor.
d. Assess the family situation, assess the level of communication in the family, and attempt to identify specific stressors or situations that could be aggravating a normal development stage in order to address them.

128. A PMH NP is working in a substance-abuse treatment clinic where the clients are subject to random, mandatory drug screening as a part of their probation for substance abuse–related offenses. If a client has a negative urine test result, the NP can be confident that the client has not abused any of the following drugs in the past 2 to 3 days EXCEPT:

a. heroin.
b. toluene.
c. cocaine.
d. marijuana.

129. A client is a 34-year-old Hispanic-American farm worker who was diagnosed last year with bipolar disorder and who has been prescribed lithium carbonate. He came to the United States from Nicaragua 18 months ago. The PMH NP is meeting him for the first time, after he has had 4 hospitalizations for his disorder and during which his lithium levels ranged from "undetectable" to 2.1 mEq/liter. What is the first step that the NP would take to assess his "health literacy" concerning his disorder?

a. Determine whether he speaks English well enough to understand explanations and directions in English or whether he needs a translator.
b. Ask him whether he was given information on bipolar disorder during and after his hospitalizations.
c. Ask him to describe in his own words what his illness is and what he must do to manage it.
d. Find out how much formal schooling he has had.

130. Which of the following is true about the heredity of bipolar disorder?

a. The risk of one identical (monozygotic) twin having bipolar I disorder if the other twin has it is 75%.
b. First-degree relatives of someone with bipolar disorder have a risk of developing bipolar disorder that is 4 to 6 times that of the general population.
c. The risk of one fraternal (dizygotic) twin having bipolar I disorder if the other twin has it is 25%.
d. If unipolar depression and bipolar I disorder are considered, then a co-twin has an even higher risk of affective illness if the index twin has bipolar I disorder, namely 100% for monozygotic twins and 50% for dizygotic twins.

131. The pathophysiology of major depressive disorder includes which of the following biochemical abnormalities?

a. Cortisol secretion following administration of 1 mg of dexamethasone will be suppressed after 12 hours in 75% of patients with clinical signs and symptoms sufficient to diagnose major depressive disorder.
b. Secretion of TSH following administration of TRH is suppressed in a significant proportion of patients with major depressive disorder relative to normal subjects.
c. CSF levels of 5HIAA are elevated in the majority of patients with major depressive disorder who commit suicide.
d. MHPG (3-methoxy-4-hydroxyphenylglycol), a metabolite of norepinephrine, is lower in the urine of patients with delusional depression than in patients with nondelusional depression.

132. Which of the following is required for the diagnosis of major depressive disorder?

    a.   At least 1 week of persistently depressed mood.

    b.   Suicidal ideation.

    c.   The symptoms cause clinically significant distress or impairment of function.

    d.   At least 4 of the following symptoms (depressed mood, loss of pleasure or interest, appetite or weight change, sleep disturbance, psychomotor agitation or retardation, fatigue, worthlessness or guilt, decreased concentration, and suicidal ideation) are present during most of 2 weeks and represent a change from the preceding 2 weeks.

133. A 25-year-old woman is brought by her family to the emergency room after complaining of having seizures again. She had been evaluated fairly recently for this same complaint, according to the family, but no medication was prescribed. The patient states that she doesn't like the neurologist and doesn't want him involved. The NP suspects that she is having pseudoseizures with a psychogenic etiology. What clinical observations or symptoms would help to confirm this possibility?

    a.   Her seizures involve bilateral tonic/clonic movements during which she remains conscious and verbal.

    b.   The patient holds her breath and becomes slightly cyanotic during an observed seizure in the ER.

    c.   She reports having the olfactory hallucination of burning rubber just before the seizures.

    d.   The patient and the family report that she is sometimes incontinent during the seizures.

134. A family brings in an elderly grandmother who is 87 years of age and who has been living with them. They express concern that she needs nursing home level of care. The patient's primary care physician evaluated her independently from the family and did not find a level of impairment or risk adequate to justify admission. The PMH NP is called in to consult on the situation. Which of the following should be prominent in the differential diagnosis?

    a.   Munchausen syndrome by proxy.

    b.   Malingering.

    c.   Substance abuse.

    d.   "granny dumping."

135. Which one of the following Axis II disorders requires the presence of an Axis I disorder as a diagnostic criterion?

    a.   Borderline Personality Disorder.

    b.   Obsessive Compulsive Personality Disorder.

    c.   Schizoid Personality Disorder.

    d.   Antisocial Personality Disorder.

136. A 32-year-old woman with Borderline Personality Disorder sees a PMH NP in her private practice for medication management every 2 weeks. When the NP responded to a phone message while on call, she obtained her cell phone number and now calls the NP up to 5 times a day for crises. The PMH NP should:

    a. change her cell phone number and make sure that she blocks her number when returning calls to her in the future.

    b. arrange to terminate services with her and refer her for more comprehensive treatment at a mental health clinic or group practice that has a DBT or other specialized approach to these patients.

    c. set limits on her phone calls, telling her that she may only leave messages on the business phone line (no more than once a day) and that she will return her calls at her discretion.

    d. tell her that the NP contract with her is for office visits every 2 weeks and that she will not speak with her in between appointments.

137. The PMH NP has obtained a position as a psychiatric nurse at a maximum-security corrections facility. Many of his clients—who are men incarcerated for serious, violent crimes—complain of anxiety or insomnia and frequently request medication for help with these symptoms. The NP's response is to:

    a. counsel them about progressive relaxation techniques—a non-medical approach to their symptoms.

    b. assume that they are attempting to manipulation to obtain drugs that will give them some kind of "high."

    c. prescribe low-dose benzodiazepine medications that will be dispensed by the nurse on duty on an as-needed basis.

    d. prescribe SSRI medications, which have no abuse potential and may help with anxiety symptoms.

138. A PMH NP receives a notice from the pharmacy management service of her patient's insurance plan that he has been obtaining benzodiazepine medication from three other practitioners besides herself, violating her agreement with him that she would prescribe these medications only if she was the sole provider. The NP decides that she will terminate treatment with this individual. The NP is concerned that he may become abusive, violent, or threatening if confronted with this directly. The best course of action is which of the following?

    a. Leave him a phone message telling him that she is canceling his next appointment, not refilling any more prescriptions for him, and terminating services as his clinician.

    b. At the next appointment, have a security guard or policeman present as she discusses the notice with him, give him a chance to respond to it, state that she believes that he is abusing these medications and may be dependent on them or addicted to them, suggest in-patient detoxification and substance abuse treatment, and inform him that she has decided that she can no longer treat him and will cease to be available as his clinician after 1 month, which will give him time to find another practitioner.

    c. Send him a registered letter (return receipt requested), in which she informs him of her decision to terminate with him as his clinician, cancel his next appointment, and tell him that she will be available for emergencies only for the next month, during which time he can seek alternative sources of treatment.

    d. Speak with him directly by phone to discuss the notice and its implications, give him a chance to respond to it, inform him of her decision to terminate with him as his clinician, suggest possibilities for in-patient detoxification and substance abuse treatment, and offer to be available by phone only for emergencies for 1 month while he seeks alternative treatment. Document the conversation fully in the medical record.

139. A challenging patient with a paranoid personality disorder has gone to an emergency room with some physical complaints. The emergency room physician notices from his medical record who the patient's psychiatric nurse is, but the patient refuses to grant permission for the ER doctor to speak with him. The ER doctor calls the PMH NP nonetheless, citing the Health Insurance Portability and Accountability Act (HIPAA), which states that clinicians may share information about patients for clinical purposes, and requests that the NP "fill him in" on the patient. What is the best response?

    a. Ask whether there is a life-threatening emergency that makes such a request legitimate under the laws of the state. If there is not, the NP should reply that he is unable to tell him anything about the patient because of confidentiality.

    b. Even though the ER physician is correct, the PMH NP should appreciate that there is a good chance that the patient will find out about the conversation, which would risk disrupting the therapeutic alliance, given his diagnosis.

    c. Because there will be nothing in writing and it's just between the doctor and the NP, provide some information to the ER doctor that will be helpful in managing the patient while he is in the ER in an effort to optimize his medical care.

    d. Ask the physician to put the patient on the phone and attempt to convince the patient that he should give permission to speak with the ER doctor.

140. A 70-year-old recently widowed patient complains of initial insomnia as she works through her bereavement and requests something from her PMH NP to help her with sleep. The best medication option is:

a. flurazepam
b. diazepam
c. temazepam
d. eszopiclone

141. In initiating and monitoring pharmacotherapy with lithium carbonate, which of the following should be performed or measured done every 6 to 12 months?

a. Electrocardiogram (ECG).
b. BUN and creatinine.
c. Serum parathyroid hormone (PTH) level.
d. Dermatology consultation for psoriasis.

142. Of the commonly prescribed antipsychotic medications for treatment of schizophrenia, which pair of the following drugs are most likely (first member of pair) and least likely (second member of pair) to cause weight gain, increased appetite, and abnormal glucose metabolism?

a. Olanzapine (Zyprexa) and aripiprazole (Abilify).
b. Quetiapine (Seroquel) and clozapine (Clozaril).
c. Risperidone (Risperdal) and paliperidone (Invega).
d. Perphenazine (Trilafon) and chlorpromazine (Thorazine).

143. A 25-year-old man complains of progressive symptoms of recurrent and persistent thoughts about germs and contamination experienced as intrusive and upsetting as well as feeling driven to perform repetitive hand washing, which has left his skin very dry and chapped. In addition to prescribing a selective serotonin reuptake inhibitor antidepressant, the PMH NP recommends referral to a practitioner that specializes in:

a. psychoanalysis.
b. therapeutic massage.
c. cognitive-behavioral therapy.
d. interpersonal psychotherapy (IPT).

144. The ethics manual of the American Psychological Association explicitly requires informed consent for psychotherapy, whereas informed consent for psychiatrists practicing psychotherapy is implicitly required in The Principles of Medical Ethics with Annotations Especially Applicable to Psychiatry. The advantages of obtaining informed consent from a patient before embarking on a course of psychotherapy include all of the following EXCEPT:

 a. informed consent ensures that the patient has been informed about the risks and benefits of psychotherapy and about available alternative treatments, which increases the ability of patients to help themselves and feel empowered in decision-making.

 b. informed consent lessens the risk of regressive dependency by deemphasizing any tendency for the patient to see the therapist as "special" or uniquely empowered to help the patient, making the patient an equal partner in the undertaking.

 c. informed consent acknowledges the uncertainty of outcomes in psychotherapy, making both the patient and therapist partners in the task of obtaining a positive result and allowing the therapist to have a more realistic role in the treatment process.

 d. informed consent, by interposing a more formal and legally based discussion between the therapist and the patient, tempers the formation of the therapeutic alliance and injects an element of doubt or negative perspective into the patient's hope for benefit.

145. The nurse-in-charge of an in-patient psychiatric unit is present when staff must intervene to forcibly restrain a 35-year-old man recently admitted with mania who has assaulted his brother, who was visiting him. The charge nurse makes the decision to place the patient in physical restraints so that he can be medicated and prevented from injuring others or himself. What is true about situations of this type?

 a. Clients in restraints must be assessed every 30 minutes for circulation, respiration, nutrition, hydration, and elimination.

 b. As soon as possible, but no longer than 1 hour after the initiation of restraint or seclusion, a qualified staff member must notify the physician of the patient's condition and obtain a verbal or written order for the restraint or seclusion.

 c. Orders for restraints or seclusion of adults must be reissued by a physician every 8 hours.

 d. A physician must evaluate the patient while in restraints every 24 hours.

146. A 56-year-old man whose wife died 1 year ago and who was recently diagnosed with inoperable lung cancer is brought to a PMH NP's clinic by his 32-year-old son, who expresses concern about his father's depressed mood. The NP concludes from her assessment that he has signs and symptoms sufficient to qualify for a diagnosis of major depressive disorder: 10-lb. weight loss, anhedonia, anergy, and some self-neglect of hygiene and clothing. He is lucid and competent, adamantly insists that he is not suicidal, does not have guns at home, is not at risk of injuring himself, and refuses recommended psychiatric hospitalization. He accepts a prescription for an antidepressant and an appointment for the next week. Two days later he dies of a self-inflicted gunshot wound. The son files a lawsuit for failure to diagnose and treat. Which of the following is true?

 a. If he deliberately concealed suicidal ideation and intent while competent and able to cooperate in a psychiatric examination, there is no liability.

 b. He should have been committed involuntarily to a psychiatric hospital for his safety because he had many risk factors for suicide.

 c. The son should have been instructed to determine whether his father had any firearms in the house and, if so, to remove them.

 d. Because he had lost 10 lbs. and was disheveled, he should have been committed involuntarily because of his inability to care for himself by reason of mental illness.

147. Which of the following organizations is responsible for the evaluation of standards for institutional healthcare?

    a. The Centers for Disease Control and Prevention (CDC).
    b. The National Center for Health Statistics (NCHS).
    c. The Joint Commission.
    d. The Agency for Healthcare Research and Quality (AHRQ).

148. The American Nurses' Association (ANA), in collaboration with the American Psychiatric Nurses Association (APNA) and the International Society of Psychiatric-Mental Health Nurses (ISPN), has outlined a set of standards of practice that includes which of the following components of the nursing process?

    a. Coordination of Care; Health Teaching and Health Promotion; Milieu Therapy; Pharmacological, Biological, and Integrative Therapies; Prescriptive Authority and Treatment; Psychotherapy; and Consultation.
    b. General Information, Predisposing Factors, Precipitating Event, Client's Perception of the Stressor, Adaptation Responses, Summary of Initial Psychosocial/Physical Assessment including Knowledge Deficits, and Nursing Diagnoses.
    c. Assessment, Diagnosis, Outcome Identification, Planning, Implementation, and Evaluation.
    d. Subjective Data, Objective Data, Assessment, Plan, Intervention, and Evaluation.

149. A PMH NP is meeting in his office with a 24-year-old man and his mother. His working diagnosis is schizophrenia, but he has become very depressed and is almost mute. His therapist and his mother agree that he should be hospitalized, but the mother would like him to be at the university hospital psychiatric unit, which will not have a bed available until the next day. The local community hospital psychiatric unit has a bed available immediately. Although he mumbles "no" to questions about suicidality, the NP feels that he should be hospitalized immediately because he is psychotic and unpredictable. The NP's supervisor is unavailable for consultation. What is the safest course of action?

    a. Allow the mother to take him home until tomorrow because she has agreed to take responsibility for monitoring him.
    b. Explain that there is no choice but to hospitalize him immediately, given his assessment, and instruct the mother to take him to the community hospital for admission.
    c. Ask the patient and his mother to sit in the waiting area while making arrangements and then call the police and the ambulance service, fill out an involuntary commitment form, and wait for the police to arrive.
    d. Outline the recommendation that the patient be admitted immediately. State that he will arrange for him to be taken to the community hospital by ambulance and that he will assist with the transfer to the university hospital psychiatric unit the next day, if possible. Explain that he would prefer to avoid an involuntary commitment action but that he is willing to do so if the family does not agree to the plan.

150. A PMH,NP has noticed that her clients who take a multivitamin daily seem to suffer less from upper respiratory infections and have less trouble with depression. She decides to perform a small study to determine whether the vitamin C and vitamin D content of the multivitamins is a factor. She obtains funding; obtains IRB approval; arranges for the preparation of identical capsules containing placebo, vitamin D, vitamin C, or both vitamins; and arranges for patients, as they come for their appointments, to be randomly assigned into the treatment groups. The contents of the capsules given to a particular patient will be unknown to her, the clinicians, and the patients. This type of clinical trial is called:

   a.   A double-blind, placebo-controlled clinical trial
   b.   A case-control study
   c.   A single-blind, placebo-controlled clinical trial
   d.   A cross-sectional study

151. Which of the following statements are true about risk of suicide?

   a.   Suicide risk declines with age, reaching its lowest level among persons 65 years of age and older.
   b.   Of all racial groups, African Americans have the highest suicide risk.
   c.   Women have a higher risk of completed suicide per attempt than do men.
   d.   Suicide risk is elevated by a history of suicide in a first-degree relative, especially the same-sex parent.

152. Motivational interviewing for reduction of high-risk behaviors includes which of the following components?

   a.   Vigorous confrontation of resistance to change.
   b.   Maintenance of a detached, impersonal attitude.
   c.   Encouragement of the client to accept the therapist as authoritative and to foster dependency.
   d.   Developing discrepancy by helping the client to see how their day-to-day behavior deviates from their ideals.

153. Which of the following situations does NOT correlate with an increased risk of vulnerability to unhealthy levels of stress?

   a.   Working more than 48 hours per week.
   b.   Having been divorced or separated in the past year.
   c.   Having a network of friends and acquaintances.
   d.   Drinking alcohol, smoking, or using drugs to relax.

154. All of the following are questions included in the CAGE screening test for alcohol problems EXCEPT:

   a.   Have you ever felt you should cut down on your drinking?
   b.   Have you ever annoyed people by your drinking?
   c.   Have you ever felt bad or guilty about your drinking?
   d.   Have you ever had a drink first thing in the morning to steady your nerves or to get rid of a hangover (eye opener)?

155. The following prevalence rates for schizophrenia in specific populations are accurate EXCEPT:

    a. General population   1%
    b. Non-twin sibling of a schizophrenic patient   16%
    c. Child with one schizophrenic parent   12%
    d. Child of two schizophrenic parents   40%

156. A 23-year-old man presents to the emergency room requesting referral for opiate detoxification and complaining of withdrawal symptoms. On physical examination, the PMH NP finds all of the following signs and symptoms EXCEPT:

    a. Rhinorrhea and lacrimation.
    b. Constricted pupils (miosis).
    c. Profuse diarrhea.
    d. Piloerection (gooseflesh).

157. A 17-year-old adolescent girl is brought to a PMH NP by her parents, who complain that she doesn't eat and is very thin. On examination it is determined that her body weight is less than 85% of normal, she has not had a menstrual period in 6 months, she worries about being overweight, and she complains that she is "too fat." Which of the following additional features allows the NP to confidently diagnose Anorexia Nervosa, Binge-Eating/Purging Type as a single diagnosis rather than Bulimia Nervosa additionally?

    a. Binging and purging occur only during episodes of anorexia nervosa.
    b. Episodes of binge eating are recurrent.
    c. Inappropriate compensatory behavior to prevent weight gain—such as self-induced vomiting, use of diuretics or laxatives, fasting, or excessive exercise—is recurrent.
    d. Binge eating and inappropriate compensatory behaviors have both been occurring, on average, at least twice per week for 3 months.

158. Which of the following features supports the diagnosis of Malingering, as opposed to Factitious Disorder?

    a. Medical history, physical examination, and laboratory evaluations do not identify specific abnormalities.
    b. The patient's symptoms have necessitated his being kept in the hospital rather than returning to prison to continue serving his sentence.
    c. The patient's symptoms are vague, ill-defined, at times overdramatized, and not in accordance with known clinical conditions.
    d. The patient has a long history of previous hospitalizations, during which his symptoms have been severe but little pathologic evidence has been identified.

159. Which of the following is the most helpful in distinguishing a syndrome of Dementia from one of Delirium?

    a. The patient has a fluctuating level of consciousness.
    b. The patient is disoriented to person, place, and time.
    c. The patient is unable to remember more than 1 of 3 objects at 3 minutes.
    d. The patient keeps asking of the whereabouts of his spouse, who died last year.

160. A PMH NP is conducting an assessment of a 37-year-old unmarried mother of 4 who works as a unit clerk at the local community hospital. In reviewing her level of functioning in various areas, which of the following stands out as needing attention and exploration?

a. Her children attend school regularly, earn above-average marks, have friends, and receive positive reports from their teachers.

b. She is financially stable, making ends meet with her salary and with some help from extended family for occasional childcare needs.

c. She obtained restraining orders, through Legal Aid services, on two former boyfriends who became abusive and exploitative.

d. Despite having to take time away from work to help her youngest child get treatment for severe asthma, she negotiated with her employer to use vacation and sick time from the coming year and took minimal unpaid leave under the Family Medical Leave Act (FMLA).

161. Which of the following is a warning sign that a nurse is in danger of crossing the professional boundary of the nurse-client relationship?

a. A married patient of the same sex, with whom the NP has worked for several years through several crises, brings the NP a small box of candy as a gift just before the Christmas holidays.

b. The nurse find herself anticipating appointments with an attractive single patient and paying special attention to how she dresses and wonders whether the patient finds her attractive.

c. A patient who is a parent confides her distress over the serious illness of one of her children and the nurse mentions that one of his children had been similarly ill in the distant past and that he can understand somewhat what she must be going through.

d. A patient of the opposite sex, whom the NP has known for some time, has confided to her that his parent died unexpectedly the previous week and spends much of the session grieving and tearful. At the end of the session, the patient embraces the NP in appreciation and she reciprocates, holding the patient in her arms for a few seconds before the patient departs.

162. A married Italian man in his 60s has a history of treatment-resistant depression. The PMH NP consults with the patient's psychiatrist, and the recommendation is to initiate treatment with an MAO inhibitor antidepressant. What is the most important reason to meet with the patient's family when prescribing this medication?

a. MAO inhibitors can cause orthostatic hypotension, which may be worse on arising; therefore, family members need to be watchful.

b. MAO inhibitors can cause sexual dysfunction; therefore, the patient's spouse should be informed so as to anticipate this possibility.

c. MAO inhibitors can interact with certain foods and over-the-counter medications and cause an abrupt increase in blood pressure, which can be harmful.

d. MAO inhibitors can disrupt the sleep-wake cycle, which can result in daytime somnolence and nighttime insomnia.

163. Evidence-based treatment approaches to Attention-Deficit Hyperactivity Disorder (ADHD) include all of the following EXCEPT:

a. progressive relaxation techniques and meditation.

b. stimulant medication and monitoring of heart rate and blood pressure.

c. behavioral parent training (BPT) and behavioral classroom management (BCM).

d. intensive peer-focused behavioral interventions implemented in recreational settings (e.g., summer programs).

164. All of the following medication interventions would be reasonable as a next step in the treatment of Major Depressive Disorder when the patient has only partially improved after 6 to 8 weeks in response to an adequate dose of a standard SSRI antidepressant (e.g., fluoxetine, sertraline, fluvoxamine, paroxetine, citalopram, or escitalopram) EXCEPT:

    a. a second SSRI.
    b. the switch to an MAO inhibitor antidepressant.
    c. a tricyclic antidepressant, such as nortriptyline or desipramine.
    d. the addition of lithium carbonate.

165. Which of the following is NOT an important reason for monitoring lithium therapy with periodic blood tests?

    a. Long-term use of lithium may be associated with a decline in renal function, as indicated by elevations in BUN and creatinine levels.
    b. Lithium may exacerbate psoriasis.
    c. Lithium has been associated with elevated levels of parathyroid hormone and hypercalcemia in some patients.
    d. Lithium can cause elevations in thyrotropin (TSH) and subclinical or clinical hypothyroidism, much more frequently in females than in males.

166. All of the following situations support the use of psychotherapy EXCEPT:

    a. the therapist maintains a neutral demeanor as a "blank canvas" to facilitate transference.
    b. the objective of the therapist is to reinforce the patient's healthy and adaptive patterns of thought and behavior.
    c. the therapist engages in a fully emotional, encouraging, and supportive relationship with the patient.
    d. one aim of the treatment is to strengthen healthy defense mechanisms, especially in the context of interpersonal relationships.

167. Which of the following statements is true concerning the use of phototherapy for Seasonal Affective Disorders?

    a. Light therapy must be used to extend the period of daylight artificially by exposure before sunrise or after sunset.
    b. The optimum time of day for treatment is during the evening.
    c. A session must last at least 2 hours for any positive effect to occur.
    d. Evidence indicates that the wavelengths of light in the blue-green end of the visual spectrum are as effective as white light.

168. Which of the following statements is NOT true about informed consent?

    a. Adult patients are assumed to have the right to consent to or refuse treatment.
    b. Sufficient information about the diagnosis, the prognosis, and the risks and benefits of the proposed treatment must be provided.
    c. The provider is not required to inform the patient of the risks and benefits of possible alternative treatments, including no treatment at all.
    d. A procedure performed without informed consent is considered battery and may be malpractice as well.

169. Nurses are mandated to report abuse or neglect in all of the following situations EXCEPT:

   a. A 12-year-old boy being seen for ADHD medication appears malnourished and has visible bruises on his forearms.

   b. A 35-year-old woman complains that her boyfriend often forces her to have sex when she is unwilling and that she is distressed by this and unsure of what to do about it.

   c. An 82-year-woman who lives with her son and daughter-in-law recounts that she doesn't know what happens to her Social Security check every month and that her family refuses to discuss it with her, telling her "it's taken care of."

   d. An 8-year-old girl tells the NP that she dislikes being left at her grandfather's house because he cajoles her into playing games during which they dress and undress in front of each other and then wrestle on the floor.

170. A 42-year-old married man brought to the hospital by police is agitated, claims not to have slept for 3 days, believes that God has revealed a special mission to him to meet with the President of the United States and confront him directly about the budget deficit, and says he will pursue this or die trying. He was found wandering on the street in his underwear in mid-January in New England, and his wife states that he has not been eating. All of the following are reasons for which he may be involuntarily committed for psychiatric care by reason of mental illness EXCEPT:

   a. he presents a danger to others, specifically to the President of the United States.

   b. he is a danger to himself because his behavior, if unchecked, would certainly cause security personnel to stop him from approaching the President of the United States, with deadly force if necessary.

   c. his lack of sleep, being underdressed for the weather, and not eating suggest that he is unable to care for himself in his current state.

   d. his wife reports that he has been spending money irresponsibly, risking financial ruin for the family.

171. Which of the following is an example of 1 of the 4 stages of cognitive development identified by Piaget?

   a. Formal Operations (12-15+ years).

   b. Preconventional Level (ages 4-10 years).

   c. Toddlerhood (learning to delay satisfaction).

   d. The Symbiotic Phase (ages 1-5 months).

172. Which of the following is NOT considered Personal Health Information (PHI) under the Health Insurance Portability and Accountability Act (HIPAA)?

   a. Biometric identifiers, including finger and voice prints.

   b. The name of the patient's attending physician.

   c. Device identifiers and serial numbers.

   d. Internet Protocol (IP) address numbers.

173. The family of an elderly patient with a recent diagnosis of terminal cancer takes his PMH NP aside and requests that the NP not inform the patient of the diagnosis because it would be too upsetting for them. The NP conducts an assessment and finds that the patient is competent and rational. The patient asks his NP to discuss the doctor's findings, and the NP focuses on the patient's mild chronic history of asthmatic bronchitis. Which ethical principle has been violated?

   a. Beneficence.
   b. Justice.
   c. Veracity.
   d. Nonmaleficence.

174. Which is the best reason for obtaining a consultation?

   a. The possibility exists that a diagnosis might be incorrect and obtaining a second opinion will provide greater protection from a lawsuit.
   b. The patient's condition is complex and interesting, and the NP knows that the consulting psychiatrist will consider the case of interest in teaching nurses and medical students.
   c. The NP's supervisor has encouraged him to obtain consultations more frequently because he doesn't seem to ask for help often enough and he or she is concerned that the NP might be overlooking subtleties or ignoring complexities.
   d. The patient's situation is complicated by many psychosocial and medical issues and the NP is not certain which course of treatment will be most advantageous; the NP believes that proper care demands additional expertise.

175. The following are 4 of the criteria used to evaluate qualitative research. Which of them is incorrectly defined?

   a. Descriptive Vividness – The researcher describes the data gathering process in sufficient detail that the reader can personally experience it. The data collected, often in the form of personal statements, should be quoted directly and extensively, because this is the raw data from the study.
   b. Methodological Congruence – The researcher presents the philosophical and methodological approach used and cites references to support their approach. The subjects, sampling method, data-gathering and data-analysis strategies, and processes for informed consent are clearly and concisely described.
   c. Analytical Precision – The methods used to determine statistical significance, study size, the number of subjects needed, and the precision and accuracy of the instruments used to measure the data are described in detail.
   d. Theoretical Connectedness – Any theory developed from the study is clearly stated, logically consistent, reflective of the data, and in accord with other available knowledge.

Answer Key and Explanations

1. C: If the psychiatric and mental health nurse practitioner (PMHNP) notes that therapists are using a variety of treatment modalities for patients with depression and he or she believes that cognitive behavioral therapy (CBT) is the most effective and takes less time than many other therapies, the best course of action is to carry out evidence-based research and present his or her findings. The PMHNP should present his or her findings to administrators as well as the therapists because administrators may be in a position to influence the choice of therapy, especially if it reduces costs.

2. A: Once a person completes gender reassignment surgery and legally changes genders, that person is then considered the reassigned gender; thus, Mikaela is considered female, so her attraction to other females would result in her sexual orientation being a lesbian. If she were attracted to males, she would be heterosexual. Although she could also be classified as homosexual, this term is more commonly used for gay males, and she is no longer considered a male. She does not report a bisexual attraction to both genders.

3. B: Up to 40% of people experience sleep paralysis, most often during adolescence, so the teen should be reassured. The associated muscle atonia occurs during the onset of sleep (hypnagogic) or upon waking (hypnopompic), and the person is unable to move for seconds to minutes. In some cases, sleep paralysis is associated with sleep-related visual, auditory, or tactile hallucinations. If both symptoms are present along with daytime somnolence, then testing for narcolepsy is appropriate. Occasional sleep paralysis by itself does not warrant testing for epilepsy. Sleep paralysis may be triggered by lack of adequate rest or by stress.

4. B: Early majority. Characteristics of innovation adopters include the following:

- Innovators: Actively seek innovation, visionaries.
- Early adopters: Apply innovations that they learn about, opinion leaders.
- Early majority: Won't bring forth an innovation but are willing to readily adopt it when proposed by others.
- Late majority: Adopt innovations only under pressure.
- Laggards: Prefer the status quo and fail-safe innovations only.

5. C: If a patient scheduled for electroshock therapy tells the PMHNP, "I'm so afraid of how much this will hurt," the most appropriate response is, "Tell me what you think is going to happen." It's important to get clarifying information to determine what the patient's misconception is in order to alleviate the patient's concerns. For example, the patient may be concerned about pain during the procedure or after the procedure.

6. D: Deadlines. The following four different types of stressors may impact a patient's quality of care:

- Environmental: Noise, pollen, traffic, temperature, and weather.
- Social: Deadlines, time demands, interactions with others, and financial concerns.
- Physiological: Aging, pain, injuries, lack of sleep, poor nutrition, and illness.
- Psychological: Negative thoughts, worries, and anxiety.

234

7. B: If, as unit supervisor, the PMHNP uses disciplinary action to control the behavior of a staff member, the type of power the PMHNP is using is **coercive**, which is the power to punish others. **Expert** power derives from knowledge and expertise. **Legitimate** power derives from educational degrees and job title. **Referent** power derives from affiliating with others who hold power in the organization.

8. A: If a PMHNP tells a patient, "If you don't stop yelling, we're going to hold you down, place you in restraints, and give you an injection," this could be considered an assault, which includes threats to cause harm. If the PMHNP actually carries through with the threat against the patient's will, then this action could be considered battery. Patients should be made aware in advance of consequences of behavior, but the patient should not be reminded of them in a threatening manner.

9. D: If, when assessing the relationship between a patient and her 10-month-old infant, the PMHNP notes that the infant showed no distress when the mother briefly left the room and did not acknowledge the mother on her return, this exemplifies the avoidant attachment style. Attachment is the emotional bond between the child and a caregiver. The avoidant attachment style often indicates that the child has learned that the mother will not respond to the child.

10. C: If, in managing a conflict among staff on the psychiatric unit, the PMHNP helped those in disagreement to reach a compromise with each side giving up something and each side gaining something, the conflict may arise again because of the losses. In some cases, that which is lost becomes more important to people on reflection than that which is gained, leading to an additional conflict.

11. B: If a 45-year-old patient is undergoing alcohol withdrawal, a medication that the PMHNP can prescribe to relieve symptoms is chlordiazepoxide (Librium). For alcoholism, the medication is usually administered IM or IV 50 to 100 mg every 2 to 4 hours. The dose is reduced over a 5- to 7-day period. Although it is most commonly used for alcohol withdrawal, chlordiazepoxide may also be used for anxiety and as a preoperative sedative.

12. A: If a patient taking the Controlled Oral Word Association Test (COWAT) test is only able to name a few items when asked to name as many items as possible starting with a particular letter, such as "D," this suggests brain damage to the frontal lobe. The COWAT is the test most frequently used to assess injury to the frontal cortex. Other tests include those that measure the patient's ability to sequence events according to time or another logical manner, to reason, and to behave spontaneously.

13. C: The area of psychology that involves the study of the mental process involved in attention, memory, and perception and how these processes affect behavior is cognitive psychology. Cognitive psychology views the functions of the mind as being similar to those of a computer with input, processing, and output. Attention aids in filtering input to allow processing. Memory involves both short- and long-term memory. Perception involves interpreting sensory input (smells, sights, touch, taste, sounds, and position).

14. B: The STAR approach to patient safety is used when delivering patient care to ensure that no mistakes are made. The components of the STAR approach include the following:

- S: Stop to concentrate on the task at hand, eliminating distractions when possible.
- T: Think about the task, what the nurse is doing, and the purpose.
- A: Act to carry out the task, ensuring it is done correctly.
- R: Review how well the task was completed and if the outcomes are as predicted.

15. D: When the PMHNP is communicating with colleagues about a problem in an email, the most appropriate message is "Please attend a 15-minute meeting at 3 p.m. to discuss coordinating time-off requests." This relays the purpose of the meeting and the expected duration, and it is neutral in tone. Using all capital letters should be avoided because this is the digital equivalent of shouting. Including the word "problems" in the message sets a negative tone.

16. A: **Whole medical systems** include homeopathic medicine, naturopathic medicine, acupuncture, and Chinese herbal medication. **Mind–body medicine** includes support groups, meditation, music, art, or dance therapy. **Biologically based practices** include the use of food, vitamins, or nutrition for healing. Manipulative/body-based programs include massage or other types of manipulation, such as chiropractic treatment. **Energy therapies** may include biofield therapies intended to affect the aura (energy field) that some believe surrounds all living things. These therapies also include therapeutic touch and Reiki. **Bioelectromagnetic-based** therapies use a variety of magnetic fields to heal.

17. B: Patients with cognitive impairment may get up and move away or go for a walk during therapy, and the PMHNP should not try to restrain the patient but should ask if he/she can walk with the person. Communicating with patients with cognitive impairment can be challenging, and patients may have very different and individual responses, so observation of the patient must serve as a guide. If responses are unclear or inappropriate, the PMHNP can say, "I didn't understand that," but he or she should not laugh or indicate frustration. The PMHNP should face the patient and maintain eye contact to help the patient stay focused.

18. D: If, when conducting observational research of patients in a group therapy setting, the PMHNP notes that patients seem to behave as they believe they should in the group setting but that this behavior does not carry over into interactions in the unit, the patients are likely responding to demand characteristics. Demand characteristics are aspects of the environment (including expectations) that affect behavior. Demand characteristics are a concern when patients are aware that they are being observed because this may cause them to change their behavior.

19. A: According to Title II and Title III of the Americans with Disabilities Act (ADA), an emotional comfort animal does not qualify as a service animal. Service animals must actually provide some type of active service and must be canine, although special requests can be made to qualify miniature horses. Psychiatric services dogs, for example, are qualified to and may be trained to identify oncoming psychiatric episodes, remind the patient to take medications, interrupt self-injurious behavior, or protect disoriented patients from danger.

20. B: Cocaine and amphetamine may produce symptoms similar to schizophrenia because they stimulate dopamine receptors, increasing the level of dopamine. Antipsychotic drugs control symptoms of schizophrenia by inhibiting these receptors. Cocaine and amphetamine cause a buildup of dopamine at the receptor sites, and this causes a sense of euphoria and pleasure, followed by depression when the effect wears off. Cocaine and amphetamine affect other neurotransmitters to lesser degrees.

21. C: According to Piaget, **concrete operational** (6–11 years) is the stage at which a child would be expected to understand conservation of physical properties and to think logically about objects and events. During the **sensorimotor stage** (birth–2 years), the child learns about the world through movement and senses. During the **preoperational stage** (2–6 years), the child begins thinking egocentrically but develops some understanding of others' minds and acquires motor skills. During the **formal operational stage**, the child can think logically and abstractly.

22. C: If a time study showed that nursing staff members spent only 25% of their time in direct patient care, 30% of their time documenting, and 45% of their time on other activities, the next step is to closely review the "other activities" that require 45% of their time because correcting this could have the greatest impact on patient care. The time spent documenting is also excessive, so documentation procedures should also be reviewed.

23. B: If a 24-year-old patient with autism spectrum disorder level 1 cannot judge the intention behind commands, often becomes distraught over simple directions ("eat your lunch now"), and ignores important directions ("leave by the fire exit"), the term for this type of deficit is **mind blindness.** This same deficit interferes with patients' abilities to recognize faces. Mind blindness may contribute to impaired social interaction. A **meltdown** may begin with a tantrum, but it is more intense because the patient totally loses control and may endanger his- or herself or others. **Stereotypy** is rigid obsessive behavior. These deficits all result in **impaired social interaction.**

24. D: Staff compliance with best practice guidelines is usually best initially with simple changes in procedures, such as instituting checklists, because the learning curve is rapid and results are generally easily quantified. Because there is no financial outlay for new equipment or a need for extensive training, setting up a pilot program is fairly simple. The PMHNP should provide strong evidence based on research that the new practice is effective, and he or she should disseminate the results of the pilot program.

25. C: If a 12-year-old child dying of leukemia tells the PMHNP that she is worried about how her parents will cope after she dies, the most appropriate response is "Perhaps you can tell your parents what your hopes are for them." Children are often afraid that talking about death with their parents will be too upsetting for the parents, but the child should be encouraged to share feelings and concerns, which can help both the child and the parents cope better.

26. A: If the psychiatric unit is changing from a primary care nursing model with all registered nurses or advance practice nurses to a team nursing model that includes LPNs and psychiatric technicians, to help combat resistance, the PMHNP should focus on the benefits of working in a team. Benefits may include more time for professional duties and assistance in providing basic care needs, such as bathing and feeding.

27. D: For a 35-year-old recently widowed woman with severe anxiety and panic attacks left with few employable skills, little money, and three children, the primary need related to Maslow's hierarchy of needs is likely to be safety/security. Although the patient apparently had a stable and happy marriage, meeting the love/belonging need, and although lower needs must be fulfilled before higher needs, it is not uncommon for people to regress under stress. Now, the patient has real concerns about supporting and providing safety for her family, so she must meet the need for safety/security before she can again progress to the next level.

28. C: When conducting psychoeducation for a patient and family members, the initial action of the PMHNP is to identify and mitigate barriers to learning. For example, if a family member is vision impaired, this will impact the development of materials; or if a member does not want to participate, the individual may not be receptive to learning. Once the PMHNP identifies barriers as well as readiness to learn, he or she can develop lesson plans and materials.

29. B: If a patient is admitted for an extended stay in a rehabilitation facility for drug and alcohol addiction, and the patient's 8-year-old child asks the PMHNP if his mother will be able to come home soon, the most appropriate response is "Not soon because your mom needs to get well first." It's important to be truthful with children and to respect their feelings and concerns rather than trying to pass their concerns off on others or to minimize them.

30. A: The evidence-based therapy recommended for adolescents with anorexia nervosa is family-based therapy. (CBT is used with adults.) Because adolescents with anorexia are not able to make good decisions about food or eating, the family is mobilized to assist the patient and carry out therapeutic interventions, such as refeeding and other efforts to restore the patient's weight to a healthy level. Because caloric intake must be high to increase weight, the family must be physically present and monitor each meal, regardless of the time needed for the adolescent to finish eating.

31. D: Acting. The three steps in the process of valuing are as follows:

1. Choosing: This involves applying the intellect to considering alternative values and then selecting those that seem appropriate for the individual.
2. Prizing: This involves the emotions and positive feelings that the person derives from the values that he or she has chosen to live by.
3. Acting: This involves behavior that supports and is consistent with the values the person espouses.

32. C: Secondary prevention for an at-risk adolescent requires some type of intervention to deal with inappropriate behavior, such as working with the patient to modify negative behaviors. The adolescent patient may receive secondary prevention measures (treatment) in the community or as an inpatient. If the patient is hospitalized, the PMHNP focuses on helping the patient to learn more appropriate problem-solving skills and helping the patient (and family) to stabilize in crisis situations.

33. B: If a patient states, "I don't understand! My daughter said that she had to leave town," an appropriate clarifying question would be "Are you confused because you don't know why she had to leave town?" Clarifying questions are used to ensure that the listener has understood the meaning (as opposed to just the words) of the patient's statement. Clarifying questions often contain some paraphrasing of what the patient has stated and may include such phrases as "Did I understand you to say…?" or "Did you say…?"

34. D: If a 9-year-old girl has vaginal tearing, bruising, and scarring, which the mother claims occurred as a result of horseback riding, and the child seems emotionally stable and repeats that she hurt herself riding, but the PMHNP suspects sexual abuse, the most appropriate response is to report suspected abuse to the appropriate authorities. State reporting laws vary somewhat from state to state, but child protective services should be notified. Children sometimes exhibit little outward emotional indications of abuse and may be coached to explain their injuries.

35. A: If a PMHNP working with a 28-year-old female patient with bulimia nervosa finds a container of laxatives hidden in the patient's bed linens, the best response is to tell the patient directly about finding the laxatives without making a judgmental statement. If consequences for violating rules have been established, then those consequences should be applied. Establishing an honest relationship is essential to the development of trust between the patient and the nurse.

36. C: Memory can be assessed in a young child beginning at about 4 years of age. Immediate memory is evaluated by asked the child to repeat words or numbers. A 4-year-old can usually remember three items. Recent memory is tested by asking the child to remember one word and having the child recall the word in 5 or 10 minutes. Remote memory is tested by asking the child to repeat something the child has learned, such as a rhyme or the child's telephone number or address.

37. D: If a patient has received long-term treatment with haloperidol as an antipsychotic agent and has developed repetitive behaviors, including tongue thrusting, lip smacking, and hair pulling, the most likely cause is tardive dyskinesia (TD), which is related to the use of conventional antipsychotics. TD may result in permanent nonvoluntary movements. Symptoms are often irreversible, but stopping or changing the medication may reduce symptoms. Patients must be monitored carefully for initial indications of TD so that medications can be changed before symptoms become severe.

38. B: If the PMHNP overhears a nurse telling a disruptive patient, "Shut up, stop acting stupid, and go to your room," the best response is to begin by describing what he or she observed without attaching a judgment (rude, inappropriate) to it, "I heard you tell the patient to shut up, stop acting stupid, and go to her room." This approach confronts the problem directly and leaves less leeway for excuses or denial.

39. A: If the PMHNP is gathering information about a patient, a tertiary source of information is medical records as well as information from other health-care providers, such as rehabilitation therapists. Primary information is only information that is derived directly from statements by the patient. Secondary information is derived from personal observation by the PMHNP or from reports of observations by family members or friends. The PMHNP should never rely on only one source of data, keeping in mind that observations may be biased or dishonest.

40. B: If the PMHNP carries out an assessment of patient satisfaction and then devises a strategy to reduce patient complaints regarding the time required for staff members to respond to patient needs, the competency skill that he or she is exhibiting is conceptual. Conceptual skills involve the ability to analyze and reach conclusions about solving problems. Other competency skills include technical skills and interpersonal skills.

41. D: If a patient with psychosis has been prescribed chlorpromazine hydrochloride (Thorazine), an antipsychotic, the PMHNP should advise the patient to avoid sun exposure because photosensitivity reactions of the skin may occur. When outside or exposed to the sun, patients should wear sunblock and protective clothing. Chlorpromazine is more likely to cause photosensitivity than are other medications in the same class. Patients should also avoid alcohol while taking the drug and should avoid activities that require good coordination, especially in the initial weeks of therapy.

42. C: According to Erikson's stages of human development, the key event during the stage of adolescence (12 to 18 years) is peer relationships. During this stage, adolescents tend to pull away from their families as they continue to assert their growing independence and to bond with their peers. This often increases conflict within a family, especially when the adolescent begins to identify with peers of whom the parents disapprove and whose values may differ from those of the parents.

43. A: With rational emotive behavior therapy (REBT), the model suggests that adversity (A—activating event) and consequences (C) are strongly influenced by beliefs (B) about the event. According to this model of therapy, people innately have both rational and irrational tendencies, so if the person has irrational beliefs about an activating event, then the consequences result in feelings of defeat, whereas if the person has rational beliefs, the consequences are more likely to be seen as constructive.

44. A: If, as part of evidence-based research, the PMHNP finds that one instrument produces the same results whenever it is used to measure a similar behavior, this suggests that the instrument has **reliability**. The three properties that are essential to a good measure are reliability, validity, and power. An instrument has **validity** if it can be shown to measure what was intended. **Power** is the ability to detect a significant effect in a sample of a population if it occurs in the whole population.

45. B: The best response to a patient experiencing auditory hallucinations, saying "Don't you hear them?" is to state "I know the voices seem real to you, but I don't hear them." This response validates the patient's perception and his or her real fear of the voices ("I know the voices seem real to you") while orienting the patient to reality ("I don't hear them"). The PMHNP should speak in a calm voice and avoid standing too close to or touching the patient without permission because these actions may increase the patient's fear and anxiety.

46. D: If the PMHNP is concerned that the state's nurse practice act needs revision to more accurately reflect the competencies of PMHNPs, the best means of promoting revision is to become active in a state nursing organization. In almost all cases, revisions are based on lobbying efforts by state and national nursing associations, such as the American Nurses Association, which can plan campaigns to gather support.

47. A: The statement by a patient that is most likely to indicate suicidal ideation and risk for suicide is "My children would be better off without me." When patients make statements indicating possible suicidal ideation, the PMHNP should address this immediately by asking if the patient has thoughts about dying and if the patient has a plan. Patients who have formulated a plan (such as taking an overdose of medications) are at higher risk than those who simply think about wanting to die.

48. C: Delusion of reference: The patient believes that everything in the environment references her, such as the patient believing that messages are being sent to her in newspapers, magazines, radio, and television and that she must decipher them. **Delusion of persecution**: The patient believes that others intend to harm her. **Delusion of control:** The patient believes that other people or objects control her actions. **Delusion of grandeur:** The patient believes that she is an important person or being, such as God.

49. B: If, when conducting evidence-based research, the PMHNP observes that a natural correlation appears to exist between two variables, he or she should consider that there may be a third-variable correlation. That is, a third variable may be affecting the other two variables and there may, in fact, be no cause-and-effect relationship between the two. Therefore, when assessing natural correlations, a researcher should always look for third-cause variables.

50. D: When using clinical pathways, patient progress is measured in relation to expected outcomes. Clinical pathways outline the expected clinical progress for specific conditions and the expected outcomes. While clinical pathways vary, they typically contain a day-by-day outline of activities (participation in exercise, eating, sleep), treatments (group therapy, medications), and expectations (including the length of stay). While clinical pathways are often used in order to minimize costs of care, their primary purpose is to promote consistent and better-quality care.

51. C: In establishing a therapeutic relationship with a patient, the PMHNP's goal for the patient at the end of the orientation phase is for the patient to develop trust in the PMHNP. The orientation phase is critical if the nurse and patient are to have a productive working phase. During orientation, the patient and the PMHNP should also develop respect for each other, identify the patient's primary problems, and estimate the expected duration of the relationship.

52. B: **Intellectualism:** Using rational intellectual processes to deal with stress and loss, such as by discussing the positive aspects of being single. **Displacement:** Transferring feelings from one person or thing to another, such as being angry with a boss and taking the anger out on a spouse. **Denial**: Completely refusing to acknowledge a situation that is stressful, such as ignoring a child's drug use. **Rationalization:** Attempting to find excuses for unacceptable behavior or feelings, such as drinking to relieve the stress of work.

53. D: The four essential elements of informed consent before a patient can make a decision about care are as follows:

1. Voluntarism: The patient must be free to make the decision without coercion, manipulation, or threats, although persuasion may be used.
2. Competence: The patient must be mentally competent to make decisions.
3. Disclosure: The health-care provider must provide full disclosure about a treatment, including what comprises the treatment, any alternate options, and the purpose of the treatment.
4. Comprehension: The patient must be able to understand the implications of the treatment.

54. B: If the PMHNP is interviewing a 20-year-old patient who has a four-year history of cyclothymia but is currently asymptomatic, the maximum period of time during which the PMHNP expects the patient to remain asymptomatic is two months (one month for children and adolescents). Symptoms include alternating periods of hypomania and mild depression. For diagnosis, the symptoms must be present for at least two years for adults and one year for children and adolescents.

55. C: According to Maslow's hierarchy of needs, the nursing diagnoses would be prioritized in the following manner (first to last):

- Physiological needs: Sleep deprivation.
- Safety and security needs: Risk for injury.
- Love and belonging: Social isolation.
- Esteem (self and from others): Ineffective coping.

The last need is for self-actualization, but Maslow's hierarchy of needs is predicated on the idea that one must meet the needs at one level before progressing to the next level, so many people are never able to meet the needs associated with self-actualization.

56. D: The FDA-approved drug for the treatment of obsessive-compulsive disorder (OCD) that the PMHNP can prescribe is fluoxetine (Prozac). Most selective serotonin reuptake inhibitors (SSRIs), such as fluoxetine, seem to show positive results with OCD, although not all are FDA approved specifically for OCD. If the medication is successful, symptoms are often reduced by 40%–60%. Some antidepressants, such as nefazodone, imipramine, and amitriptyline, show little effect.

57. B: During the stage of toddlerhood, the child should learn to delay gratification and feel satisfied when delaying self-gratification is pleasing to others. According to Peplau's interpersonal relations theory, if patients have not completed tasks of toddlerhood, as adults they may use exploitive and manipulative behavior with others, exhibit envy and suspiciousness toward others, hoard, exhibit miserliness, exhibit inordinate neatness/punctuality, have difficulty relating to others, and alter personality characteristics to fit the situation. A patient who has not completed toddlerhood tasks requires complete acceptance in order to feel safe and secure.

58. A: If, as leader of an interdisciplinary team, the PMHNP notes that one team member who has worked on the unit for more than 20 years frequently criticizes younger and less experienced nurses, the best initial approach to resolving this is to ask the experienced nurse to serve as a mentor. This shows recognition of the nurse's skills and may help to alleviate some anxiety the nurse may have about being displaced by younger nurses.

59. C: The structure in the brain that plays a role in emotional memories and other emotional processes is the amygdala, which is part of the limbic system, which also includes the hippocampus and the hypothalamus. The amygdala triggers reactions, such as laughing, crying, and screaming with fright, and it has a primary role in encoding events as fearful. The amygdala is the brain structure that evaluates stimuli to determine if they are good or bad.

60. D: Most people with reasonable cognitive ability understand that smoking is bad for their health, so threatening them or scaring them is not likely to motivate them to quit. Realistically, success rates for smoking cessation are often low, so the PMHNP should consider that not everyone will be successful at quitting and should provide information as a preventive measure about symptoms of concern, such as increasing cough, purulent or bloody sputum, and increased shortness of breath.

61. D: The behavior that would differentiate aggression from anger is making verbal threats because this often means that the patient's anger is escalating and the person's response may be disproportionate to the situation. Other indications of aggression include restless behavior and pacing back and forth, shouting in a loud voice, and using obscenities. The person may be very suspicious and exhibit disturbed thought processes and increased agitation and overreaction to stimuli. Aggressive patients almost always have an intent to hurt someone or something.

62. A: Under provisions of the American with Disabilities Act (ADA) related to people with psychiatric disabilities, employers are required to provide reasonable accommodations. This does not mean that the ADA requires the hiring of people with psychiatric disabilities, holding a position open during an employee's absence, or providing for any and all requests that people make. The employee must still be able to carry out the job for which he or she was hired, although accommodations such as flexible work hours or break time and a quieter space to work are reasonable.

63. B: If, during a severe storm, four psychiatric unit staff members are unable to report for duty, leaving the unit understaffed, the PMHNP should proceed by prioritizing patient care needs to ensure that the most important needs (such as medications) are attended to first. Some needs, such as assistance with bathing, may be bypassed for the day. Asking patients to assist is not appropriate, and the administration may not be able to provide additional staff.

64. C: If a 28-year-old female patient who experienced sexual abuse as a child expresses distorted feelings of guilt and shame, blaming herself for the abuse and exhibiting low self-esteem, the most effective therapeutic approach is likely to be CBT. CBT helps patients to change their patterns of thinking and to feel better about themselves. CBT is a relatively short form of therapy, often taking only a few weeks or months of weekly meetings with a therapist.

65. D: If a patient with a right-sided above-elbow (AE) amputation has become increasingly depressed because of persistent severe phantom limb pain, and the PMHNP suggests the use of a mirror box to create the illusion that the limb has been restored, then this therapeutic treatment is based on neuroplasticity. Viewing the limb as intact helps to create new mapping in the brain, eventually allowing the person to "move" the phantom limb to reduce discomfort.

66. A: If a patient who has been using heroin is admitted to the psychiatric unit, the patient is likely to exhibit withdrawal symptoms within 6 to 12 hours after the last dose of heroin because heroin is relatively short acting. Withdrawal symptoms usually peak within 1 to 3 days and subside by the end of a week. Typical withdrawal symptoms include nausea and vomiting, abdominal cramping, myopathy, dysphoric mood, fever, diarrhea, rhinorrhea, and insomnia.

67. D: If a patient with antisocial personality disorder tells the PMHNP (who is sensitive about her weight) that other staff members are making fun of her appearance and state that she is "fat and lazy," the PMHNP should remain calm, avoid showing a reaction, and advise the patient that his comments are inappropriate. Pathological personality traits common to antisocial personality disorder include antagonism characterized by manipulation, deceit, callousness, and hostility. The patient often uses dishonesty, lack of empathy, and hostility to manipulate others.

68. A: The most appropriate documentation regarding an incident with a disturbed patient is "Patient threw a plate at his father, grabbed him by the shirt, and threw him onto the floor." This statement is objective because it is describing the actions of the patient without attaching labels or interpretations (violent, aggressive, upset). Because this incident involved another person, an incident report must be filed, and any actions that were carried out in response to the incident should be detailed.

69. B: The statement by a patient in CBT for major depressive disorder suggesting that she is applying principles learned in therapy is "I can't fix this situation, so I'm going to think about taking a vacation." One of the goals of CBT is to help patients think differently about situations and to use thought-stopping exercises when they begin to obsess over problems, such as a situation they can't fix. Patients use imagery, such as imagining being on a vacation, to help to have more positive thoughts.

70. A: If the PMHNP notes during a patient interview that the patient consistently expresses surprise at information of which the PMHNP knows that he is already aware, the display rule that this behavior exemplifies is **intensification**. **Deintensification** is muting expression. **Masking** is feeling one emotion and expressing another, and **neutralizing** is feeling an emotion but not expressing it.

71. A: The lithium level for maintenance should be 0.5 to 1.5 mEq/L. If the level increases to 1.5 to 2 mEq/L, then the next dose of medication should be withheld and the serum level of the drug should be tested. A further increase to 2 to 3 mEq/L is of considerable concern because the patient may exhibit moderate signs of toxicity. The patient requires immediate IV fluids as well as withholding of lithium. A level of 3 mEq/L or greater is life threatening and requires emergent intervention, sometimes including dialysis to lower lithium levels.

72. C: If a patient has intellectual disability and an IQ of 45 (moderate disability), a realistic maximal expectation is that the patient may be capable of working in a sheltered workshop because he or she should be capable of performing some activities independently while requiring some supervision. The patient should be able to achieve an academic level comparable to second grade. He or she may exhibit some speech impediments and have difficulty with peer relationships because of an inability to understand or adhere to social conventions.

73. A: A symmetrical pattern of bruising and petechiae up and down the back, chest, and shoulders, and across the forehead probably indicates coining (*cao gio*). This is a practice that is common in Southeast Asia and can appear as severe bruising, but the bruises are not random in the same way that is expected with abuse. An ointment is first applied to the skin, which is then rubbed firmly with a coin (or sometimes a spoon) until discoloration occurs as a method to rid the body of "bad blood" that may be causing illness.

74. B: If the PMHNP is prescribing lithium for a patient with bipolar disorder, a drug that should not be taken concurrently is hydrochlorothiazide because thiazides may increase the risk of lithium toxicity. Lithium interacts with numerous other medications (anticonvulsants, antipsychotics, loop diuretics, angiotensin-converting enzyme [ACE] inhibitors), so the PMHNP should always carefully review medication lists and check with a pharmacist if he or she is unsure about the possibility of a drug interaction.

75. C: An example of feedback that is directed at an action/state that the patient cannot modify is "You have memory problems because of your alcohol abuse" because the patient cannot undue the physical damage that has been caused by any specific action. The patient can modify behavior based on the other feedback. The patient can modify behavior if he has made an inappropriate comment, can try to control or explore the reasons for his anger, and can also attempt to make eye contact with his son during a subsequent visit.

76. D: According to CBT, the type of automatic thought exemplified when a patient states "My mother thinks I'm a failure" is **mind reading** because the patient is assuming to know what is in another person's mind (although this would not hold true if the mother actually stated that the patient was a failure). An example of **discounting positives** is "Of course I passed the test. The teacher made it too easy." **All-or-nothing thinking** leaves no room for another interpretation: "Everyone knows I'm stupid." **Personalizing** brings everything back to the individual, "He's successful because of my advice and help."

77. A: In a group process, the three major types of roles that group members assume within the group are:

1. **Completing group tasks:** Roles may include coordinating, evaluating, energizing, orienting, and elaborating.
2. **Supporting the group process:** Roles may include compromising, encouraging, following, harmonizing, and gatekeeping.
3. **Fulfilling personal needs**: Roles may include being aggressive, dominating, blocking, help-seeking, monopolizing, seeking recognition, and seducing.

Although completing group tasks and supporting group processes function to make the group effective, roles involved in fulfilling personal needs may interfere with the overall functioning of the group.

78. D: If a 68-year-old patient with Alzheimer's disease has been showing only mild symptoms on rivastigmine (Exelon) and suddenly had a marked increase in confusion, the medication that may be causing this confusion is oxybutynin. Rivastigmine is a cholinergic drug, and oxybutynin is an anticholinergic drug. Cholinergic drugs mimic the effect of acetylcholine and stimulate cholinergic receptors, but anticholinergic drugs block these receptors, decreasing the effect of the rivastigmine and similar drugs used to treat Alzheimer's.

79. D: The most appropriate intervention for severe confusion and agitation in a patient with dementia related to Alzheimer's disease is nonpharmacological measures, such as altering the environment, using distraction, allowing the patient to pace, and identifying triggers. Numerous studies have shown that antipsychotics are no better than placebos and that their use results in increased risk and adverse effects. Anticonvulsants also show no benefit. SSRIs have not been shown to reduce agitation, confusion, or depression in patients with Alzheimer's disease.

80. C: If a new member of a team on the psychiatric unit failed to follow unit safety protocols when a patient became aggressive and, as a result, sustained injuries when attacked by the patient, in a just culture model, the appropriate response would be coaching and further training because the PMHNP engaged in at-risk behavior by ignoring safety protocol. Human error and unintentional mistakes are dealt with by consolation and support, whereas reckless behavior requires punitive action.

81. B: According to the four phases of alcoholic drinking behavior (Jellinek), blackouts are a characteristic of phase II, early alcoholic. Phases of alcoholic drinking behavior include the following:

- Phase I, prealcoholic: Using alcohol to relieve stress (often learned behavior from childhood).
- Phase II, early alcoholic: Sneaking drinks, experiencing blackouts, and reacting defensively about drinking.
- Phase III, crucial alcoholic: Binge drinking, losing control to physiological dependence, displaying anger and aggression, and showing a willingness to sacrifice almost everything for alcohol.
- Phase IV, chronic alcoholic: Disintegrating physically and emotionally, being intoxicated most of the time, and experiencing life-threatening adverse effects.

82. A: Because of constant need, homeless people are most likely to be motivated by self-interest, so offering free food, water, and hygiene products is probably the best method to use to encourage participation. Although funding may be limited, sometimes community members will contribute or organizations, such as the Salvation Army, so the PMHNP may need to consider partnering with or working with other community resources, including homeless shelters and food kitchens, because these organizations can refer the homeless.

83. B: If a patient is undergoing opioid withdrawal, the medication that is often prescribed to relieve symptoms is clonidine (Catapres). Although the medication does not reduce the cravings associated with withdrawal, it helps to relieve the patient's anxiety, agitation, and discomfort (muscle aches, cramping, diaphoresis, rhinorrhea). Patients who experience fewer withdrawal symptoms are less likely to relapse. Patients also often receive other drugs during withdrawal, including methadone or buprenorphine, which are also used for maintenance.

84. D: If a patient who was voluntarily committed to a psychiatric facility wants to leave and is restrained from doing so by the PMHNP, this may constitute **false imprisonment** because the patient has the legal right to leave, even against medical advice. **Assault and battery** may occur if a patient was treated without consent or threatened. **Intentional torts** are voluntary purposeful actions intended to bring about a physical or mental consequence. **Negligence** is providing substandard care.

85. A: The electrolyte imbalance of most concern with polydipsia, which is characterized by excessively drinking water (more than 3 liters per day), is hyponatremia because of the diluting effect that the water has on the blood and the inability of the kidneys to excrete urine fast enough. Polydipsia may occur with schizophrenia as well as in those with developmental disabilities. If untreated, the patient may develop seizures and experience cardiac arrest. Treatment of polydipsia generally requires hospitalization. Clozapine is often used to control symptoms.

86. C: If a 55-year-old patient complains of increasing memory loss, a drug that may induce memory impairment is atorvastatin (Lipitor). The FDA added cognitive impairment, including memory loss and confusion, to the list of safety information regarding statins. Research has found that patients taking cholesterol-lowering drugs have about four times the risk of developing cognitive impairment compared to those not taking the drugs, although symptoms tend to recede if the medication is discontinued.

87. B: If, during a patient interview, the PMHNP notes the patient rubbing her hands together, sitting tensely, answering abruptly, and avoiding eye contact and tells the patient, "I can see that you are upset," this therapeutic technique is called observing. The PMHNP is stating a factual observation about what is seen or heard from the patient in order to encourage the patient to verbalize her feelings and concerns.

88. D: If a Mexican immigrant suffering from depression and multiple health complaints agrees to take an antidepressant but insists that he also needs to receive treatment by a *curandero* for *susto* (loss of soul), the best response is to be supportive and facilitate *curandero* treatments. The *curandero* is a healer who is believed to heal the body and the soul using various rituals, herbs, and massage. The PMHNP should review any herbs used in the rituals to make sure they don't interact with the patient's prescription medications.

89. C: If a patient with bulimia nervosa is very angry at the PMHNP because of the restrictions that the PMHNP has prescribed after meals to prevent the patient from purging, but the patient denies she is angry and accuses the PMHNP of being angry with her, this is an example of projection. Projection is a defense mechanism in which the patient projects her own feelings, which she may find unacceptable, onto someone else.

90. C: Inconsistencies in social, medical, and functional data are not uncommon, so the PMHNP should first consult with the source of inconsistent data to try to determine the reason for the inconsistency. In some cases, the inconsistency may result from errors or misstatements. In other cases, the patient's condition may have changed from one assessment to another. The patient usually serves as the primary source of information, but other sources can include family, friends, employers, physicians, other health-care providers (such as home health nurses and physical therapists), and medical records

91. B: The **Mini-Cog test** requires the person to remember and later repeat the names of three common objects and to draw the face of a clock with all 12 numbers and with the two hands indicating a specified time. The **MMSE** requires a number of tasks, including counting backward from 100 by 7s, providing the patient's current location, repeating phrases, following directions, and copying a picture of interlocking shapes. **IADL** measure eight activities necessary for adults to function independently (including shopping, food preparation, telephone use, and managing finances). The **Confusion Assessment Method** is used to assess development of delirium, not dementia.

92. D: If the PMHNP is the manager of the unit and has hired two new graduate nurses to work on the unit, the PMHNP should expect that the nurses will likely need the most guidance related to delegating tasks. New graduate nurses often feel insecure about delegating and tend to try to do everything by themselves, especially if they are unsure of the skills and roles of other staff members.

93. C: If the PMHNP has discovered that Medicare and Medicaid are routinely being charged for services that patients have not received and records are being falsified, the most appropriate action is for the PMHNP to file a *qui tam* lawsuit. This is a whistleblowing action under the False Claims Act against those defrauding the federal government. Many states have similar laws. With a *qui tam* lawsuit, the person who files the complaint is entitled to a percentage of the recouped funds.

94. A: Psychogenic nonepileptic seizures are best treated with antianxiety medications and psychological counseling because they are related to emotional trauma and stress rather than abnormalities in electrical discharges. Indications of pseudoseizures include inconsistent motor movements (such as bilateral asynchronous motions and shaking the head from one side to the other), normal electroencephalogram (EEG) findings, specific triggering events (pain, lights), and a lack of seizure activity during sleep. A primary indication of psychogenic nonepileptic seizure is resistance to antiepileptic drugs. Pseudoseizures may also have organic causes, such as migraines.

95. B: Anorexia and weight loss associated with topiramate (Topamax) may exacerbate the patient's tendency toward anorexia. Sedation may occur initially but usually subsides. Dulling of cognition may occur, but starting with a low dose and increasing it gradually may negate this effect. Many other anticonvulsants are associated with weight gain and increased appetite, and this is sometimes a concern for adolescents. Generalized clonic-tonic seizures can occur at any age and usually have abrupt onset with loss of consciousness for 1 to 2 minutes.

96. A: The theory of cognitive dissonance (Festinger) states that individuals attempt to escape dissonance and avoid inconsistencies between their beliefs and actions. If dissonance occurs, then beliefs and ideas are more likely to change than actions or behavior. To avoid dissonance, people may avoid individuals or situations in which dissonance occurs. When faced with dissonance, the person can:

- Change one cognition (piece of knowledge) to match others or change all to bring them in line.
- Eliminate one cognition or add more to bring about consonance.
- Alter the importance of the cognitions.

97. C: The PMHNP should monitor adolescents taking atypical antipsychotics, such as olanzapine and risperidone, for weight gain. Patients' baseline weights should be noted and monitored frequently because patients may gain up to 20 pounds in the first months of treatment. Adolescents may need nutritional counseling and should be encouraged to participate in physical exercise. Adolescents are often concerned about body image issues, so weight gain is one of the reasons that adolescents may be noncompliant with treatment.

98. B: The PMHNP prescribes antipsychotic medications for patients, even though the PMHNP is aware that the medications have numerous adverse effects that may impair overall health, basing treatment on the ethical principle of beneficence because the intent is to do good and the good overcompensates for the bad. This corresponds to the principle of double effect, wherein the principles of beneficence and nonmaleficence appear to be in conflict.

99. D: These symptoms—depression, lethargy, weight gain, hair loss, dry skin, sensitivity to cold, and slow pulse—are consistent with hypothyroidism, so the initial diagnostic tests that are indicated to determine potential causes for depression include thyroid-stimulating hormone (TSH), T3, and free T4. Normal free T4 values range from 0.8 to 1.5 ng/dL. Normal TSH values range from 0.4 to 4.0 mIU/L. The TSH value is especially important because it often increases first to compensate for a decrease in the free T4 value, so the free T4 value may stay within normal range for a while. Normal free T3 values range from 2.6 to 4.8 pg/mL.

100. A: If the PMHNP is basing her leadership style on expectancy theory (Vroom), which deals with motivation, she is expected to focus on positive reinforcement. Expectancy relates to how the person perceives that his or her needs will be met based on previous experience. According to this theory, motivation in the workplace is associated with positive feedback and the positive relationship between performance and outcomes. Feedback should be positive and specific.

101. C: Activism should begin with knowledge, so the first step that a PMHNP should take if he wants to become a leader in health-care reform and the role of the PMHNP is to become knowledgeable about the current health-care system. From this knowledge base, the PMHNP can determine what area or areas of health care he wants to focus on and which organization(s) might be the best fit.

102. A: The ethnic group with the highest rates of suicide in the United States is Caucasians, whose rates are double that of other ethnic groups. The ages at which patients are most at risk of suicide are 15 to 24 and 65 and older. Males have a higher rate of completed suicide, probably because they often choose more lethal methods (such as gunshots), whereas females have a higher rate of attempted suicide. Females, who often choose overdoses of pills, are more likely to be rescued.

Mometrix

103. D: Examples of **decisional responsibilities** include allocation of resources, employee evaluations, hiring and firing staff members, planning, job analysis, and job design. **Informational responsibilities** include serving as a spokesperson, monitoring staff and activities, and disseminating information. **Interpersonal responsibilities** include conflict negotiation/resolution, networking, staff development, and provision of rewards (salaries) and punishments (disciplinary action).

104. B: If the PMHNP is the project manager for a quality improvement project that requires multiple activities and stages of development over a 12-month period, the best method of illustrating the sequence of tasks is by developing a program evaluation and review technique (PERT) flowchart. Events are ordered, activities supporting those events are coded (A–Z), durations are assigned to each event, and a flowchart is developed that visually represents the project flow from beginning to end.

105. C: If a patient being treated for antisocial personality disorder became very agitated and refused to participate in activities, the PMHNP best engages in reflective thinking by reviewing interactions to determine how to better deal with the patient. Reflective thinking may be carried out during or after an event or activity, and it involves thinking about the steps the PMHNP takes and evaluating them to determine if they are effective or if other steps would be more effective.

106. A: The type of organizational structure in which the PMHNP would likely need to report to more than one manager is the matrix structure. For example, the PMHNP may need to report to a functional manager (nursing) as well as a project manager (substance abuse or Alzheimer's). Problems can arise with managers competing for the individual's time.

107. D: Virtual reality allows patients to experience an environment in the digital world and in the relative safety of the treatment facility, so it is best used for exposure therapy. For example, a flight simulation program can allow patients who have a fear of flying to experience entering an airplane and taking off, but the patient can remain in control of the degree of exposure she can tolerate and can terminate the experience if desired.

108. C: If the PMHNP discovers that a coworker has posted information on a social media site about a patient who is well known in the community, giving the person's name and diagnosis and describing the patient's condition, the PMHNP should immediately notify the administration of a breach in confidentiality and should not attempt to deal with this personally. This is a serious Health Insurance Portability and Accountability Act of 1996 (HIPAA) violation that requires notification of the patient and the Department of Health and Human Services that will best be handled by the organization's risk management personnel.

109. C: If the PMHNP has been offered a leadership position but feels unprepared, the best solution is to find a mentor, especially someone that the individual has worked with and respects. Most new leaders are apprehensive and recognize that they will have learning curves, but having someone to discuss situations with on a regular basis and to ask for guidance can be invaluable. Asking subordinates for guidance signals a lack of confidence.

249

110. A: If a 16-year-old patient with diabetes mellitus, type 1, since age 4 has been hospitalized three times for failing to follow dietary and medication protocols because of peer pressure to conform, the patient may benefit from assertiveness training to learn how to address her diabetes with her friends so that they can better understand her medical needs. The patient should also be assessed for depression and anxiety, which are common findings in adolescents trying to deal with developmental issues and a serious illness because these factors may lead to dietary and medication noncompliance.

111. D: Because the Patient Self-Determination Act ensures that patient have access to health information, the PMHNP can withhold information about a patient's diagnosis from the patient only if the patient has requested the PMHNP do so or the patient has been found to be mentally incompetent and unable to comprehend the information. The PMHNP must evaluate each individual to determine the best method of sharing bad news with him or her.

112. C: Under the doctrine of *respondeat superior*, if the PMHNP is an employer, then the PMHNP is legally responsible for the employee's actions and can be held liable because the employee administered the incorrect dose of the medication during employment and the act was within the realm of employment. For this reason, it's especially important to train and supervise staff well and to ensure that all communications are clear and well understood.

113. B: The best collaborative response is the one that includes "you": "Let's talk about ways to allow you to get more rest." The patient has a legitimate concern and should be encouraged to provide input rather than the PMHNP simply stating a solution or lack of a solution. In some cases, simply rescheduling medications or treatments may help to resolve the issue. If, in fact, there is no real solution, discussing the issue with the patient can help the person feel that his or her concerns are at least being acknowledged.

114. D: **Duty owed to the patient** is the element of malpractice that is violated if the PMHNP gives a patient a sedative and fails to monitor the patient's response. **Breach of duty owed** is failing to adequately communicate changes in the patient's condition to the primary health-care provider. **Foreseeability** is failing to ensure that minimum standards of care are met. **Causation** is failing to provide necessary education to the patient.

115. A: Although all of these are important, in communicating with an interdisciplinary group, the most critical skill is listening. The other actions, such as making eye contact, using attentive body language to show interest, and verbal tracking, are used to support listening and are part of active listening in which the listener gives feedback to the speaker. Verbal tracking includes keeping track of the conversation and paraphrasing or summarizing to indicate attention to the speaker's words.

116. C: If the organization has flattened the chain of command and widened the span of control (often done as a cost-cutting measure to reduce the layers of authority), as a supervisor, the PMHNP should expect that this will mean increased numbers of staff to manage. The span of control represents the number of staff the individual manages. A wider span of control can make adequate supervision more difficult.

117. D: The **Revised Children's Manifest Anxiety Scale (RCMAS)** assesses anxiety in children and adolescents (6–19) with 37 yes–no questions, and it can be read to young children. The **Hamilton Anxiety Scale (HAS)** provides an evaluation of overall anxiety and its degree of severity for children and adults. This scale is frequently used in psychotropic drug evaluations. The **Beck Anxiety Inventory (BAI)** is a tool for adolescents and adults that ranks 21 common symptoms related to anxiety, according to the degree that they have bothered the client in the previous month. The **Beck Depression Inventory (BDI)** is a widely used, self-reported, multiple-choice questionnaire consisting of 21 items, which measures the degree of depression for persons ages 17 to 80 years.

118. B: SWOT analysis is used to evaluate internal and external factors that can affect work. Opposing factors are considered with strengths (S) and weaknesses (W) focused on internal factors and opportunities (O) and threats (T) focusing on external factors. During SWOT analysis, a diagram is developed that outlines positive and negative opposing factors. Internal factors to consider include human resources, financial resources, processes, physical resources, and historical events. External factors to consider include the general economy, rules and laws, national/international events, demographics, sources of finances, and nursing trends.

119. C: According to Rogers' Innovation–Decision Process, individuals can bring about personal change and accept innovations in the following five stages: (1) knowledge, (2) persuasion, (3) decision, (4) implementation, and (5) confirmation. However, individuals may reject change at any stage in the process, so it is important for an agent of change to remain vigilant and ensure that individuals are apprised of benefits of change at every stage and are encouraged to persist.

120. B: If an observant Muslim patient is hospitalized during the month of Ramadan, staff members should expect the patient to refuse to eat or drink from sunup to sundown as part of observance. Otherwise, the patient will generally carry on as usual. Although people who are ill are excused from the requirement to fast, many patients will insist on remaining observant. The staff should make arrangements for food to be served to the patient before dawn and later in the evening.

121. A: In a recovery-oriented system of care, a patient who is discharged after treatment for drug or alcohol addiction should expect referral to community resources. The recovery-oriented system may involve multiple treatment approaches (because what works for one patient may not work for another), and it makes use of community agencies and resources to help the patient with recovery while recognizing that multiple episodes of treatment may be needed.

122. D: When helping individuals to resolve conflicts, the PMHNP realizes that the most difficult conflicts to resolve are value-based because people are often unwilling to consider a change in values or belief systems. Additionally, values are subjective, so it can be difficult to provide objective evidence to convince people. Because of this, value-based conflicts often remain unresolved. Other types of conflicts include goal based, fact based, and approach based.

123. A: If the administration has asked the PMHNP for guidance on eliminating lateral violence (bullying among coworkers) from the workplace, the initial recommendation should be to conduct an anonymous survey. Lateral violence is almost always underreported because of the fear of reprisal, and many staff members will not talk openly about the problem but may be more forthcoming in an anonymous survey. The results can show the extent of lateral violence and help to determine appropriate interventions.

124. C: Staring. The STAMP acronym is used to identify behaviors that pose the risk of violence, as follows:

- **S**taring: Prolonged glaring at an individual.
- **T**one and voice volume: Increased volume and sarcastic or sharp retorts.
- **A**nxiety: Flushed, hyperventilating, dilated pupils, rapid speech, confusion, disorientation, and physical indications of pain.
- **M**umbling: Slurred, incoherent speech, criticizing just loud enough to be overheard, and repeating the same statements or questions.
- **P**acing: Walking back and forth, flailing, and being resistive of health-care interventions.

125. A: **Illusion:** The patient misinterprets real external stimuli, such as perceiving the picture of the red roses as a monster with blood dripping from its mouth. **Delusion:** The patient has false personal beliefs despite evidence to the contrary, such as a somatic delusion in which he or she has false ideas about the functioning of his/her body. **Hallucination:** The patient experiences false sensory perceptions (auditory, visual, tactile, gustatory, and olfactory). **Magical thinking:** The patient believes that thoughts have power to control people, situations, or things.

126. C: Most aggressive acts are committed against people who are known to the aggressor, usually family members. The exceptions to this general rule are male adolescents, who may act violently against acquaintances who they know only slightly or against complete strangers.

127. D: The important first step is a thorough assessment of the situation, i.e., asking lots of questions before making any suggestions. Subsequently, the practitioner can assess the client's level of education and vulnerability concerning high-risk behaviors, determine whether separate therapists are indicated, and determine the degree to which the behavior is normative or pathological.

128. B: Toluene is a constituent of solvents that are abused through inhalation. Like most of the substances abused through inhalation, toluene is not detected by urine drug screenings. Other means of assessing inhalant abuse, such as detecting the odor of the inhalant on the subject's breath (where it may persist for many hours) or finding products of abuse stored in unusual locations, must be sought.

129. A: Given this history, the patient is unlikely to have a strong grasp of the English language, adding an additional degree of difficulty to developing his "health literacy," that is, his "capacity to obtain, process, and understand basic health information and services needed to make appropriate health decisions." Being able to provide information and education in a language that he can understand is the first step, preceding even an assessment of his understanding.

130. B: The majority of studies show a concordance of 40% for monozygotic twins and 0 to 10% for dizygotic twins. When unipolar depression and bipolar I disorder are considered, the risk is 69% for identical twins and is 19% for fraternal twins when the index twin has bipolar I disorder.

131. B: The response of TSH to TRH is blunted in a significant proportion of patients with major depressive disorder. The dexamethasone suppression test is positive (that is, cortisol is not suppressed) in only about 50% of patients with major depressive disorder. CSF levels of the serotonin metabolite 5HIAA are significantly reduced in patients who commit suicide. MHPG is elevated in the urine of patients with delusional depression compared with patients without delusional depression.

132. C: Either depressed mood or loss of interest or pleasure must be present for 2 weeks. Suicidal ideation need not be present for the diagnosis, but at least 5 of the listed symptoms must be present for 2 weeks. There must be clinically significant distress or impairment of function caused by the symptoms.

133. A: Patients may remain conscious during unilateral, partial motor seizures; however, the spread of the seizures to both cerebral hemispheres (indicated by bilateral tonic/clonic movements) is always associated with loss of consciousness. The other symptoms are frequently seen during seizure disorders.

134. D: Munchausen by proxy (factitious disorder by proxy) usually involves a parent who presents a child repeatedly for treatment with physical complaints or conditions that turn out to be fabricated or produced by the parent, who is motivated by a wish to adopt a sick role vicariously through the child. Malingering would usually be manifest by the adoption of feigned or exaggerated symptoms in order to obtain nursing home admission, when the patient has minimal signs and symptoms. If the patient has an occult substance abuse problem that causes serious impairment at home but not when sober, as here when seen by the physician, it could explain the disconnect. However, the family is usually aware of and reports the substance abuse. "Granny dumping," the attempt to offload a burdensome elder onto the healthcare system, must be considered prominently in the differential diagnosis, given the limited information.

135. D: Antisocial Personality Disorder requires evidence of a Conduct Disorder with onset before age 15 years.

136. B: Patients with this degree of behavioral dyscontrol should not be managed by a solo practitioner in a private office setting. The NP needs to terminate services and help her find an alternative venue that will more comprehensively manage her neediness and dilute her transference over a wider group of clinicians.

137. A: Many incarcerated individuals have antisocial personality disorders and will attempt to manipulate or con susceptible prison staff, often seeking drugs or diagnoses that will gain them special treatment. Malingering (making up symptoms to gain an advantage) is common in this population. Individuals feigning symptoms for this purpose will generally be uninterested in non-medical approaches, allowing some differentiation between a malingering population and those with a genuine problem.

138. D: The PMH NP is not required to expose herself to undue risk of injury or even abuse from a potentially violent patient. The compassionate and correct way to terminate services is to speak with the patient directly, by telephone if an office visit will present too great a risk, and inform them of the decision and why she is making it, offering to help arrange additional treatment for substance abuse issues. Full documentation in the medical record and in a registered letter and the offer to be available on an emergency basis for 1 month will protect the NP against any accusation of abandonment. Offering to help arrange in-patient detoxification will protect her against any liability should the patient refuse and then have withdrawal complications.

139. A: If state confidentiality statutes are more restrictive than the federal guidelines of HIPAA, the former take precedence. Here, there has been no compelling reason presented to the NP that would supersede his explicit contract of confidentiality with the patient about his privileged information. Although the consequences of sharing information without his permission may be greater, given his paranoid personality disorder, that alone should not be the rationale for deciding to share confidential information or not. Also, attempting to speak with the patient if he has not requested it would generally be too involved or intrusive to be positive for the treatment alliance with this type of patient.

140. C: Both flurazepam and diazepam have long elimination half-lives and are not recommended for use in patients over the age of 65 years. Eszopiclone is likely to be more expensive than the other agents listed, which are available in generic form. Temazepam has an intermediate half-life, is FDA-approved for insomnia, and is well-tolerated and inexpensive.

141. B: Deterioration of kidney function with long-term lithium use is a significant risk, requiring BUN and creatinine to be monitored at least annually. Whereas lithium can cause T wave changes in the ECG and can exacerbate or precipitate psoriasis in some patients, there is no need to monitor these areas in any regular way. Lithium has been associated with elevations in serum parathyroid hormone and serum calcium, but not frequently enough to be routinely monitored.

142. A: The newer second-generation antipsychotic medications have demonstrated a tendency to significantly increase appetite, weight, and glucose intolerance. Clozapine and olanzapine are the most likely, risperidone and quetiapine are less likely, and ziprasidone (Geodon) and aripiprazole are least likely to be associated with these adverse effects.

143. C: Although Obsessive Compulsive Disorder is clearly an Axis I condition mediated by abnormalities in brain function and neurotransmitter balance, good empirical evidence indicates that the application of behavioral techniques such as exposure and response inhibition are effective in motivated patients for improving symptom control.

144. D: The hazard of psychotherapeutic informed consent is that it interferes with the establishment of initial rapport and therapeutic alliance by fostering discouragement and a negative suggestion about the possible outcome of the treatment. The other choices are the benefits of informed consent for psychotherapy.

145. B: Patients in restraints or seclusion must be observed and assessed every 10 to 15 minutes for circulation, respiration, nutrition, hydration, and elimination. Orders for restraints or seclusion must be reissued by a physician every 4 hours for adults (every 2 hours for those aged 9 to 17 years and every 1 hour for children younger than 9 years), and a physician must evaluate the patient while in restraints or seclusion every 8 hours (18 years and older) or every 4 hours (younger than 18 years). (The Joint Commission Guidelines)

146. A: In the absence of any stated or implied suicidal ideation or intent and without evidence of very significant self-neglect, involuntary hospitalization in this case would have been beyond the scope of the usual statutes governing such interventions, which usually require "likelihood of serious harm" or "substantial risk" of injury to self or others. If the patient is assessed as competent, the clinician cannot be held liable for the patient's deliberate withholding of suicidal ideation or intent and of information about possession of lethal means or for the patient's failure to seek help when such suicidal ideation or intention arose.

147. C: The CDC provides information for health protection and disease prevention, including environmental health and occupational health and safety and infectious disease monitoring. The NCHS compiles health statistics to guide policy formation in the health care field. The AHRQ develops clinical guidelines and promotes evidence-based medical practices. The Joint Commission performs periodic reviews of hospital care, including areas of operations, staff performance, physical facilities, and standard operating procedures. If the institution meets standards of practice in these areas, it is given initial or ongoing accreditation. The Joint Commission is a non-profit organization that has been accrediting institutions since 1951. Accreditation by the Joint Commission is often required by health insurance plans for coverage of services.

148. C: The elements of answer (a) are those of the Implementation component of nursing process. The elements of answer (b) are those of the Assessment component of the nursing process. The elements of answer (d) are those of the Documentation aspect of the nursing process.

149. D: Although family members might be willing to "take responsibility," they are not trained mental health professionals and the NP will be liable for any adverse outcome resulting from delaying the admission overnight. Even expecting the mother to follow through on taking her son to the community hospital is risky, because she could decide to drive him home instead. An involuntary commitment without discussion with the family would be needlessly challenging to the therapeutic alliance, unless the assessment is that the patient would run away if he knew that he would be taken to the community hospital immediately, instead of waiting for a bed to become available at the university hospital. Sending the patient voluntarily by ambulance is the best route, if the family agrees, with involuntary commitment as the fallback option.

150. A: When both the subject and the investigator are "blind" to the treatment option being given, it is a "double-blind" trial. When only the subject is unaware of which treatment is being given, it is a "single blind" trial, which is considered to be subject to investigator bias because the latter knows the treatment being given and may be influenced to assess it as more effective in the subjects receiving it. Cross-sectional studies make observations in subjects at a single point in time, whereas a case-control study identifies subjects with the condition and compares them with a sample of subjects without the condition to determine which other factors are associated with the difference in outcomes.

151. D: Suicide risk increases with age and is highest in persons older than 65 years. Whites have the highest rate of suicide, followed by Native Americans, African Americans, Hispanic Americans, and Asian Americans. Women attempt suicide at a higher rate than do men, but men succeed more often.

152. D: Motivational interviewing is a client-centered approach that involves "rolling with the resistance" rather than confronting it, expressing empathy and viewing the situation from the client's perspective, supporting self-efficacy by explicitly embracing client autonomy, and developing discrepancy.

153. C: Some of the many factors that increase stress levels are social isolation, financial instability, job loss, divorce or separation, and physical illness. Signs of stress include irritability, loss of interest, sleep disturbance, weight loss, increased use of alcohol or drugs, increased use of sick time from work, and increased levels of physical complaints and symptoms.

154. B: The correct form of question "b" is "Have people annoyed you by criticizing your drinking?" The others are correct formats from the CAGE (Cut down, Annoyed, Guilty, Eye opener) assessment for alcohol problems.

155. B: The prevalence of schizophrenia among non-twin siblings of a schizophrenic patient is 8%. Being a dizygotic twin of a schizophrenic patient raises the prevalence rate to 12%, and being a monozygotic twin of a schizophrenic patient raises the prevalence rate to 47%.

156. B: Opioid Withdrawal Syndrome is associated with severe muscle cramps and bone aches, profuse diarrhea, abdominal cramps, rhinorrhea, lacrimation, piloerection or gooseflesh, yawning, fever, pupillary dilation (mydriasis), hypertension, tachycardia, and temperature dysregulation.

157. A: If a patient binges and purges only during periods of time when other signs and symptoms qualify the patient for a diagnosis of Anorexia Nervosa, Bulimia Nervosa will not be diagnosed additionally. The correct diagnosis in this situation is Anorexia Nervosa, Binge Eating-Purging Type.

158. B: In both Factitious Disorder and Malingering, false or grossly exaggerated physical or psychological symptoms are intentionally reported. Careful assessment both excludes other causes and often allows documentation of direct evidence of fabrication based on the non-physiological or non-anatomical nature of the symptoms, changes in symptoms, or observations (e.g., witnessing a patient deliberately contaminate a wound that mysteriously refuses to heal). There may be a pattern of such "illnesses" in both cases. Malingering is associated with a clear external incentive or secondary gain from assuming a sick role, such as avoiding military service or incarceration, avoiding work, obtaining financial rewards such as disability payments or other financial compensation, obtaining drugs, or evading criminal prosecution. Factitious Disorder is associated with a more internal motive, that is, to assume the sick role.

159. A: Deficits in cognition can be similar in delirium and dementia, but the distinguishing characteristics are twofold: delirium manifests with an alteration in alertness or level of consciousness and with a reduced capacity for cognitive processing, both of which appear within a short time frame; most dementias are slower in onset, and cognitive decline usually takes place in the setting of clear sensorium (although Dementia with Lewy Bodies can be characterized by altered sensorium and prominent perceptual distortions, such as hallucinations).

160. C: Despite evidence of resolve and appropriate self-care in dealing with difficult ex-boyfriends, a pattern of involvement in abusive relationships may exist that bears examination and intervention.

161. B: There are no absolute rules about self-disclosure, accepting small gifts, or touch, because the diverse cultural backgrounds and sociocultural situations of clients may make an action appropriate in one situation but inappropriate in another. However, it is never appropriate to allow romantic feelings or thoughts to interfere with clinical care. In such cases, supervision should be sought, and the situation should be monitored closely; it may become necessary for the client to be referred to another practitioner.

162. C: Any member of the family who prepares meals should be educated about the potential tyramine reaction that can occur with the ingestion of aged cheeses, certain sausages and other fermented protein products, and some alcoholic beverages (beer and wine). The presence of these products in food may be masked during preparation; therefore, both the food preparer and the patient should be aware of the risk.

163. A: A number of adequately designed and controlled studies have demonstrated the efficacy of stimulant medications, BPT, BCM, and peer-focused behavioral interventions in recreational settings in both children and adults with ADHD.

164. B: MAO inhibitor antidepressants—such as phenelzine, tranylcypromine, and isocarboxazid—are reserved for use until at least 3 or 4 other antidepressant options have failed to be helpful, because of the risk of toxic interactions with dietary items and other medications. The MAO inhibitor selegiline, applied as a patch, may circumvent some of these issues and may be categorized as a third- or fourth-line treatment.

165. B: No evidence indicates that lithium levels worsen psoriasis at the high end of the therapeutic range or are associated with improvement in psoriatic lesions at the lower end of the therapeutic range; therefore, blood monitoring is not helpful for managing lithium-associated psoriasis.

166. A: The aim of supportive psychotherapy is to help the patient through a difficult period by strengthening, supporting, and highlighting the patient's already existing strengths and assets. The duration of both the sessions themselves and of the course of therapy may be brief. Techniques of psychoanalysis meant to foster free association or even to provoke anxiety and uncertainty, such as the therapist presenting a "blank screen," tend to undermine or diminish usual defense mechanisms rather than strengthen them, as is the goal of supportive psychotherapies.

167. D: Phototherapy works better by increasing the intensity of light exposure rather than by increasing its duration, appears to be most effective when administered in the morning, and can have positive effects with as little as 30-45 minutes of exposure per day. Blue-green light may be the most effective part of the visual spectrum for treating depression.

168. C: The courts now require that practitioners relate sufficient information about alternative treatments that may be advantageous to the patient, discuss the possible risks and benefits associated with them, and discuss the option of no treatment.

169. B: The principle of autonomy holds that adults have the ability and the right to make reasonable and responsible choices for themselves. An adult woman in an abusive relationship may request counseling and even shelter, but the health practitioner is not mandated to report the situation to any civil or criminal authority, independent of the patient's willingness or consent. Doing so without the patient's consent would be a violation of confidentiality.

170. D: Financial indiscretion is not considered a reason for involuntary commitment for mental illness in most jurisdictions.

171. A: Piaget's 4 stages of cognitive development are Sensorimotor (birth to 2 years), Preoperational (ages 2-6 years), Concrete Operations (ages 6-12 years), and Formal Operations (ages 12-15+ years); Kohlberg's levels of moral development are Preconventional (ages 4-10 years), Conventional (ages 10-13 years and into adulthood), and Postconventional (from adolescence onward); Peplau's stages of personality development are Infancy (learning to count on others), Toddlerhood (learning to delay satisfaction), Early Childhood (identifying oneself), and Late Childhood (developing skills in participation); and Mahler's theory of separation-individuation includes the Autistic Phase (birth to 1 month), the Symbiotic Phase (ages 1-5 months), and the Separation-Individuation Phase (ages 5-36 months).

172. B: PHI does not include the name of the patient's physician, because this is not information that "identifies the individual or with respect to which there is a reasonable basis to believe the information can be used to identify the individual" (U.S. Department of Health and Human Services, 2003).

173. C: Veracity is the duty to tell the truth and not intentionally deceive or mislead clients. Occasions when the truth would produce harm or interfere with the recovery process are rare. The principle of autonomy holds that the patient is presumed rational and responsible, retaining the right to determine their own destiny and to be fully informed about their condition. Withholding the truth would violate this principle as well. In this case, the nurse is attempting to act under the principles of nonmaleficence (to do no intentional harm to the client), beneficence (to benefit or promote the good of others), and justice (to treat all individuals, including the family, equally and fairly); however, the primary duty is to the patient.

174. D: The chief reason to obtain consultation is to determine a professional assessment of whether a patient's situation is beyond the NP's experience or knowledge to handle properly. Another reason to obtain consultation would be to honor the patient's requests for a second opinion, which should generally be facilitated. Although a second opinion provides a sharing of medical-legal responsibility, this is not the primary reason to obtain such.

175. C: Analytical Precision is not concerned with statistics and instruments. It refers to the decision-making process by which researchers synthesize concrete data (words of the subjects) into an abstract that clarifies the meaning and the importance of the study. The last of the 5 criteria is Heuristic Relevance: The researcher clarifies the significance of the study, its applicability to public health or community nursing, and its likely influence on future research.

How to Overcome Test Anxiety

Just the thought of taking a test is enough to make most people a little nervous. A test is an important event that can have a long-term impact on your future, so it's important to take it seriously and it's natural to feel anxious about performing well. But just because anxiety is normal, that doesn't mean that it's helpful in test taking, or that you should simply accept it as part of your life. Anxiety can have a variety of effects. These effects can be mild, like making you feel slightly nervous, or severe, like blocking your ability to focus or remember even a simple detail.

If you experience test anxiety—whether severe or mild—it's important to know how to beat it. To discover this, first you need to understand what causes test anxiety.

Causes of Test Anxiety

While we often think of anxiety as an uncontrollable emotional state, it can actually be caused by simple, practical things. One of the most common causes of test anxiety is that a person does not feel adequately prepared for their test. This feeling can be the result of many different issues such as poor study habits or lack of organization, but the most common culprit is time management. Starting to study too late, failing to organize your study time to cover all of the material, or being distracted while you study will mean that you're not well prepared for the test. This may lead to cramming the night before, which will cause you to be physically and mentally exhausted for the test. Poor time management also contributes to feelings of stress, fear, and hopelessness as you realize you are not well prepared but don't know what to do about it.

Other times, test anxiety is not related to your preparation for the test but comes from unresolved fear. This may be a past failure on a test, or poor performance on tests in general. It may come from comparing yourself to others who seem to be performing better or from the stress of living up to expectations. Anxiety may be driven by fears of the future—how failure on this test would affect your educational and career goals. These fears are often completely irrational, but they can still negatively impact your test performance.

> **Review Video: 3 Reasons You Have Test Anxiety**
> Visit mometrix.com/academy and enter code: 428468

Elements of Test Anxiety

As mentioned earlier, test anxiety is considered to be an emotional state, but it has physical and mental components as well. Sometimes you may not even realize that you are suffering from test anxiety until you notice the physical symptoms. These can include trembling hands, rapid heartbeat, sweating, nausea, and tense muscles. Extreme anxiety may lead to fainting or vomiting. Obviously, any of these symptoms can have a negative impact on testing. It is important to recognize them as soon as they begin to occur so that you can address the problem before it damages your performance.

> **Review Video: 3 Ways to Tell You Have Test Anxiety**
> Visit mometrix.com/academy and enter code: 927847

The mental components of test anxiety include trouble focusing and inability to remember learned information. During a test, your mind is on high alert, which can help you recall information and stay focused for an extended period of time. However, anxiety interferes with your mind's natural processes, causing you to blank out, even on the questions you know well. The strain of testing during anxiety makes it difficult to stay focused, especially on a test that may take several hours. Extreme anxiety can take a huge mental toll, making it difficult not only to recall test information but even to understand the test questions or pull your thoughts together.

> **Review Video: How Test Anxiety Affects Memory**
> Visit mometrix.com/academy and enter code: 609003

Effects of Test Anxiety

Test anxiety is like a disease—if left untreated, it will get progressively worse. Anxiety leads to poor performance, and this reinforces the feelings of fear and failure, which in turn lead to poor performances on subsequent tests. It can grow from a mild nervousness to a crippling condition. If allowed to progress, test anxiety can have a big impact on your schooling, and consequently on your future.

Test anxiety can spread to other parts of your life. Anxiety on tests can become anxiety in any stressful situation, and blanking on a test can turn into panicking in a job situation. But fortunately, you don't have to let anxiety rule your testing and determine your grades. There are a number of relatively simple steps you can take to move past anxiety and function normally on a test and in the rest of life.

> **Review Video: How Test Anxiety Impacts Your Grades**
> Visit mometrix.com/academy and enter code: 939819

Physical Steps for Beating Test Anxiety

While test anxiety is a serious problem, the good news is that it can be overcome. It doesn't have to control your ability to think and remember information. While it may take time, you can begin taking steps today to beat anxiety.

Just as your first hint that you may be struggling with anxiety comes from the physical symptoms, the first step to treating it is also physical. Rest is crucial for having a clear, strong mind. If you are tired, it is much easier to give in to anxiety. But if you establish good sleep habits, your body and mind will be ready to perform optimally, without the strain of exhaustion. Additionally, sleeping well helps you to retain information better, so you're more likely to recall the answers when you see the test questions.

Getting good sleep means more than going to bed on time. It's important to allow your brain time to relax. Take study breaks from time to time so it doesn't get overworked, and don't study right before bed. Take time to rest your mind before trying to rest your body, or you may find it difficult to fall asleep.

> **Review Video: <u>The Importance of Sleep for Your Brain</u>**
> Visit mometrix.com/academy and enter code: 319338

Along with sleep, other aspects of physical health are important in preparing for a test. Good nutrition is vital for good brain function. Sugary foods and drinks may give a burst of energy but this burst is followed by a crash, both physically and emotionally. Instead, fuel your body with protein and vitamin-rich foods.

Also, drink plenty of water. Dehydration can lead to headaches and exhaustion, especially if your brain is already under stress from the rigors of the test. Particularly if your test is a long one, drink water during the breaks. And if possible, take an energy-boosting snack to eat between sections.

> **Review Video: <u>How Diet Can Affect your Mood</u>**
> Visit mometrix.com/academy and enter code: 624317

Along with sleep and diet, a third important part of physical health is exercise. Maintaining a steady workout schedule is helpful, but even taking 5-minute study breaks to walk can help get your blood pumping faster and clear your head. Exercise also releases endorphins, which contribute to a positive feeling and can help combat test anxiety.

When you nurture your physical health, you are also contributing to your mental health. If your body is healthy, your mind is much more likely to be healthy as well. So take time to rest, nourish your body with healthy food and water, and get moving as much as possible. Taking these physical steps will make you stronger and more able to take the mental steps necessary to overcome test anxiety.

> **Review Video: <u>How to Stay Healthy and Prevent Test Anxiety</u>**
> Visit mometrix.com/academy and enter code: 877894

Mental Steps for Beating Test Anxiety

Working on the mental side of test anxiety can be more challenging, but as with the physical side, there are clear steps you can take to overcome it. As mentioned earlier, test anxiety often stems from lack of preparation, so the obvious solution is to prepare for the test. Effective studying may be the most important weapon you have for beating test anxiety, but you can and should employ several other mental tools to combat fear.

First, boost your confidence by reminding yourself of past success—tests or projects that you aced. If you're putting as much effort into preparing for this test as you did for those, there's no reason you should expect to fail here. Work hard to prepare; then trust your preparation.

Second, surround yourself with encouraging people. It can be helpful to find a study group, but be sure that the people you're around will encourage a positive attitude. If you spend time with others who are anxious or cynical, this will only contribute to your own anxiety. Look for others who are motivated to study hard from a desire to succeed, not from a fear of failure.

Third, reward yourself. A test is physically and mentally tiring, even without anxiety, and it can be helpful to have something to look forward to. Plan an activity following the test, regardless of the outcome, such as going to a movie or getting ice cream.

When you are taking the test, if you find yourself beginning to feel anxious, remind yourself that you know the material. Visualize successfully completing the test. Then take a few deep, relaxing breaths and return to it. Work through the questions carefully but with confidence, knowing that you are capable of succeeding.

Developing a healthy mental approach to test taking will also aid in other areas of life. Test anxiety affects more than just the actual test—it can be damaging to your mental health and even contribute to depression. It's important to beat test anxiety before it becomes a problem for more than testing.

> **Review Video: Test Anxiety and Depression**
> Visit mometrix.com/academy and enter code: 904704

Study Strategy

Being prepared for the test is necessary to combat anxiety, but what does being prepared look like? You may study for hours on end and still not feel prepared. What you need is a strategy for test prep. The next few pages outline our recommended steps to help you plan out and conquer the challenge of preparation.

STEP 1: SCOPE OUT THE TEST

Learn everything you can about the format (multiple choice, essay, etc.) and what will be on the test. Gather any study materials, course outlines, or sample exams that may be available. Not only will this help you to prepare, but knowing what to expect can help to alleviate test anxiety.

STEP 2: MAP OUT THE MATERIAL

Look through the textbook or study guide and make note of how many chapters or sections it has. Then divide these over the time you have. For example, if a book has 15 chapters and you have five days to study, you need to cover three chapters each day. Even better, if you have the time, leave an extra day at the end for overall review after you have gone through the material in depth.

If time is limited, you may need to prioritize the material. Look through it and make note of which sections you think you already have a good grasp on, and which need review. While you are studying, skim quickly through the familiar sections and take more time on the challenging parts. Write out your plan so you don't get lost as you go. Having a written plan also helps you feel more in control of the study, so anxiety is less likely to arise from feeling overwhelmed at the amount to cover.

STEP 3: GATHER YOUR TOOLS

Decide what study method works best for you. Do you prefer to highlight in the book as you study and then go back over the highlighted portions? Or do you type out notes of the important information? Or is it helpful to make flashcards that you can carry with you? Assemble the pens, index cards, highlighters, post-it notes, and any other materials you may need so you won't be distracted by getting up to find things while you study.

If you're having a hard time retaining the information or organizing your notes, experiment with different methods. For example, try color-coding by subject with colored pens, highlighters, or post-it notes. If you learn better by hearing, try recording yourself reading your notes so you can listen while in the car, working out, or simply sitting at your desk. Ask a friend to quiz you from your flashcards, or try teaching someone the material to solidify it in your mind.

STEP 4: CREATE YOUR ENVIRONMENT

It's important to avoid distractions while you study. This includes both the obvious distractions like visitors and the subtle distractions like an uncomfortable chair (or a too-comfortable couch that makes you want to fall asleep). Set up the best study environment possible: good lighting and a comfortable work area. If background music helps you focus, you may want to turn it on, but otherwise keep the room quiet. If you are using a computer to take notes, be sure you don't have any other windows open, especially applications like social media, games, or anything else that could distract you. Silence your phone and turn off notifications. Be sure to keep water close by so you stay hydrated while you study (but avoid unhealthy drinks and snacks).

Also, take into account the best time of day to study. Are you freshest first thing in the morning? Try to set aside some time then to work through the material. Is your mind clearer in the afternoon or evening? Schedule your study session then. Another method is to study at the same time of day that you will take the test, so that your brain gets used to working on the material at that time and will be ready to focus at test time.

Step 5: Study!

Once you have done all the study preparation, it's time to settle into the actual studying. Sit down, take a few moments to settle your mind so you can focus, and begin to follow your study plan. Don't give in to distractions or let yourself procrastinate. This is your time to prepare so you'll be ready to fearlessly approach the test. Make the most of the time and stay focused.

Of course, you don't want to burn out. If you study too long you may find that you're not retaining the information very well. Take regular study breaks. For example, taking five minutes out of every hour to walk briskly, breathing deeply and swinging your arms, can help your mind stay fresh.

As you get to the end of each chapter or section, it's a good idea to do a quick review. Remind yourself of what you learned and work on any difficult parts. When you feel that you've mastered the material, move on to the next part. At the end of your study session, briefly skim through your notes again.

But while review is helpful, cramming last minute is NOT. If at all possible, work ahead so that you won't need to fit all your study into the last day. Cramming overloads your brain with more information than it can process and retain, and your tired mind may struggle to recall even previously learned information when it is overwhelmed with last-minute study. Also, the urgent nature of cramming and the stress placed on your brain contribute to anxiety. You'll be more likely to go to the test feeling unprepared and having trouble thinking clearly.

So don't cram, and don't stay up late before the test, even just to review your notes at a leisurely pace. Your brain needs rest more than it needs to go over the information again. In fact, plan to finish your studies by noon or early afternoon the day before the test. Give your brain the rest of the day to relax or focus on other things, and get a good night's sleep. Then you will be fresh for the test and better able to recall what you've studied.

Step 6: Take a practice test

Many courses offer sample tests, either online or in the study materials. This is an excellent resource to check whether you have mastered the material, as well as to prepare for the test format and environment.

Check the test format ahead of time: the number of questions, the type (multiple choice, free response, etc.), and the time limit. Then create a plan for working through them. For example, if you have 30 minutes to take a 60-question test, your limit is 30 seconds per question. Spend less time on the questions you know well so that you can take more time on the difficult ones.

If you have time to take several practice tests, take the first one open book, with no time limit. Work through the questions at your own pace and make sure you fully understand them. Gradually work up to taking a test under test conditions: sit at a desk with all study materials put away and set a timer. Pace yourself to make sure you finish the test with time to spare and go back to check your answers if you have time.

After each test, check your answers. On the questions you missed, be sure you understand why you missed them. Did you misread the question (tests can use tricky wording)? Did you forget the information? Or was it something you hadn't learned? Go back and study any shaky areas that the practice tests reveal.

Taking these tests not only helps with your grade, but also aids in combating test anxiety. If you're already used to the test conditions, you're less likely to worry about it, and working through tests until you're scoring well gives you a confidence boost. Go through the practice tests until you feel comfortable, and then you can go into the test knowing that you're ready for it.

Test Tips

On test day, you should be confident, knowing that you've prepared well and are ready to answer the questions. But aside from preparation, there are several test day strategies you can employ to maximize your performance.

First, as stated before, get a good night's sleep the night before the test (and for several nights before that, if possible). Go into the test with a fresh, alert mind rather than staying up late to study.

Try not to change too much about your normal routine on the day of the test. It's important to eat a nutritious breakfast, but if you normally don't eat breakfast at all, consider eating just a protein bar. If you're a coffee drinker, go ahead and have your normal coffee. Just make sure you time it so that the caffeine doesn't wear off right in the middle of your test. Avoid sugary beverages, and drink enough water to stay hydrated but not so much that you need a restroom break 10 minutes into the test. If your test isn't first thing in the morning, consider going for a walk or doing a light workout before the test to get your blood flowing.

Allow yourself enough time to get ready, and leave for the test with plenty of time to spare so you won't have the anxiety of scrambling to arrive in time. Another reason to be early is to select a good seat. It's helpful to sit away from doors and windows, which can be distracting. Find a good seat, get out your supplies, and settle your mind before the test begins.

When the test begins, start by going over the instructions carefully, even if you already know what to expect. Make sure you avoid any careless mistakes by following the directions.

Then begin working through the questions, pacing yourself as you've practiced. If you're not sure on an answer, don't spend too much time on it, and don't let it shake your confidence. Either skip it and come back later, or eliminate as many wrong answers as possible and guess among the remaining ones. Don't dwell on these questions as you continue—put them out of your mind and focus on what lies ahead.

Be sure to read all of the answer choices, even if you're sure the first one is the right answer. Sometimes you'll find a better one if you keep reading. But don't second-guess yourself if you do immediately know the answer. Your gut instinct is usually right. Don't let test anxiety rob you of the information you know.

If you have time at the end of the test (and if the test format allows), go back and review your answers. Be cautious about changing any, since your first instinct tends to be correct, but make sure you didn't misread any of the questions or accidentally mark the wrong answer choice. Look over any you skipped and make an educated guess.

At the end, leave the test feeling confident. You've done your best, so don't waste time worrying about your performance or wishing you could change anything. Instead, celebrate the successful completion of this test. And finally, use this test to learn how to deal with anxiety even better next time.

> **Review Video: <u>5 Tips to Beat Test Anxiety</u>**
> Visit mometrix.com/academy and enter code: 570656

Important Qualification

Not all anxiety is created equal. If your test anxiety is causing major issues in your life beyond the classroom or testing center, or if you are experiencing troubling physical symptoms related to your anxiety, it may be a sign of a serious physiological or psychological condition. If this sounds like your situation, we strongly encourage you to seek professional help.

Thank You

We at Mometrix would like to extend our heartfelt thanks to you, our friend and patron, for allowing us to play a part in your journey. It is a privilege to serve people from all walks of life who are unified in their commitment to building the best future they can for themselves.

The preparation you devote to these important testing milestones may be the most valuable educational opportunity you have for making a real difference in your life. We encourage you to put your heart into it—that feeling of succeeding, overcoming, and yes, conquering will be well worth the hours you've invested.

We want to hear your story, your struggles and your successes, and if you see any opportunities for us to improve our materials so we can help others even more effectively in the future, please share that with us as well. **The team at Mometrix would be absolutely thrilled to hear from you!** So please, send us an email (support@mometrix.com) and let's stay in touch.

> **If you'd like some additional help, check out these other resources we offer for your exam:**
> **http://mometrixflashcards.com/NP**

267

Additional Bonus Material

Due to our efforts to try to keep this book to a manageable length, we've created a link that will give you access to all of your additional bonus material.

> **Please visit**
> **https://www.mometrix.com/bonus948/npfamilypmh** to access
> **the information.**